Algrove Publishing Limited
1090 Morrison Drive
Ottawa, Ontario
Canada K2H 1C2

Canadian Cataloguing in Publication Data

Main entry under title:

    Popular mechanics shop notes for ...

(Classic reprint series)
Includes indexes.
Originally published: Chicago : Popular Mechanics Co., 1905-
"Compiled from the "Shop notes" department of Popular mechanics
    magazine, and "Written so you can understand it;" tells easy
    ways to do hard things" --Added t.p., v. 1.
Contents: v. 1. 1905 - v. 2. 1906 - v. 3. 1907 - v. 4. 1908 - v. 5. 1909 - v. 6. 1910 - v. 7. 1911 -
    v. 8. 1912 - v. 9. 1913 - v. 10. 1914 - v. 11. 1915 - v. 12. 1916 - v. 13. 1917 - v. 14. 1918 -
    v. 15. 1919 - v. 16. 1920 - v. 17. 1921 - v. 18. 1922 - v. 19. 1923.
ISBN 0-921335-87-3 (v. 11) - ISBN 0-921335-91-1 (v. 12) - ISBN 0-921335-94-6 (v. 13) -
ISBN 0-921335-96-2 (v. 14) - ISBN 0-921335-98-9 (v. 15) - ISBN 0-921335-93-8 (v. 16) -
ISBN 0-921335-95-4 (v. 17) - ISBN 0-921335-97-0 (v. 18) - ISBN 0-921335-99-7 (v. 19) -

    1. Do-it-yourself work. 2. Industrial arts. I. Title: Shop notes for ... II. Series: Classic reprint series (Ottawa, Ont.)

TJ1160.P66 2000   600   C99-900763-7

Printed in Canada
#10900

Publisher's Note

Virtually every woodworking magazine in the English-speaking world has a shop notes section and has published an accumulation of them in book form. This was all started in 1905 with the first annual issue of *Popular Mechanics Shop Notes*, a compilation of advice on jigs, fixtures, methods of work, processes and projects. The earlier issues focussed primarily on metalworking, but with tips for a variety of other trades liberally sprinkled throughout. As years went by, the contents shifted more and more to woodworking and handyman projects. Each book is profusely illustrated. The line drawings of the earlier issues were supplanted by superb engravings until photographs started to creep in during the 1920s. Each year has its charm but all issues share the attribute of being clear, concise and widely informative.

Leonard G. Lee, Publisher
Ottawa
September, 1999

WARNING

This is a reprint of a book compiled in the early 1900s. The book describes what was recommended to be done in accordance with the knowledge of the day.

It would be advisable to treat all corrosive, explosive and toxic materials with much greater caution than is indicated here, particularly any materials that come in contact with the body.

Similarly, some of the recommended projects were dangerous then and remain so now. All of this material should be regarded with a judicious eye and necessary precautions taken.

POPULAR MECHANICS

SHOP NOTES

FOR

1923

EASY WAYS TO DO HARD THINGS

OF DAILY USE
TO EVERY MECHANIC

Vol. XIX—Table of Contents, Pages 3927-3934

PUBLISHED BY
POPULAR MECHANICS COMPANY
CHICAGO, ILLINOIS, U. S. A.

PRINTED IN U. S. A.

Mold for Making Concrete Blocks

BY A. J. R. CURTIS

THE mold illustrated can be made from wood by any mechanic and used to produce concrete building blocks for quite a good-sized building. The bottom, ends, and sidepieces are made from thoroughly kiln-dried white pine, 2 in. thick, strengthened with 2-in. square cleats. The cores are merely tapered sections of 6 or 8-in. square posts. The wearing edges of the sides and ends are protected with strap iron, screws being used to attach both the cleats and strap-iron reinforcing. Handles of ½-in. rod

painted inside and out with any kind of light oil that will fill up the pores of the wood and keep out water. If the inside faces have been properly planed and sanded, the oil surfaces will produce correspondingly smooth surfaces on the blocks. Only enough free oil should be left on the forms to prevent the concrete from sticking, the surplus being removed with a piece of waste.

The blocks may be cast either face down or face up, as preferred, and it is recommended that only plain-face blocks

The Upper Photograph Shows the Concrete-Block Mold, Opened, with Its Cores and Clamps; Below, Left, the Clamps Applied and the Cores in Position to Cast a Concrete Block. The Face of the Block can Be at Either the Top or Bottom of the Mold. Right, One of the Blocks Cast in the Homemade Mold, Showing the Hollows at the Center. These Openings Make the Block Lighter and Improve Its Insulating Qualities

or pipe through the cores are provided, so that they can be removed from the mold after the block has been cast. Carpenters' or cabinetmakers' quick-acting clamps provide the best means for holding the parts together rigidly, although simple strap-iron hooks and wooden wedges can be used if clamps are not available.

Before using the mold, it should be

be made, as they are simpler and better-looking than the rock-face block. If the face of the block is to be down, a facing mixture is first placed in the mold to a depth of ¾ in., and the remaining space in the mold box is filled with ordinary concrete, mixed as wet as possible, yet so that it will stand up without sagging when the mold is removed. If the facing is to be placed on the upper side, the mold is filled to within ¾ in. of the top, and struck off with a template, after which the facing mixture is placed. Of course, all the concrete must be tamped thoroughly, and this is best done with a small foundry rammer, or one so constructed that the mixture is thoroughly compacted around the cores and in the corners.

The plain-concrete backing may be made of a mixture of 1 part cement to 3 or 4 parts of clean gravel, varying in size from minute particles to ¾-in. pieces. The facing should consist of a mixture of 1 part cement to 2 or 3 parts of white sand, marble dust, or granite, the proportion and color of the ingredients determining the color and texture of the finished article. Cement-stucco mixtures, in a variety of colors and textures, may be obtained from building-material dealers. After the block has been thoroughly compacted in the mold and the top struck or floated off, a straight, true pallet, made from 2-in. plank and cleated on the back, is clamped to the top of the mold, which is then turned over until the block rests on the pallet. The cores are then withdrawn, the mold carefully removed, and the block set away in a warm, moist place to season. The blocks should be carefully protected against sun, draft, and frost, preferably being stored where the temperature can be kept as high as possible and where the blocks can be sprinkled frequently, commencing as soon as this can be done without injury to the block. It is almost fatal to let blocks become dry during the first two weeks.

Engine Grates Made from Old Tires

While doing some threshing, the ashes were allowed to accumulate underneath the grates of the steam tractor, the result being a ruined set of grates. Not wanting to wait for several days until new grates could be received from the supply house, several old wagon tires were obtained, and, after cutting, were straightened out without heat. The iron bars thus obtained were cut into lengths to fit the grate racks, longer strips being provided at the sides for holding the grate in place. Three holes were drilled through each piece. The separate bars were spaced by old nuts and washers, the whole being held securely together by round rods, threaded on the ends, inserted through the holes, and drawn up tight with nuts.

Tinning Small Work

The work to be tinned is placed in warm water, to which a little sulphuric acid has been added, to clean the pieces of grease and dirt. Some powdered sal ammoniac is then added to the water and vigorously stirred until entirely dissolved. The work is then removed, washed in clean water, and placed near the fire to dry. A shallow pan, such as a frying pan, is obtained, and the bottom perforated. This pan should be small enough to allow it to be dipped into the pot of melted tin. The work is placed in the bottom of this perforated container, and a little sal ammoniac is sprinkled over the surface of the melted metal; then, after all smoke from the metal has disappeared, dip the pan containing the articles into the tin, lift it out, and shake well to get rid of the excess metal, at the same time sprinkling a little sal ammoniac over the work, to prevent too thick a coating. The articles are cooled quickly by dumping them into water, which also produces a bright finish.

A Convenient Ratchet Wrench

The original ratchet wrench of the type shown was made by using the ratchet from an old chain drill, and an elaboration of the idea resulted in a complete set of such wrenches to fit standard-size nuts.

By making the wrenches from carbon steel and casehardening, it is possible to screw or unscrew nuts and bolts

RATCHET

that are so located as to be inaccessible to wrenches of the usual kind. The nuts are screwed down by means of a drift and hammer, as shown; to unscrew the nut the wrench is turned over so that the teeth point in the opposite direction, the hammer and drift again being used.

Removing Stains from Concrete

Stains on concrete and stucco are mostly caused by dirt and dust washed down from the windows. These can readily be removed by scrubbing with a heavy bristle or wire brush and water.

Occasionally stains are caused by iron dissolved in rain water. These are really rust stains, and come from iron piping, nails, etc. Often they resist scrubbing with plain water. In this case, a dilute solution of hydrochloric acid (muriatic acid) used with a plain bristle brush, is effective. After scrubbing, rinse well with clean water. Protect the hands with gloves when applying the acid.

A Reel for Drawing Paper

For most drafting rooms, detail paper is bought in large rolls that are heavy and awkward to handle when merely stood on end in a corner, as is quite often the case. By this system much paper is wasted through careless handling, and it was for the purpose of reducing this waste and placing the roll in a convenient position, that the reel in the drawing was devised.

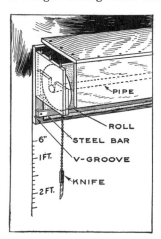

It was built as shown, the frame being screwed to the wall, and pieces of 1-in. material were attached inside each end as a support for the pipe roller. The top and front of the reel were made in a unit and held in place by dowels, so as to be readily removable. The paper, as it leaves the roll, runs underneath a ¼ by 1¼-in. iron bar that serves as a guide when cutting paper from the roll, assuring a smooth, square cut, which is also greatly facilitated by the V-groove in the backboard of the reel.

The device is mounted about 6 ft. above the floor, and a scale in feet and inches is painted on the wall, making it possible to draw out a sheet of the exact size required and cut it off quickly and smoothly, with square corners.—J. H. Kay, Cleveland, Ohio.

Limousine Sled for Winter Touring

The limousine sled shown in the drawing is the product of a locality where winter comes early and stays late, and

A Limousine Sled, for Use in Localities Where Arctic Winters Are the Rule and Passable Roads the Exception at This Season of the Year

where roads, that are none too good normally, are even worse at this season. The runners of the sled are made of heavy plank, suitably crossbraced and shod with tire iron. The comfortable body is built to convenient dimensions and provided with windows on all sides, and a door. In this particular vehicle, a comfortably upholstered seat from an old automobile gives a touch of luxury.—John Hirdler, Minneapolis, Minn.

Making Crates of Maximum Strength

The annual waste and damage that are the direct results of packing and shipping goods in improperly made cases and crates amount to a staggering total. It has only been within comparatively recent times that serious thought has been given to

the matter of correct packing and crating. In most boxes and crates, it will be noticed that a great deal of the box is fastened together by driving the nails in parallel to the grain. This is all wrong, and should be avoided, because the nails will pull out readily. The best way to get the maximum strength at the corners of a box or crate, where it is most needed, is accomplished by arranging the pieces at the corners in either of the two ways shown in the drawing, and driving the nails into the wood at right angles to the grain.

A Stick Hydrometer

Due to the rapid evaporation of alcohol from the antifreezing solution in the automobile radiator, the owner is never quite certain as to the efficiency of his alcohol-water mixture, without frequent tests.

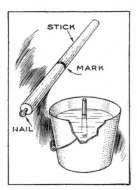

A simple test gauge, operated on the same principle as a hydrometer, can be made from a circular stick of wood, with a nail driven into one end to hold it upright. The proper alcohol-water mixture is made up, and the stick is inserted into the bucket, the depth to which it sinks being marked. The stick is kept either under the seat of the car or in the garage. Whenever there is any doubt as to the percentage of alcohol in the water, it is tested, and alcohol added until the test gauge sinks to the previously marked level.

Flat-File Attachment

It is not generally known that a handle placed on the front end of a flat file greatly facilitates its use. Anyone who

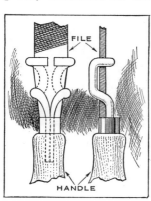

has used a flat, rough file for any length of time knows how awkward it is to keep on filing after the left hand has become sore and blistered from the continual contact with the file's rough surface. A good method of attaching such a handle is to bend a piece of drill rod to the shape shown in the drawing. After bending, grind off half the diameter of the two ends so that when brought together they can be driven tightly into a hole drilled in the wooden handle. The piece is then split at the front to form a spring grip. The front or split part of the attachment should be much narrower than the width of the file, so that when it is pushed on there will be sufficient tension to grip the file tightly. The lines showing the teeth on the end of the file have been omitted from the drawing for the sake of clearness; it is not necessary to grind off the teeth, although it may be found advisable to grind the edges of the file to a more abrupt taper. The size of drill rod to use will depend largely upon the size file with which it is to be used, $\frac{1}{4}$ to $\frac{5}{16}$-in. stock being sufficiently heavy for 8 to 12-in. files.

Self-Centering Dividers

A pair of machinists' dividers can be made self-centering by the simple addition of a perpendicular centering rod and

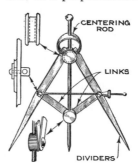

a link arrangement, by means of which the rod is always held at the center. A hole is drilled through the spool and bow for the center rod, which is free to move vertically. This rod passes through a hole in the stud riveted at the center of the links. The links are fastened to the legs of the dividers, and, as the adjustment is changed, move up or down the centering rod.—Albert Hochheimer, West, Ia.

Pocket for Loose-Leaf Notebook

For carrying clippings, and similar small notes, in a loose-leaf notebook, a pocket can be added to the book, which will keep them all together and prevent them from dropping out each time the book is opened.

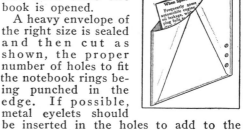

A heavy envelope of the right size is sealed and then cut as shown, the proper number of holes to fit the notebook rings being punched in the edge. If possible, metal eyelets should be inserted in the holes to add to the strength of the pocket and prevent its being easily torn out of the book.

Repairing Small Ammonia Compressors

BY J. V. ROMIG

OWNERS of small ice plants are usually rather chary of undertaking the overhauling and repair of their compressors, although many are quite competent to perform the repair work if they understood just how to go about it. It is to give this instruction to owners, or repairmen unfamiliar with refrigeration equipment, that this article is written.

The first thing necessary is to go over all pipe connections, studying the plant thoroughly, until the operation of each part is completely understood, and a firm grasp of the method of controlling the ammonia obtained. It is surprising how easily the ammonia is made to do as desired, when the operation of the system is understood.

Compressors should be thoroughly examined and overhauled at least once a year, and the winter is the best time to do this, as, once the desired temperature has been attained in the cold-storage room, it will remain at a low degree much longer than in a warmer season. Figs. 1 and 2 show cross-sectional views of two typical compressors; these should be studied carefully so that the instructions may be followed intelligently.

When the desired temperature has been obtained in the storage boxes, ice-cream cabinets, ice tanks, or whatever the machine may be cooling, pump a good vacuum on the system, then close the line suction valves, one of which is shown in Fig. 3, and pump down again. Stop the compressor, then close valves A and B, Fig. 3, as tight as possible. There is now no pressure on the suction side, and the pressure remaining on the high-pressure side of the cylinder may be by-passed

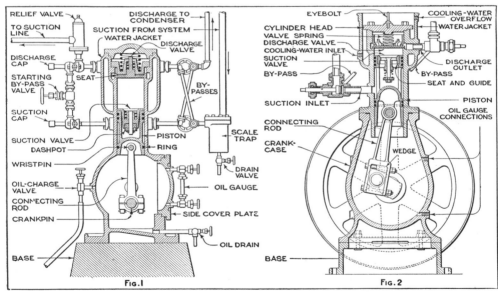

Sections through Typical, Small Single-Acting Ammonia Compressors: Note Carefully the Arrangement of the By-Passes, Suction and Discharge Valves. The Cross By-Pass Valves are Closed at All Times When the Machine is Running

by opening the starting by-pass valve E, Fig. 3; the pressure will then equalize on both ends of the cylinder. Place a bucket of water below the hose on the oil-charge valve, Fig. 1, open the valve, and the ammonia in the cylinder will be absorbed by the water. Do not keep the hose in the water too long, or all the ammonia will be absorbed by the water, and a vacuum may form in the cylinder, drawing in some of the water, and requiring subsequent sponging. Drain the oil from the crankcase, then take off the side cover plate and the cylinder heads; very little smell will be noticed if the instructions have been carried out carefully. Remove the connecting-rod nuts, caps, and shims, and turn the flywheel until the pistons are at the top of the stroke; then the discharge valve and false head, if such is fitted, can be removed, eyebolts inserted into the piston head, and the pistons and connecting rods drawn out. Carefully examine the suction-valve seats; if pitted badly, they must be reground, using fine emery and oil, as in grinding in automobile-engine valves. See also that the balancing springs on the suction valves exert just enough force to overcome the weight of the valves and dashpot plungers; if they are too "light," remove the cage, take out the valve, and stretch the spring until the proper tension is secured; if the spring holds the valve off its seat, compress it a little. Clean out any scale or grit that may be found around the piston cavities, then take the slip ring, used to compress the piston rings when inserting the piston into the cylinder, and slip it half over each ring in turn, observing how much the ring is open at the gap when compressed. If the gap measures more than .02 in., new rings should be fitted.

Rings that have an angular oil groove

not in line when inserting the piston into the cylinder, and that they stay staggered. Next examine the discharge valve; this usually shows some pitting, due to particles of scale getting between valve and seat; if necessary, regrind to a continuous surface with emery and oil. By a continuous surface is meant one in which there may be some pits, but which do not overlap each other, so that the valve will not leak. Too much emphasis cannot be laid upon the necessity of doing this part of the work well; the writer has found that very many cases of poor operation were due to bad high-pressure seats.

Replace the pistons in their proper cylinders, and, by turning to the top of the stroke, see how much clearance there is between the piston head and the top of the cylinder walls; if this is more than .02 in., the top halves of the connecting-rod bearings are worn, and should be replaced. Too great clearance is also a prolific source of inefficiency, as the space holds a comparatively large volume of highly compressed gas, and allows it to expand on the downstroke, partly filling the cylinder. Allow as little clearance as possible without permitting the metals to touch. All bearings should be tested for wear by placing a pinch bar under the shaft, in the case of the shaft bearings, or under the cap, in the case of the connecting-rod bearings, and, using a block as a fulcrum, raising the shaft or piston assembly; the bearings must be tight enough so that no play will be felt. If too much end play exists in the crankshaft, this can be taken up by a fiber washer, placed between the cover plate and crank web.

The key in the flywheel should be tested for shake, as it is very likely to work loose; if allowed to run when loose, it will develop a bad knock. Remove all accumulated dirt in the crankcase, and reassemble. After assembling, turn the machine over slowly to see that everything is clear, then pump out the air entrapped in the cylinder through the discharge cap, Fig. 1. If, while the machine was open, a leak in either of the main control valves A or B, Fig. 3, was noticed, it will be found neces-

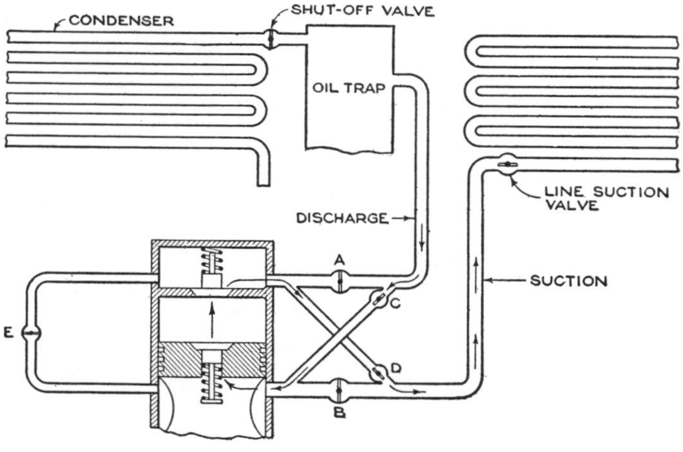

FIG. 3
Diagram of the Pipe Connections: The Arrows Show the Direction of the Gases When Pumping from the Discharge Side to the Suction Side

cut in the outer face give the best results, and should be fitted so that the gap is no wider than .006 in. "Stagger" the gaps, that is, see that the gaps are

sary to reseat these valves; to do this, the stems and bonnets must be removed, and the ammonia must be prevented from escaping while the valves are open. To repair valve A, proceed as follows: Close the shut-off valve between the cylinder and condenser, close also valves A and B, and open the cross-by-pass valves C and D; run the machine until the oil trap frosts up well. This pumps the gas from the discharge side, through the by-passes, into the suction side, as shown by the arrows. Close valves C and D, then the bonnet and stem may be removed from valve A.

It will probably be found that the lead seats are spun up, as shown in the center drawing of Fig. 4, which shows a double-seat valve head. To reseat, heat the head with a blowtorch until the lead melts and flows freely in the groove. Add a little new lead, and skim off the oxidized surface lead. If care is exercised, both seats may be renewed without unscrewing the two parts of the head, but the repairman with no experience in this work will probably find it better to unscrew the head and repair each seat separately. When replaced in the valve body, screw tightly in place, and use a monkey wrench on the valve wheel when seating for the first time; this will make a tiny circular impression on the new seat, and it will hold tight. If the valve has a steel disk instead of a soft seat, regrind as instructed for the cylinder valves.

To repair valve B, pump a vacuum on the system, close the line suction valves, and again pump a vacuum. Now close valve A, after stopping the compressor, and the line between the cylinder and the line suction valve will have no gas in it. Open valve E, and dissipate the gas in water as explained before; valve B can then be opened and repaired. When replaced, pump out the entrapped air through the discharge cap and replace the cap before opening valve A. These valves should be repacked when dismantled, and a little oil applied on the stem and threads. Various types of globe, angle, and expansion valves are shown in Fig. 4; with

what has been said, no trouble should be experienced in repairing any of these. One thing should be borne in mind, however; when placing valves on a line, always present the bottom of the seat or disk toward the source of the greatest pressure, that is, always have a valve shut

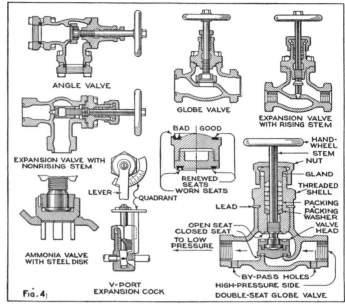

ANGLE VALVE

EXPANSION VALVE WITH NONRISING STEM

AMMONIA VALVE WITH STEEL DISK

GLOBE VALVE

EXPANSION VALVE WITH RISING STEM

BAD | GOOD

RENEWED SEATS

WORN SEATS

LEVER — QUADRANT

LEAD

OPEN SEAT
CLOSED SEAT
TO LOW PRESSURE

V-PORT EXPANSION COCK

HAND-WHEEL
STEM
NUT
GLAND
THREADED SHELL
PACKING
PACKING WASHER
VALVE HEAD

BY-PASS HOLES
HIGH-PRESSURE SIDE
DOUBLE-SEAT GLOBE VALVE

Fig. 4

Sections of Typical Globe, Angle, and Expansion Valves: The Center View Shows the Head of a Double-Seat Valve

against the pressure; if the pressure comes on top of the valve, the stuffing box will be under pressure always, and it will be difficult to keep it from leaking.

Examine the crankshaft stuffing box and repack, placing the new rings with the gaps staggered, to prevent leakage; it is well to smear the new rings with a little thin graphite grease.

Before starting up an overhauled compressor, pour in a new supply of ice-machine oil, bringing the level up to ½ in. in the gauge glass. Be sure to get the proper kind of oil, as any oil which has not a low freezing point will cause endless trouble.

Another point worth noting is to renew all cotter pins; cotter pins *may* be bent more than once without breaking, but use new ones, and be safe.

Do not turn any valve, or open any part, on an ammonia compressor, without tracing over every part of the system, or without being sure what the effect will be, and also be sure that there is a near and free exit, so that a quick escape may be made if the gas comes out too strongly.

Fixture for Forming Flat Springs

The drawing shows the construction of a fixture for forming flat springs quickly, conveniently, and uniformly. A bedplate,

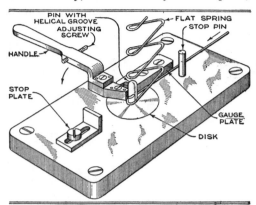

A Fixture for Conveniently and Quickly Forming Specially Shaped Flat Springs Uniformly

which may be of cast iron, is machined and provided with screw holes at the corner for attachment to bench or table, and a hole is bored out at the center to receive a steel disk, which should be a free-running fit, but without shake. A drive-fitted pin is inserted into the center of the disk. A helical groove, with a pitch equal to that desired in the spring, is cut into this central pin. A gauge plate is fastened to the plate for guiding the wire and for preventing vertical movement of the disk. A sliding, adjustable stop plate is also provided, to make the spring of uniform width. The forming handle is fastened to the disk and should stop against the gauge plate, as shown; as the handle must clear the center pin and stop plate, it should be offset, and provided with an adjusting screw which comes into contact with the stop pin, and serves to keep the coils of the spring parallel.—S. H. Johnson, Westville, Conn.

Efficiency of Wood Fuels

Two pounds of dry wood of any nonresinous species have about as much heating value as a pound of good coal. A ton of coal may be taken as the equivalent in heating value of a cord of heavy wood, 1½ cords of medium-weight wood, or two cords of light wood.

The following is an approximation of the number of cords of seasoned wood of various kinds needed to give the same amount of heat as a ton of coal, on the basis of 80 cu. ft. of wood, with a mois-

ture content of 15 to 20 per cent to the cord: one cord of hickory, hard maple, beech, birch, oak, ash, elm, locust, longleaf pine, and cherry; 1½ cords of shortleaf pine, Douglas fir, western hemlock, sycamore, red gum, and soft maple; and two cords of cedar, cypress, redwood, basswood, poplar, catalpa, spruce, and white pine.

Resin gives twice as much heat as wood, weight for weight. Hence, such woods as the pines and firs have more heating power per ton than nonresinous woods. The resinous woods in the list are considered as having an average amount of 15 per cent of resin.

The fuel value of the wood depends in many cases not alone upon its heating power, but also upon such qualities as easy ignition, rapid burning, freedom from smoke, and uniform heat. As a rule, soft woods burn more readily than hard woods, and light woods more readily than heavy woods. The pines give a quicker, hotter fire, and are consumed in a much shorter time than birch, whereas birch gives a more intense flame than oak. Oak, however, gives a very steady heat.

Case Holds Tags Numerically

An adaptation of the device shown in the drawing can be used to deliver con-

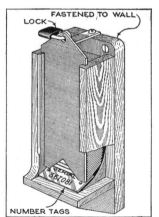

secutively numbered tags or plates, such as used for marking machinery, automobiles, and the like, and is suitable for the accommodation of plates that are made up and stored in advance of the parts being made.

The holder is made from hardwood with a compartment the exact size of the plates, the lower end of the slot being curved, as shown, so that the plates will move forward and downward as the bottom one is removed. A sliding front that fits into grooves in the sides is removable for replenishing the supply of plates; to prevent tampering with the contents, the holder can be locked.—G. A. Luers, Washington, D. C.

Castings for Six-Inch Bench Lathe

In response to our request, Mr. J. V. Romig, the author of the article on "Making a Six-Inch Bench Lathe," published in our October issue, has kindly consented to furnish the necessary castings for this lathe, to any who contemplate building one. They will, of course, be rough castings, and the price will be nominal; if machined castings are ordered, a higher charge will be made to cover the cost of the work.

Further information may be obtained by writing to the editor of this department.

A Gasket Lock Joint

When the pressure-head gasket blew out of the hoisting cylinder of an ash

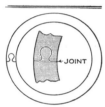

hoist, just at the time of day when it was most needed, a delay of several hours would have been necessary to have removed the piston-rod cables, sheaves, and other parts, to replace a solid gasket. However, by cutting the gasket joint as shown, a non-slipping splice was made, and the job completed in less than half an hour.—U. S. Sprout, Lancaster, Pa.

Jack Made from Axle Housing

Jacks around the service station are often "borrowed" without being returned. To avoid the cost of providing jacks for those lost in this manner, one station used jacks of the type shown in the drawing; these were made in their own shop. Sections of the axle housing of light

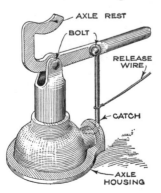

automobiles were used, cutting them as shown and fitting a forged lifting bar and hook, to hold the jack in its raised position. Such jacks are always returned, as they are too large to fit in the tool box or under the seat of an auto.

Radial Shop Crane

A crane suitable for the garage and machine shop, that involves no structural changes in roof or wall beams and re-

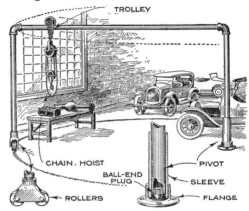

A Radial Shop Crane for the Garage and Machine Shop That can be Pushed to Any Point of Its Circular Path

quires no separate guides, is constructed, as illustrated, from pipe, making it sufficiently simple and inexpensive for any shop, even though it be used infrequently. A center pivot, consisting of a section of pipe and a closed-end floor flange, supports one end of the crane in the manner shown in the detail. The outer end of the crane is supported upon rollers so that the device can easily be pushed around.

Brake-Lining Fixture

The usual method of riveting new lining to the brake and transmission bands of automobiles consists in clamping a punch in a vise, to back up the rivet while the head is being upset with the hammer. This requires considerable effort to keep the punch and rivet together. The idea illustrated by the drawing makes the riveting job

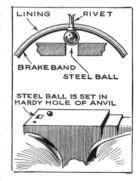

somewhat simpler and requires nothing more than a large steel ball, placed in the hardy hole of an anvil. The rivet is set on this, and the end hammered over. The first blow makes a small depression in the rivet, and the ball rests in this.

Making Leather Fillets for Wood Patterns

Leather fillets glued into the corners of wooden patterns are often used, and while they may be bought ready-made, it is oc-

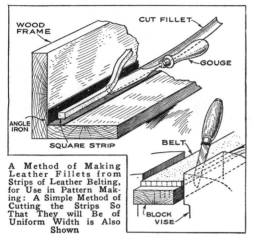

A Method of Making Leather Fillets from Strips of Leather Belting, for Use in Pattern Making: A Simple Method of Cutting the Strips So That They will Be of Uniform Width is Also Shown

casionally necessary that a special size be made in the shop.

A good method is to cut an old leather belt into strips of square cross section, in the manner illustrated in the lower part of the drawing. A wooden block, the same width as the belt, is clamped in a vise, the top of the block being lower than the tops of the vise jaws. A knife is then stuck into the block, at a distance from one of the jaws equal to the required width of the strip, and the belt is pulled through, as shown, cutting off one strip. The block is now planed down to the width of the remaining piece of belting and the operation repeated. Thus the strips will be of uniform width.

A form is then made by nailing together two pieces of board at right angles, with a right-angled strip of heavy tin or sheet iron nailed into the corner. One of the square leather strips is placed in the corner and either a gouge pushed along it while holding one end of the strip, or the gouge is held stationary and the leather strip pulled against its edge. If the resulting fillet is a little rough, it may be smoothed by wrapping fine sandpaper around a hardwood dowel and rubbing it along the surface of the leather, still held in the corner of the form; or it may be sandpapered after being glued into the pattern.

Another way to make such a fillet is to glue the uncut square strip to the pattern and hold it in place temporarily by driving

in a series of brads diagonally, allowing the heads to project. When the glue has set, the brads are pulled out, and the strip is cut with the gouge, and sandpapered. If a fillet is glued into place after being cut to shape, it is usual to press it down into position by means of a small rod, with a brass ball on the end, of the same radius as the fillet.—H. H. Parker, Oakland, Calif.

Tap Wrench Aids in Using Breast Drill

When drilling with a breast drill, to overcome the catching of the drill that necessitates backing it up, the following remedy is a good one: Take a tap holder from a set of taps and dies, slip the shank of the drill through the tap holder, and tighten down as when holding a tap. Allow enough of the drill shank to stick through to engage in the drill chuck. The tap holder now acts as a flywheel and the centrifugal motion carries the drill past the little catches unnoticed; the drilling is thus made much easier.—Orin C. Watkins, Salem, Ore.

Vulcanizing without a Vulcanizer

Repairing slits in boots, hot-water bottles, or similar rubber goods that are too large to fit into one of the small gaso-

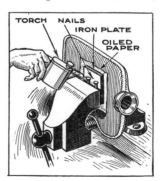

line vulcanizers, used for mending punctured automobile tubes, is done with the makeshift vulcanizing apparatus shown in the drawing. The surface around the slit is treated as in patching

a tube; that is, it is cleaned with gasoline for a generous distance around the aperture and the surface roughened slightly with sandpaper. A good coat of vulcanizing cement is applied and allowed to dry for a few seconds, and a neat patch of vulcanizing rubber is put in place and smoothed down until it adheres evenly.

Then, taking two sheets of iron, as near the size of the patch as possible, one is placed against the patch and the other on the opposite side of the article being mended. A piece of waxed paper is placed between the plate and patch to prevent sticking. The whole is then clamped in a vise, as shown in the drawing, using a couple of nails between the vise jaw and the iron plate, to permit a free play of flame from the alcohol torch used to supply the heat. The flame is kept playing on the plate against the patch, which is kept hot for about 10 minutes, then allowed to cool for another 10 minutes before removing the work for inspection. — Harry W. Poor, Boston, Massachusetts.

Tool for Inserting Auto Universals

The tool shown in the drawing will be found of particular value in automobile

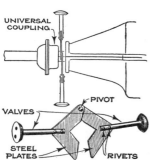

garages and service stations making a specialty of light-car repairs; it is used for inserting the end of the universal joint into its socket in the transmission.

Two sheet-iron plates, triangular in shape, are hinged together at one side, as shown, and a square opening, the size of the universal-joint shaft, is cut in the center. Old valves, welded or riveted to the separate plates, are used for handles. With the tool in position around the universal shaft, the latter can be turned and centered so that it can be inserted into its socket in the transmission.

Motoring through Snow

When driving an automobile through deep snow, it is well to remember that letting some air out of the tires will give a broader traction surface; this is as efficacious in sand as in snow. While tire chains usually are effective, the wheels will sometimes spin; and it is advisable for the winter tourist to carry a pair of mudhooks for such occasions. Do not get alarmed if the radiator boils, so long as it contains enough water to cover the cylinder heads. Snow can be melted for the **radiator** by placing a bucket full under the radiator drain cock, and allowing some of the hot water to flow into it.

Snap-Ring Bending Fixture

The fixture shown in the drawing may be made in any machine shop at but slight cost, and will be found very useful in

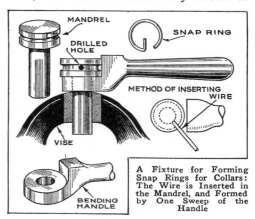

A Fixture for Forming Snap Rings for Collars: The Wire is Inserted in the Mandrel, and Formed by One Sweep of the Handle

forming snap rings for collars used on small shafts, and for various other purposes. A circular mandrel is turned with a grooved collar, and a hole, slightly larger in diameter than the diameter of the wire used, is drilled in the center of the groove. Flats are filed on the mandrel shank to prevent it from turning in the vise.

A handle, the boss of which is bored to fit freely on the shank of the mandrel, is shaped as illustrated, and the fixture clamped in the vise. The wire, cut to length, is inserted in the hole in the mandrel, and one turn of the handle completes the ring.

Mitering Odd-Shaped Molding

Cutting molding that has a very narrow back, although full and round in the

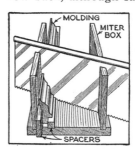

face, is somewhat difficult because the work rocks and slips on its narrow base. The easiest and surest way of making a correct miter, or joint, is to slip in strips of wood of suitable thickness between the sides of the miter box and the work, to provide a support for the latter, as shown in the drawing. If a great deal of molding of one style is to be cut, these strips can be permanently attached to the miter box.

Novel Arrangement of Drawing-Table Drawer

The illustration shows a novel method of attaching a drawer to a drawing table, in which the drawer, instead of the board, is attached to the legs. The reason for

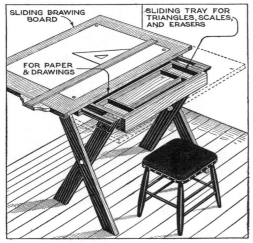

A Novel Arrangement for a Drawing Table: The Drawer is Fastened to the Legs, and the Drawing Board Moves Back over It

this is, first, that it is not necessary to move back when opening the drawer, and, second, that the drawer, being usually filled with books and paper, is much heavier to move than the top. Furthermore, the board is often tipped up at the back so that the drawer is disposed to slide out, and, as the drawer has considerable depth, the supports are more conveniently attached. A sliding tray is made to receive scales set on edge, so that one may be selected conveniently with a very slight opening of the drawer. The divisions in the sliding tray can be made to meet the requirements of individual cases.—G. M. Beerbower, Tarrytown, N. J.

Soldering Jewelry

It is of first importance that soft solder be avoided as far as possible in repairing articles of gold and silver, and even filled and plated jewelry can be repaired with hard solder. To repair a ring, the shank of which requires soldering, bury the setting in a crucible of wet sand, place a small piece of charcoal against one side, and coat the break, previously cleaned by scraping or filing, with borax; charge with solder and blow a flame against the ring until the solder runs in.

Articles that require protection against discoloring in the process of soldering, should be coated with a mixture of burnt yellow ocher and borax, adding a little gum to make it cover the article completely. Allow it to dry, charge with borax, solder, and boil in a weak pickle composed of nitric or sulphuric acid in water. One important point is to wash the piece well in hot water, with a little ammonia added, to remove any dirt and grease, before undertaking any repairs.

If the article is made of colored gold, boil out in a pickle of muriatic acid and water, but never coat with any protecting mixture. To repair gold-filled work, melted solder is required; this may be made in the proportion of 1 oz. fine silver, and 10 dwt. hard brass wire, to which 2 dwt. of zinc is added just before pouring. Or, for strong silver use only the silver and brass.

For repairing most bright gold work, use an alloy composed of 3 dwt. fine silver, 3 dwt. gold, and 2 dwt. fine copper.

A good solder for soldering spectacle frames or other steel parts is made by melting together equal parts of silver and copper.—Geo. M. Millard, Toronto, Ont.

Tools for Valve Combined with Tire Gauge

A tire gauge, used in an eastern tire-service station, was incorporated into the

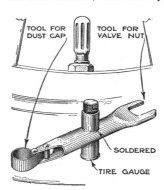

three-in-one tool illustrated. This tool can be used for gripping the dust cap or valve nut, according to the end used, and is made by drilling a hole through a piece of thin steel tubing and soldering the tire pressure gauge in this hole. One end of the tubing is flattened, and a slot cut to fit around the valve nut. At the opposite end, a strip of sheet brass is riveted to form a toggle that takes a tight hold of the dust cap.

❡ Pure Venetian red is the most durable color known for outside woodwork. If applied with pure linseed oil, it will last as long as the woodwork.

Moving Big Trees Economically

By A. M. HUSTEAD

HAVING obtained a contract for moving several large trees from their original location to another, a landscape-service firm successfully accomplished the work without the use of special apparatus. For the transportation of a 16-in. hard maple, a trench was dug around the tree at a distance of about 4 ft. from the trunk and about 4 ft. deep, or to a depth sufficient to catch most of the surface roots. During the time the tree was being dug loose, it was well guyed to prevent it from falling over. The ball of

pulleys, cables and a check rope, to prevent a too sudden drop into the hole, as this might cause the ball to crack, with ultimate loss of the tree.

After the tree was in place, the dirt was backfilled, thoroughly tamped, and puddled in with a stream of water. It is of the utmost importance that the earth be well tamped around the ball and that no air pockets be allowed to form, as these are detrimental to root function, and will, therefore, retard the normal growth.

Showing the Method of Trenching around the Tree and the Appearance of the Root Ball: Many of the Feeder Roots are Cut in This Operation, and This Requires a Subsequent Thinning Out of the Branches

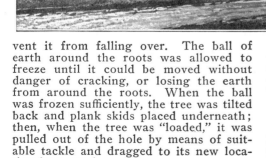

Above, the Tree being Dragged to Its New Location by a Motor Truck: The Root Ball must be Frozen So Solidly as to Avoid Splitting It or Losing Earth around the Roots. Left, Lowering the Tree down an Incline into the New Hole: A Check Rope around the Ball Prevents a Too Sudden Drop

vent it from falling over. The ball of earth around the roots was allowed to freeze until it could be moved without danger of cracking, or losing the earth from around the roots. When the ball was frozen sufficiently, the tree was tilted back and plank skids placed underneath; then, when the tree was "loaded," it was pulled out of the hole by means of suitable tackle and dragged to its new location by a truck.

The hole into which the tree was transplanted was dug with an incline from the bottom to the surface so that the tree could be slid into position by means of

In moving a tree, many of the feeder roots are necessarily cut off, and this will require thinning out the branches. From this particular tree two wagon loads of brush were removed without spoiling its original symmetry.

⁋It is well to remember, when round holes are to be accurately sized, that the properly designed round broach has demonstrated its value for this work even in comparison with roughing and finishing reamers. The work is produced at a greater speed and a considerably lessened cost for tool maintenance.

A Simple Windmill Regulator

Many devices have been applied to windmill-driven pumps supplying water to tanks, to regulate automatically the operation of the windmill as the water in the tank becomes too high or too low.

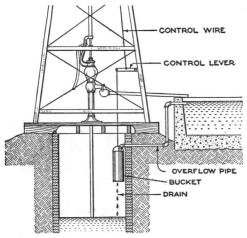

An Automatic Regulator for a Windmill-Operated Pump on the Farm That Keeps the Tank Filled with Water at All Times and Prevents Overflowing

Most of these arrangements are operated by a float or other device in the tank, and are easily rendered inoperative if the float leaks, or the mechanism rusts.

The arrangement shown in the drawing suffers from none of the shortcomings of floats. A 5-gal. cream can is suspended in the well from the end of the control lever by means of a strong wire. A small hole in the bottom of the bucket allows the water to drip out so that it is emptied about every three hours. As the weight is released, the pump clutch is automatically thrown in, and water is pumped into the tank until it reaches the level of the overflow pipe, which drains into the bucket; as the bucket is filled with water the pump is automatically disengaged, so that the container is prevented from overflowing.—S. E. Gibbs, Corydon, Ia.

Deodorizing the Glue Pot

Quite often the glue pot exudes an odor that is almost unbearable; this is often caused by bad glue, but more frequently by the brush. Copper-bound brushes are the most desirable, and, when quitting work for the day, they should be taken out of the pot and hung up until the next morning. Only a few minutes are required to soften up the brush, and

when treated in this fashion, all or most of the disagreeable odor will disappear. While in no way affecting the adhesive qualities of the glue, a few drops of some oil, like oil of sassafras, clove, wintergreen, or cinnamon in the glue pot, is very effective in purifying the vapor arising from the glue.

Repairing Grooves Worn in Shaft

When a ring-oiling box is found that continues to give trouble from heating, it is generally because one of the rings has stopped turning at some time and worn a groove around the shaft; this groove prevents the oil brought up by the ring from being properly distributed, and, of course, the bearing will not be lubricated. These grooves are not usually noticed until the machine is taken down for repairs of some sort, as they are not noticeable so long as the machine is in operation. If the box is oiled by hand, it will run properly, but if the rings are depended upon to carry the oil, the bearing cannot help but run hot.

When grooves are found in a shaft, particularly if the bearing is an important one, it is essential that they be repaired. Sometimes a new shaft may be put in, but to do this, the machine will often be shut down when it is most needed. Also, the shaft may be turned down small enough to eliminate

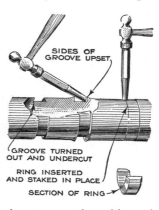

the grooves, but this makes a new bearing necessary, which is impossible in case the bearing is solid and a gear or pulley goes on the end outside the bearing.

Another method to bring the shaft back to its original condition in a short time is illustrated by the drawing. The grooves are squared out and slightly undercut, and a small punch is then used to bring the sides of the groove parallel by upsetting the metal above the surface of the shaft. A metal ring is turned up with beveled sides to fit into the dovetail groove in the shaft. The ring is sawed in half and the sections placed in the groove, the metal that was upset being staked back in place to hold the ring securely to the shaft. If this operation is done carefully, the shaft will be the same size as before, and the ring can be turned to the exact diameter of the shaft, making it difficult to tell where the ring was applied. Small shims can be inserted to compensate for the metal removed when the ring was sawed. On very small shafts the ring can be held in place with solder, but this does not work so well on larger pieces.—James Ellis, Memphis, Tenn.

Calciminer's Brush Holder

A holder, permanently attached to the calcimine pail in such a manner that the brush may drip into the vessel, will prove of convenience to the workman. A hook is formed, as illustrated, from a piece of round iron, flattened at one end and attached to the bucket with screws, if a wooden bucket is used, or with rivets, if a metal one. The handle of the brush rests on the rim of the pail and under the hook, where it may be instantly disengaged.—Jesse L. Blickenstaff, N. Manchester, Ind.

Making a Square from Scales

The drawing shows a convenient little clamp attachment whereby two ordinary machinist's steel scales can be converted into a square, or attached end to end to form a single long scale. The clamp is made from a block of flat steel, slotted to the desired depth to take the scales. The ends of the thumbscrews are turned to a conical point of such an angle that the conical surface is parallel with the face of the scale. It will be seen that with the screws in this position, the action of tightening them rolls the edges of the scales together automatically. Both screws have right-hand threads and knurled heads.

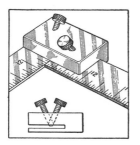

Safety Device for Punch Presses

A manufacturer has designed and installed on his punch presses a safety device that forces the operator to use both hands to trip the press, thus making

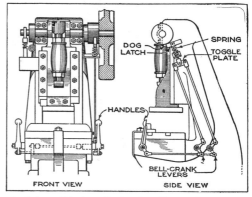

A Safety Tripping Device for Punch Presses, the Operation of Which Requires Both Hands, So That They cannot be Caught under the Descending Ram

sure that the employe's hands will not be under the ram when it descends.

The drawing shows the operating principle of the arrangement. A toggle plate, the center of which is connected to the tripping latch of the press, is controlled by rods hinged to each end. To cause the tripping lever to operate, both rods must move downward at the same time; if only one is moved, the toggle plate will turn about its center and impart no motion to the tripping latch.

Two cast-aluminum handles, one on each side of the press, are pivoted on studs screwed into the press bed. The motion of the handles is transmitted to the toggle plate by $\frac{1}{4}$-in. cold-rolled steel rods and bell-crank levers. The handle at the left-hand side transmits its motion to the toggle through a $\frac{5}{8}$-in. cold-rolled steel shaft extending from the left to the right side of the press. Slots are cut in the toggle plate where the connecting rods are attached, so that the operator will have to push both handles far enough to trip the latch.

This type of safety tripping device is considered more satisfactory than the air-operated device, as its action does not depend upon the use of air pressure, or any other agency but the control of the operator.—Edward H. Tingley, Dayton, Ohio.

❡ Overprinted blueprints can be bleached by flowing very hot water over them.

Holder for Crankcase Bolts

An improvised spring holder, that facilitates the removal or insertion of the crankcase bolts on certain types of automobiles, is shown in the drawing. With such a tool, the bolt is prevented from turning, while both hands are free to place the nuts and washers in position and screw them down. There is nothing complicated about the device, which consists of a wrench socket, of a size to hold the bolts, fastened to one end of an iron rod, which is hinged at its opposite end to an old auto-spring leaf.

In use, the end of the spring is held down with the foot, and this holds the wrench over the bolt head until the nut has been screwed down from above.

Counterbore for Square-Bottom Hole

The drawing shows a counterbore that was designed to make a flat-bottom hole in a case where a teat projecting from the bottom of the hole, as left by the ordinary flat-end drill, was not permissible. Usually, with a tool of this character, considerable trouble is encountered in keeping it sharpened, when it is made in one piece, as there is no clearance at the center. In the tool illustrated, a hole is drilled axially to accommodate a small drill, held in place by a setscrew, the thrust and compensation for wear on the drill being cared for by the adjusting screw in the top. It is no great trick to grind a drill to cut a square bottom, and the clearance necessary to grind the body is provided by the axial hole.—John Homewood, Ontario, Calif.

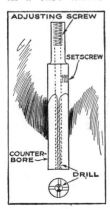

Speed of Conveyor Belts

The National Safety Council recommends the following speeds for belts conveying loose material, such as grain or sand: for belts under 16 in. wide, a maximum speed of 300 ft. per minute, while 450 ft. per minute should be allowed for belts of from 16 to 24 in. in width. For belts wider than 24 in., a speed of 600 ft. per minute is permissible. Belts carrying packages are generally run no faster than 60 to 100 ft. per minute.

Price and Quantity Dial Calculates Cost of Fuel to Motorists

A garage proprietor selling gasoline to motorists has installed the calculator shown in the drawing on his gasoline-measuring pump, saving his own time and that of his customers.

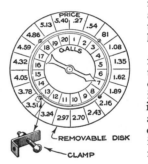

The dial is made from a piece of tin of suitable diameter, in this instance about 8 in., with a pointer at the center. The disk is divided off into the proper number of segments, as illustrated. The price for one or more gallons of fuel is indicated on the outer circle; the number of gallons is shown on the inner one. Of course, any changes in the retail price of the fuel will make it necessary to alter the figures on the outer circle to conform to the new price. Where prices are subject to frequent changes, cardboard circles can be lettered and applied to the sheet-metal disk with shellac. The device is attached to the measuring pump with small bolts and clamps similar to the one shown.—F. J. McMillan, Morristown, Ohio.

Machining and Finishing Ebonite

Ebonite, which is sometimes called vulcanite and hard rubber, and which is largely used for electrical purposes, is also of great use in the chemical industry, owing to the resistance it offers to chemical reagents. It is stable toward air, light, and changes in temperature up to about 175° F. It can be softened in boiling water and then bent and shaped as desired; the shape or impression is retained on cooling, but if the material is subsequently softened by heat it will return to its original form. In machining it, the tool must be sharp, and to prevent overheating, the cut must not be too heavy. If the tool and the work are not kept cool, the former will rapidly lose its edge and the work will be burnt. In polishing ebonite, the surface should first be rubbed smooth with powdered pumice and then buffed, using a tripoli compound, and running the cloth polishing wheel at high speed, the work being held lightly against the wheel. In making ebonite, sheet-metal foils are used as a backing for the plastic material during the process of vulcanization, and this gives the finished sheets their well-known glazed appearance. Owing to the fact that this surface is slightly metallic it should be removed when the material is used for electrical work, else the insulation will be low, owing to surface leakage.

Battery Service-Station Aid

The arrangement shown in the drawing is one of the labor-saving features of a well-planned storage-battery service station. The valve is fitted close to the wall, and from it the water-supply pipe is run overhead to a point about the center of the sink. A short vertical piece of pipe has a length of rubber hose attached to it,

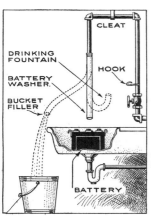

as in the illustration. When washing out battery cells, the hose can be swung to any angle. Other conveniences of this arrangement are that the hose can be used as a drinking fountain, or to fill buckets, as indicated by the dotted lines.

¶To remove a bolt that is "set" or "frozen," or that one has reason to believe cannot be driven out, use as large a wrench as can be handled and tighten down the nut, even if it twists off. This will stretch the bolt and reduce its diameter slightly so that it can be driven out with comparative ease.

Bending Large Sheets of Metal

In a case where several large galvanized-iron tanks were to be made, they were so large that two full-sized sheets of metal were required for the sides and bottom. These pieces had to be bent at right angles for their entire length and the ends riveted together on the bottom. The problem was to bend these sheets to leave a square corner. To start at one end and bend as the work went along was first tried, but it was found that the metal stretched and warped, so

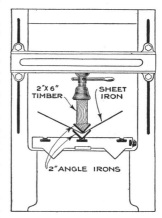

that this method would not answer. The planer was then rigged up as an angle press, and the results were perfect.

Two pieces of 2-in. angle iron were cut to the length of the sheet metal. One length was placed in the T-slot of the planer table and the stock laid on this. A triangular piece of wood was nailed to a 2 by 6-in. timber, 6 ft. long; this was placed on the second angle-iron strip, and a screwjack fitted between it and the crossrail of the machine. By turning the jackscrew, the sheet of metal was bent for its entire length in one operation, and no kinks were formed.—Edwin J. Bachman, Fullerton, Pa.

Drilling Tile

A contractor discovered that one of his men was drilling holes in tile bathroom fixtures about four times as fast as the other workers. Asked to explain his method, the worker demonstrated how cut nails were used in place of the ordinary twist drill. He filed the heads of two nails so that the nails would lie close together, and put them into his brace as he would a drill. He started the hole with the point of a screwdriver, or similar tool, and then applied the nails, which penetrated into the tile much faster and with less loss than the twist drill. When the nails become dull, they are thrown away and a new pair inserted.—Armstrong Perry, New York City.

Valve Grinder Made from Hand Drill

If an old hand drill, or breast drill, of the type in which the spindle runs up through both bevel pinions and into the handle, can be obtained, it may be converted into a tool suitable for valve grinding. The gears are removed and the upper pinion pinned to the spindle. Then, over half of the teeth on the bevel gear are filed or ground off down to the root depth; a smooth surface should be left even with the roots of the teeth to bear against the upper pinion. Enough gear teeth must be removed to prevent interference of one pinion with the other; that is, they must clear one pinion before starting to mesh with the other. As the spindle will now continually reverse its motion as the operating handle is turned, the drill chuck is likely to loosen, so it must be pinned or setscrewed, or removed altogether, and the valve-grinding tool be fastened directly to the end of the spindle.

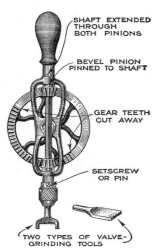

SHAFT EXTENDED THROUGH BOTH PINIONS

BEVEL PINION PINNED TO SHAFT

GEAR TEETH CUT AWAY

SETSCREW OR PIN

TWO TYPES OF VALVE-GRINDING TOOLS

Using Wood Alcohol

Great caution should be observed in the use of any mixtures containing wood alcohol. This is the most deadly poison used in daily commerce; one teaspoonful has been known to cause blindness, and one ounce, death. The poison may be absorbed into the body through the nose, mouth, or skin, so that even the inhalation of the fumes, or the contact of the liquid with the hands, or any other part of the body, may cause poisoning just as though the alcohol were taken into the system through the mouth.

Sudden blindness, with vomiting and abdominal pain, should always cause suspicion of wood-alcohol poisoning, and no time should be lost in having the patient treated by a physician.

Denatured alcohol should be substituted for wood alcohol wherever possible, as this has no ill effect on the system

It has been suggested that, in establishments using quantities of wood alcohol, the word "methanol" be used to label the liquid, as this describes the product specifically, while removing the tempting suggestiveness of the word "alcohol." This term, of course, should be accompanied by the word "Poison," as, even though the temptation to drink the liquid might be removed, the danger from absorption and inhalation would still be present.

One Wrench for Two Taps

By using a supplementary double bushing, of the type shown in the drawing, and placing this in a standard tap wrench with an adjustable handle, two taps can be accommodated at one time. This is a very handy arrangement when a hole is to be rough and finish-tapped. By using the taper tap to rough out the hole, it is only necessary to reverse the tool to complete the hole, using the bottoming tap. The bushing or holder can be made of any good grade of steel.

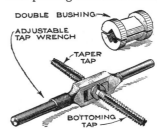

DOUBLE BUSHING

ADJUSTABLE TAP WRENCH

TAPER TAP

BOTTOMING TAP

Gauge for Sharpening Gravers

It is a very difficult matter for users of gravers, such as those used in engraving metals, to get the correct cutting angle when sharpening them on an oilstone. This is so because the tool must be held at just the right angle, and not be allowed to rock. To overcome this difficulty, and, at the same time, make it possible to sharpen the tool at any desired angle, the tool shown in the drawing was made from a T-handle tap wrench. The handle was cut off, and a hole, large enough to accommodate the gravers, drilled along the axis of the wrench shank. A guide, made of steel, 1 in. square by ¼ in. thick, and beveled on one edge at the proper clearance angle for the gravers was bored out to fit over

the nose of the chuck, to which it is held by a small thumbscrew, the chuck being first turned down parallel at the place where the guide fits. A zero line was scribed on the nose of the chuck, and the face of the guide graduated in degrees, as indicated.

In use, it is unnecessary to remove the graver from its handle, the tool being inserted through the hole in the center of the one-time tap wrench. The angle of the side faces of the cutting edge can be varied by loosening the thumbscrew on the guide and changing the position of the chuck with reference to the graduations on the block.—Charles E. Stark, North Attleboro, Mass.

Accurate Holes for Hinge Screws

In fastening a hinge to a door, or box, it is first necessary to drill small holes in the wood for the screws. The hinge is placed in the proper position and held there while one hole is marked off with a pencil. The hinge is then removed and the hole drilled, after which the hinge is replaced and a screw driven to hold it in place while the remaining holes are

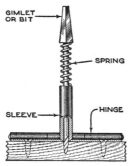

drilled, using the hinge as a template. In order to make this work a little more accurate, the device shown in the drawing was designed. It consists of an ordinary square-shank gimlet, or drill, of the proper diameter, with a spring sleeve on the outside. The sleeve is beveled at the lower end to the same angle as the countersink in the screwholes. Between the drill shank and sleeve, a spiral spring is placed; the pressure of this spring keeps the sleeve always in contact with the work so that the drilled hole is accurately centered.—Charles Homewood, Ontario, Calif.

⁋An open flame should never be used for the purpose of discovering leaks in acetylene tanks. Leaks can generally be detected by the odor of the gas, and their location can be determined by applying soapy water to the surface of the tank, and watching for the bubbles formed by the escaping gas.

A Handy Riveting Anvil

Many riveting jobs require the work to be placed on an offset, to accommodate parts of the work while the rivets are being set, and this is particularly the case on channel iron and work of similar section.

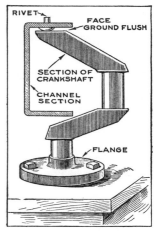

An old automobile crankshaft can be utilized to make a very convenient anvil of this character, as indicated in the drawing, with very little trouble. The shaft is cut off between two crankpins and the cut face ground, or otherwise smoothed off, to provide a plane surface. The section is bolted to a suitable support by means of screws, or bolts, through the flywheel flange. An anvil of this type will prove a useful fixture in the garage for such work as relining brakes, repairing lamp casings, and other work where an opening under the face of the anvil is required.

Rubber Trough for Acid Carboys

Acid carboys are bulky and difficult to handle unless they are mounted on some form of pouring device. If no device of this character is available, it is a very difficult matter to pour acid without more or less splashing and spilling, with resulting damage to clothing and surrounding objects.

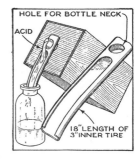

By using a suitable length of automobile inner tube as a trough to guide the acid, all the potential loss and damage can be prevented. A hole is cut into one end of the tube section to fit over the neck of the carboy, and the upper wall is cut away as shown, leaving the sides to guide the fluid into the receiving container.

Boiler-Compound Feeder

The steam boiler-compound feeder illustrated has features not possessed by the usual arrangement. A piece of large-

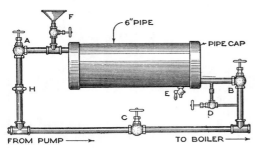

An Arrangement for Feeding Boiler-Compound Solutions into Steam Boilers with the Feed Water: The Supply of Compound can be Forced in as Fast or Slow as Desired by Proper Manipulation of the Valves

diameter pipe, closed at the ends with caps or flanges, is used as a receptacle for the solution. By opening the valves A and B and closing C, the pump discharge will be forced into the boiler, carrying the compound solution along with it. By leaving A and C open, B closed, and the ⅛-in. valve D slightly open, a slow feed of compound will be secured. It is nearly impossible to get a slow feed by leaving the valves A and B slightly opened. The tank can be emptied of water through the draincock E and filled with the compound through the valve F, the upper end of which is fitted with a funnel. Some engineers may prefer to have the union H located between the tank and valve B; a small union or right and left-hand coupling is used to connect the ⅛-in. pipes. The addition of a glass indicator on the tank, while not necessary, would be an improvement.

Hardened Hasp Staple Prevents Sawing

The staple of an ordinary padlock hasp is made of soft steel or iron, and it is usually an easy matter to saw it off and release the hasp; less trouble than to pry off the hasp or saw the lock. A way to prevent this is to make a special staple of drill rod, hardened and tempered, or of casehardened soft steel. If one is unfamiliar with casehardening, the use of drill rod is preferable, as this need only to be heated, quenched, and the temper drawn. The length of rod, which should be of the largest diameter that will pass through the slot in the hasp, is annealed, and each end is threaded. Old dies should be used if possible, as drill rod is hard on new

ones; the S. A. E. thread, as used by automobile repairmen, is preferable to the U. S. S., as less metal is removed.

Then the rod is bent to form the staple, heated bright red, and plunged into water. After testing for hardness with an old file, the piece is brightened up with emery cloth and again heated until the polished surface turns to a deep blue, when it is again plunged into water. If tempered correctly, the staple will be too hard to saw easily, but not hard enough to be brittle. After pushing the arms through the staple plate, nuts are screwed onto the ends and these are sunk into the wood beneath the plate.

Eyelets in Draftsman's Triangle

The draftsman's triangle can be arranged so that it is raised out of contact with the paper at each corner, thereby lessening the chance of blurred lines. A hole is drilled through the triangle at each corner; shoe eyelets, which can be obtained from any shoe repairer, are inserted in the holes, and heads are formed upon them. The short legs will keep the instrument from contact with the paper, but do not interfere in any way with its regular use.—C. B. Smith, Chicago, Ill.

Plane Handle Made Adjustable

The plane handle illustrated is made so that it can be pushed toward the adjusting nut to meet the requirements of different users. Ordinarily, the position of the handle with relation to the adjust-

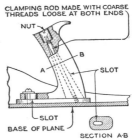

ing nut is such that it can be conveniently reached by only a few persons.

A tapered slot is cut into the handle, as indicated in the drawing. The clamping rod is made with a coarse thread at each end, and makes a loose fit in the nut and bottom of the plane. This makes possible an adjustment of the handle forward for the particular convenience of short-fingered users, or backward for the user whose fingers are long. The adjustment is made by loosening the nut, moving the handle the required distance in either direction, and retightening the nut.—M. E. Duggan, Kenosha, Wis.

An Improved Stone Boat

For building garden walls, stone fences, laying foundations, or similar masonry work that requires the transportation of heavy stones or other weighty masses, the old stone boat can well be resorted to. The farmer perhaps appreciates the utility of this "vehicle" better than anyone, and he knows that it is easier to move heavy objects horizontally than vertically. However, the stone boat that is now helping the settlers of cut-over lands to avoid the dangers of hernia and strained backs in the clearing of their land, is built along different lines from the old type.

Large weights that are to be moved by a stone boat are usually dragged by a team of horses, yet one man can pull a surprisingly heavy object with it, and two men can make quite a showing; if handled carefully, a light car can also furnish the pulling power without undue strain.

The making of a stone boat of the type illustrated requires only two pieces of plank, about 8 ft. long, a wooden crosspiece, two straight bolts, and two ring bolts, together with the necessary length of chain. The planks are pointed at one end, and the two squared ends are bolted to the crosspiece, which should be of about 2 by 8-in. stuff and less than 2 ft. long. A space of several inches is left between the planks at the crosspiece, to permit the rear ends to move together when pull is applied to the forward ends. On fastening the ring bolts to the front end, about 1 ft. from the point, the stone boat is complete. A chain attached to the ring bolts enables the draw-

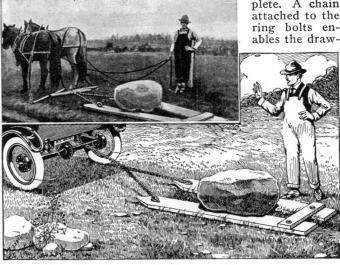

A Stone Boat for Moving Heavy Bowlders or Tree Stumps: This Type of Boat Itself Lifts the Load, Thus Relieving the Operator of Much Heavy Work and Clearing the Land More Rapidly

bar pull to be applied at a convenient distance from the pointed ends of the planks.

This particular type of stone boat works like a pair of scissors. Placed behind a stump or bowlder, it opens up as the pulling power forces its two pointed planks apart. As the pull is steadily applied the load is lifted or rolled onto the stone boat and then hauled away. Where a team, or other pulling power, is available the operator has no work except to adjust the pointed planks and the chain—this stone boat loads itself.—Mark G. Troxell, Madison, Wis.

Making Gun Greases

During the war, the deterioration of arms and equipment of different kinds from rusting was a serious matter, and the government spent much time and money in extensive experiments upon "slushing oils" for the prevention of rust. As a result of this work, the following formulas were developed and gave excellent results:

Resin (preferably H-grade) 1 part, vaseline 10 parts, and kerosene 1 part. The resin is melted and mixed with the previously heated vaseline. The mixture is stirred well while cooling, and then the kerosene is added. If a more solid grease is desired, a little candelilla wax may be substituted for a part of the vaseline. The more wax used, the more solid will be the resulting grease. In government tests, this mixture almost perfectly preserved bright-steel plates that were exposed to outside winter weather for eight months.

Two other formulas are given for semi-solid greases, as follows: Formula A; candelilla wax 3 parts, resin (preferably, but not necessarily, H-grade) 6 parts, and vaseline 50 parts; Formula B; 2 parts carnauba wax, 5 parts resin, and 50 parts vaseline. The materials in the above formulas should be heated together to about 250° F., until all the ingredients are melted, and the mixture thoroughly stirred while cooling. They are best applied so as to cover the surfaces completely. When it is desired to remove the grease, slightly warm the article protected by it, and wipe off with a clean cotton cloth.—Chas. E. Mullin, Philadelphia, Pa.

An Emergency Fan Belt

In an emergency, when a fan belt breaks or is lost, a serviceable substitute, that will hold until the proper kind of

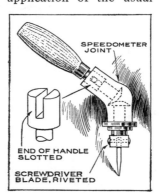

belt can be obtained, can be made from tire tape. Such a belt is made by looping about four layers of tape to make an endless ring of the proper diameter. Each layer is slightly staggered as in the sectional view. A diagonal wrapping in each direction is then applied for further strength. Under some conditions, when the belt is not lost, it can be repaired with tape strips.

Roller for Decorators' Stencils

Nearly all stencil brushes will tear the ties and fine lines of complicated decorators' stencils and patterns. To overcome this, I make use of a tool that works faster and gives better results than the brush, and saves the stencil. A wooden roller, about 3 in. in diameter, has a slot, ½ in. deep, cut parallel with its center. The roller is covered with a piece of plush or felt, preferably the former, about an inch longer than the circumference of the roller, the excess material being forced into the slot and tacked to hold it in place. Pins are driven into the ends of the roller, and a handle is made from stiff wire and bent over the pins. The paint, or calcimine, is spread on a board, or slab, and the roller is run over this until the plush or felt covering is sufficiently charged with color; the roller is then run over the stencil.—C. F. Herbert, Chicago, Ill.

Concrete Piles without Forms

Although concrete piling is no novelty, a method of using bored holes as forms for foundation piles for a summer cottage may be of value in many instances. To secure solid footings for the sills in the case in question, an 8-in. post-hole auger was used, and the holes were bored about 5 ft. deep and 6 ft. apart. Sill levels were established and the holes filled with the concrete mixture to the ground level. Short sleeves or forms of 8-in. stovepipe were then forced into the soft concrete in each hole until the tops were on the established sill level. These extension-sleeve forms were then filled with concrete, with suitable anchor bolts imbedded in it.—T. W. Ingersoll, Buffalo, Minnesota.

Geared Offset Screwdriver

A screwdriver, for use where the space above the screw head does not permit the application of the usual straight-handle type, is made, as shown in the drawing, from a speedometer joint, in which two bevel gears rotate shafts held at an angle to each other. There are usually two such joints on each speedometer, at the points where the flexible shaft is connected. The joint is modified by riveting a screwdriver blade to one end and fitting a handle to the second shaft, as indicated. In use, the casing about the gears forms a convenient hold for the palm of the left hand, while the right hand is used to turn the handle.

Ammonia for Cooling Hot Bearings

When a 100-hp. motor, running at 1,800 r.p.m. and driving a blower used to furnish the induced draft to a battery of six boilers, developed a hot bearing on the pulley side, it created a problem that was satisfactorily solved by cooling the overheated bearing with chemically pure ammonia.

The heating was caused by excessive

tightness of the belt, but although the tension was decreased immediately this was noticed, the bearing failed to cool, and as it was impossible to shut down the motor until the bearing cooled off, and flooding the bearing with oil produced no result, the ammonia treatment was used as a last resort. A small amount of chemically pure liquid ammonia was mixed into an emulsion with the oil, and the mixture was carefully and slowly fed into the bearing drop by drop; it sputtered at first, but after about 15 minutes' steady application, the bearing had cooled nearly to normal. The oil was then changed, and no further trouble was experienced. If the liquid ammonia is not chemically pure and nearly free from water, the water in the mixture will decrease the lubricating property of the oil sufficiently to render it useless for high-speed bearings. This system of cooling bearings by utilizing the rapid-evaporating qualities of ammonia has since been used many times with perfect success.—C. E. Diehl, Mammoth, Utah.

Tool Clamps Auto-Transmission Springs

When replacing the cover of the light-automobile planetary transmission after repairs have been made, much difficulty is experienced in compressing the springs enough to get them between the ears of the transmission bands. The tool shown in the drawing is specially adapted for this purpose; it will compress the springs and

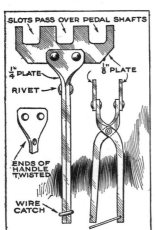

hold them so that they can be inserted easily. The tool consists of a simple pair of tongs or pliers provided, on each jaw, with a slotted plate that fits over the springs. A link or catch in one of the handles slips over the opposite handle and retains the adjustment. The use of such a tool will immediately reduce the time of placing the transmission cover, especially when new lining has been placed on the brake bands.

Rack Makes Delivery Car of Touring Car

A baker made use of his passenger car to deliver the products of his shop to customers, by adding a rack that fitted neatly and securely into the back-seat frame after the cushion had been removed. A light but substantial wooden frame was made, covered with wallboard, and a notch cut in the underside of the frame

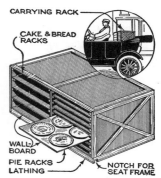

bottom, to fit over the edge of the frame that retains the cushion. The whole rack was suitably reinforced with lattice strips, and shelves were made from wallboard, sliding on light strips. A central partition divides the rack into two compartments. This arrangement is easily removed from the passenger car and saves its user the cost of a commercial truck. The original rack has eight shelves with a capacity of 64 pies, but the shelving can be adjusted as desired.—O. H. Hampsch, Nashville, Tenn.

Scraping Battery Terminals

Scraping the scale from the terminals of storage-battery plates is a tedious and time-consuming job, requiring a strong arm for continued work when done in the ordinary manner. By making and using a scraper of the type shown, in which the blade from an ordinary hand scraper is attached to a

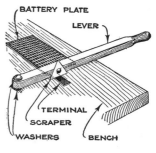

lever, the obstinate scale, on the positive plate in particular, can be removed with but a single operation for each surface, and the leverage makes greater speed possible. The lever is permanently attached to the bench top and has just enough vertical play to permit the insertion of the plate terminal underneath the scraper blade.—H. Sibley, Pasadena, Calif.

A Superior Eye-Splice

Unless the workmanship has been very good, an eye-splice of the ordinary kind will become loosened, and eventually pull

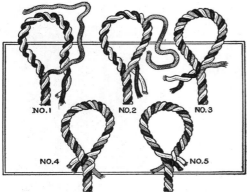

NO.1 NO.2 NO.3

NO.4 NO.5

The Various Operations Required to Make an Eye-Splice Superior to the Usual One: The Steps Require but Little More Time than the Old Way

out when the rope is subjected to intermittent but excessive strain. In order to prevent this, the splice, shown in the drawing in the successive operations of making it, has been devised, and as can be readily seen, the rope must break before the splice will pull out. The splice is built on the principle of the one-strand grommet. A bight is made in the rope, one strand is unlaid, and then relaid around the eye in reverse order. The three ends are then worked under and over after the usual manner of making a short splice, or finishing an eye-splice. The work can be done in very little more time than is usually required for the other type, while the strength is greatly increased.—G. Dallas Hanna, San Francisco, Calif.

A Handy Drill-Press Drift

A handy drift for knocking out sockets or taper-shank tools, made as shown in

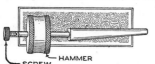

HAMMER

SCREW

the drawing, does away with the necessity of using a hammer, and leaves one of the operator's hands free to catch the socket or tool as it is released.

Made of ¼-in. flat stock, it is turned down at one end to form a guide for the sliding weight which takes the place of the usual hammer; the screw in the end prevents the hammer from sliding off. The side of the hammer is made concave

to provide a better grip for the fingers. The drift is used in the same manner as ordinary ones, the blow of the hammer against the end of the tapered drift releasing the socket or tool.

Tractor Started with Carbide

For starting my tractor in cold weather, I have a small tin can with a few ³⁄₁₆-in. holes punched in it. A handful of waste is dipped in water and the surplus squeezed out. Four or five pieces of calcium carbide, the size of a pea, are placed in the middle of the wad, which is placed in the can. The can is shoved into the intake, and the flywheel turned over until the engine fires, which is usually on the first or second turn. As soon as the engine is operating properly, the acetylene-generating can is removed and placed in the toolbox.—Russell Adams, Seward, Oklahoma.

Tester for Auto Ignition

An efficient tester for the ignition circuit of an automobile can be made from a circular block of wood, a screwhook, and some nails, as shown in the drawing. The nails are driven through the wooden

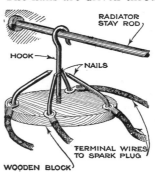

RADIATOR STAY ROD

HOOK

NAILS

TERMINAL WIRES TO SPARK PLUG

WOODEN BLOCK

disk, around the edge, and are bent over so that the points are at the proper distance from the central screwhook, by which the tester is suspended from the radiator stay rod. The spark-plug terminal wires are slipped over the nails and the motor turned over. Perfect sparking at the tester indicates that the ignition units are operating up to the spark plugs. For six and eight-cylinder engines a larger number of nails will be required, as one is needed for each spark-plug wire.

¶ In some drafting rooms the practice is followed of making long dashes for invisible lines, not only because they require less time, but also to preclude the possibility of a short dash near a dimension being mistaken for the figure 1, and read as part of the dimension.

TESTING MOTORS, GENERATORS, and TRANSFORMERS

By KENNETH C. COGGESHALL

Part I—Motors

TESTS on motors, generators, and transformers are usually made to ascertain if the apparatus can carry additional load without injury; to make certain that the rating guarantees have been fulfilled; to see if the temperature rise is within safe limits; to determine the efficiency of the apparatus under varying loads, or to find the most economical conditions of operation.

It is often necessary to find the resistance of the windings, and this is done by connecting a voltmeter and ammeter in the circuit, as shown in Fig. 1, using a direct-current supply. The basis of this method, known as the fall-of-potential method, is Ohm's law, which states that the resistance of any circuit, in ohms, is equal to the electromotive force, in volts, divided by the current strength in amperes. Expressed as a formula, this is:

$$R = \frac{E}{I},$$

where R is the resistance in ohms, E the voltage, and I the current strength in amperes. The values of E and I are read from the meters simultaneously. It should be understood that the resistance of a winding increases with a rise in temperature, consequently, for purposes of comparison, it is best to note and record the temperature of the winding when the test is made.

The power input to a direct-current motor is measured as shown in Fig. 2, the connections being very similar to those of Fig. 1. While the motor is running under various loads, several readings of the ammeter and voltmeter are recorded, and the average value of E and I obtained. The product of the average values of E and I is expressed in watts, and represents the power input to the motor. The formula is:

$$P = E \times I,$$

where P represents the power, expressed in watts; E and I are, of course, the voltage and current strength as in measuring resistance. If the power is to be expressed in horsepower units, the product of E and I is divided by 746, as 746 watts are equivalent to one horsepower

(Hp.); the formula then becomes:

$$Hp. = \frac{E \times I}{746}.$$

By comparing the ammeter reading with the full-load current value, as shown on the motor nameplate, a fair estimate of the load on the motor may be made, where no more accurate method of determining the load is available.

The efficiency of a machine is the ratio of the output to the input, or the power given out divided by the power supplied. Motor efficiency may be determined either by the measurement of its losses, or by actually measuring the output by mechanical or other means. The mechanical method, while not so accurate, is the simpler, and is the only one that will be described here. As shown in Fig. 3, a **Prony** brake is used to measure the horsepower produced. This consists of a pair of brake blocks, clamped on the pulley of the motor; a long lever fastened to one of the blocks, and a spring balance. If L represents the distance, in feet, from the center of the pulley to the center of the spring balance; W the pull or weight shown on the scale, and N the number of revolutions per minute of the motor, then

$$Hp. = \frac{2 \times 3.142 \times L \times N \times W}{33,000};$$

by making the length L equal to 5 ft. 3 in., the formula may be simplified to

$$Hp. = \frac{N \times W}{1,000};$$

that is, simply multiply the number of revolutions per minute by the weight shown on the scale, and divide by 1,000. If this result is multiplied by 746, the number of watts delivered is obtained, and if this figure is divided by the input, as calculated from the meter readings, the efficiency of the motor is obtained. The formula is:

$$Efficiency = \frac{746 \times \left(\frac{N \times W}{1,000}\right)}{E \times I},$$

Another formula,

$$Efficiency = \frac{8.52 \times L \times N \times W}{E \times I},$$

may be used; in this formula, N is the

number of revolutions per *second*. The result of either of these formulas, multiplied by 100, will give the percentage of efficiency.

It is often desirable to know at what load a motor operates most efficiently; some motors, for example, show their peak efficiency at a slight overload, others, again, at slightly under full load. To test, take readings at various loads, up to 50-per-cent overload, as compared with the nameplate rating. Using these values, calculate the output for each reading, and for each output value compute the per cent efficiency. This information can then be put into graphical form, as shown in Fig. 4. The curve will show the point of highest efficiency, as that point will be the peak of the curve.

Tests on alternating-current machinery cannot be carried out in the same manner as on direct-current apparatus. Another instrument, the wattmeter, must be employed to measure the actual power input or output. This is necessary because the voltage and current alternate in value from positive to negative, completing each second as many cycles as the frequency of the generator; the current strength also either leads the voltage or lags behind it, usually the latter, therefore the product of the volts and amperes is not the actual, but only the apparent power. The true or actual power is shown by the wattmeter, which is designed to compensate for what is known as the power factor.

The apparent power, in watts, is indicated by the formula:

$$P = E \times I,$$

but the actual power is

$$P = E \times I \times Pf.,$$

and the power factor (Pf.) is equal to the actual watts divided by the apparent watts, that is,

$$Pf. = \frac{\text{Actual watts}}{\text{Apparent watts}}.$$

The connections for testing a single-phase a.-c. motor are shown in Fig. 3. Taking the values of E, I, and P, where P is the wattmeter reading, then

$$Pf. = \frac{P}{E \times I}.$$

The kilowatt (Kw.) input is

$$Kw. = \frac{E \times I \times Pf.}{1,000} = \frac{P}{1,000}.$$

If a **Prony-brake** test is made, then

$$\text{Efficiency} = \frac{746 \times \left(\frac{N \times W}{1,000}\right)}{P},$$

that is, multiply the number of revolutions per minute by the weight, divide by

1,000, multiply by 746, and divide the last result by the wattmeter reading.

The formula

$$\text{Efficiency} = \frac{8.52 \times L \times N \times W}{P}$$

can also be used, N again being the number of revolutions per *second*.

To test a three-phase a.-c. motor, six instruments are necessary, as shown in Fig. 6, except where a switching system is provided, as in Fig. 7, when the tests may be made with but three instruments. The total input, in this case, is the sum of the wattmeter readings. If the load is very light, it is possible that one of the wattmeters will show a negative value. To obtain a reading, reverse the current leads. In this instance, the actual watts input is the reading of the positive wattmeter minus the reading of the one the connections of which were reversed.

It should be realized that the values found for each phase are not one third of the total, and that, considered individually, they mean nothing. In reality, the apparent power is equivalent to the product of E and I multiplied by the square root of 3, that is,

$$\text{Apparent power} = E \times 1 \times 1.73,$$

in which

$$E = \frac{E_1 + E_2}{2}, \text{ and } I = \frac{I_1 + I_2}{2}.$$

The total power is

$$P_1 + P_2;$$

and the power factor

$$Pf. = \frac{P_1 + P_2}{E \times I \times 1.73}.$$

In these formulas, it must be remembered that E and I are the average readings. E_1 is the reading of the upper voltmeter (Fig. 6); E_2, the reading of the lower one; and similarly for I_1, I_2, P_1, and P_2. The average values of E are obtained, as stated in the formula, by adding the readings of E_1 and E_2 and dividing by 2. The average values of I are obtained in the same way.

By using a Prony brake to determine the horsepower output, the efficiency at any load can be computed, and the data recorded graphically.

$$\text{Efficiency} = \frac{8.52 \times L \times N \times W}{P_1 + P_2},$$

N being the number of revolutions per *second*. If the full-load efficiency is known, the output in horsepower may be calculated thus:

$$Hp. = \frac{(P_1 + P_2) \times \text{Efficiency}}{746}.$$

In order that the operator may be able at any time to estimate quickly the output of the motor when the input is

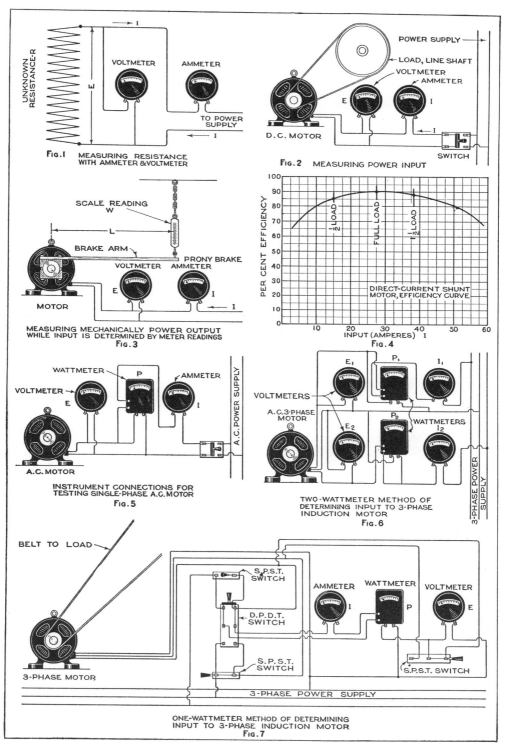

Fig. 1 Shows the Method of Measuring Resistance; Figs. 2 and 3, Connections for Power Tests on Direct-Current Motors, and Figs. 5 and 6, Connections for Testing Single and Three-Phase Alternating-Current Motors. Fig. 7 Shows How a Three-Phase Motor may be Tested with Only Three Instruments

known, an efficiency curve, as shown in Fig. 4, should be plotted.

A very rough check of the power input can be made with only a voltmeter and ammeter connected in one phase. Compare the readings with the nameplate data. If the voltmeter reading is as specified, then the ammeter reading, as compared with the nameplate value, will indicate whether the motor is over or underloaded.

In calculating either input or output, the values of E, I, P, L, N, and W must be read as nearly simultaneously as possible, dividing the work between several persons if necessary.

Wedge Holds Door for Planing

Carpenters, when planing doors, hold their work in a vertical position by inserting the end in a notched board horizontally between the door jambs. However, the work is not held rigidly, and it must be supported by the workman. A

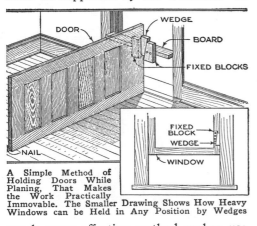

A Simple Method of Holding Doors While Planing, That Makes the Work Practically Immovable. The Smaller Drawing Shows How Heavy Windows can be Held in Any Position by Wedges

much more effective method makes use of tapered blocks affixed to the edge of the board, then, by inserting a wedge and tacking the door down to the floor at the opposite end, the work is practically immovable. Windows that overbalance their sash weights to such an extent that they cannot be kept up, can be wedged into position in much the same manner, as shown in the lower illustration.—Wm. E. King, Monessen, Pa.

Protecting Sprinkler Heads

To be sure that an automatic-sprinkler system is in good order the sprinkler heads should be carefully watched. Sprinkler heads having four different melting points are made; the lowest is 160° and the highest 360°. The latter are used in boiler rooms, drying rooms, and other places where there is a high temperature at all times. Extreme care should be used in replacing the sprinklers, so that only those of the proper melting point are used. To get the greatest pro-

tection from the system, however, the heads should have the lowest melting point that can be safely used. Where chemical fumes or moisture come into contact with and corrode the heads, the protection is decreased, because the thin skin of oxide on the surface increases the temperature required to melt the fusible metal. This trouble can be overcome by covering the heads with a waxlike substance that melts at a temperature somewhat lower than that required to melt the head. In a case where the likelihood of corrosion is great the heads should be changed frequently. Under some conditions, as in woodworking shops, paper mills, and the like, the heads become coated with flying particles of sawdust or paper pulp, which hardens and thus reduces their effectiveness. Paint or calcimine, that is accidentally smeared over the heads when painting, also lowers their efficiency. When painting or calcimining, the sprinkler heads should be protected by tying small paper bags over them, removing the bags when the work is finished.

Clothespins Aid in Replacing Auto Cylinder Head

The last two bolts on the light-automobile cylinder head, are located directly underneath the dash, and must be in

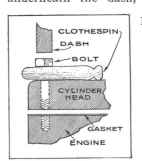

place while the head is inserted on the engine block. To push the head into place with these bolts protruding results in the gasket being bent or torn. The usual practice is to have a helper who holds the bolts while the cylinder head is being put on or taken off. A simple solution to this problem consists in the application of two clothespins, one underneath the head of each bolt, as shown in the drawing.

Sharpening Tools with Mill File

That a fine flat mill file may be used for sharpening and dressing tools is a fact that many mechanics have overlooked completely. Possibly it is not generally realized that the edges of scissors, tin-snips, screwdrivers, and numerous other tools, are softer than the file and can be dressed down to a sharp cutting edge. It is advisable to keep an old file with a broad surface for this purpose, and use it by clamping the tool to be sharpened in the vise. Occasionally a tool too hard to file will be met with, and for this reason the use of an old file is advised. In sharpening scissors, especially when used for cutting cloth, the file-sharpened edges are better than oilstoned ones. The file marks should run downward and inward on both cutting edges; the wire edge left by the file is removed by simply closing the scissors as in cutting.

Emergency Pinch Dogs

We had occasion to use a large number of small pinch dogs on a pattern job, and after we had used all we could find, we

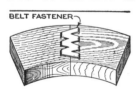

still needed several dozen more, and the shop boy came to the rescue with a box of belt fasteners. These were cut up so as to leave about three points on each side, and we discovered that the makeshift article was better than the regular manufactured pinch dog, as it not only drew the pattern segments together but prevented any lateral movement. Furthermore, any length suitable is easily made, they are cheap, and will not break at the corners like the factory-made article.—C. M. Graham, Waterloo, Ia.

Insuring the Sweeping of Corners

One concern, which found that the janitors, when sweeping, consistently slighted the corners, has now painted all the corners in the factory white. The paint extends about a foot up the walls, and an arc of about 1-ft. radius is painted on the floor.

Where corners are dark, this brightens them up, and dirt is easily seen. The corners are not slighted now.—A. Mac-Cullough, Chicago, Ill.

Bridge Models Show Problems Clearly

A little time spent in the drafting room in the making of models similar to those

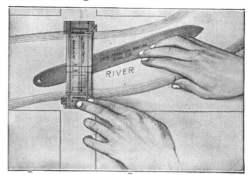

Paper Models for Showing the Relation of a Proposed Bridge to the Shipping That Must Pass Through, Makes It Possible to Present the Situation Clearly to Those Unfamiliar with the Problems Involved

illustrated will save a great deal of useless argument in consultation with engineers, business men, and commissions in large cities. It will be immediately apparent to even those most unfamiliar with the problems involved, just what size boat can pass up the river and through the proposed bridge. The outline model of the bridge is adjustable so that the distance between the abutments can be increased or shortened. It is only necessary to place the models, which are cut from ordinary Manila drawing paper, on a map of the proper scale to make the situation self-explanatory.

Bushings Removed with a Tap

A simple and convenient method of removing a small bushing consists in cutting into it with a tap slightly larger than the internal diameter of the bushing. With the tap in place, a punch or drift is used to drive the bushing out from the opposite side, in cases where this is possible.

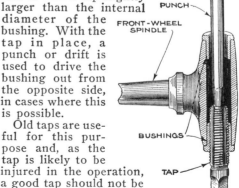

Old taps are useful for this purpose and, as the tap is likely to be injured in the operation, a good tap should not be used unless absolutely necessary, and then only with great care. Coarse-threaded taps are better than finer ones for this purpose.

Useful Attachment for Square

By fitting up his combination square as shown in the drawing, so that a cold-rolled steel rod can be inserted and tight-

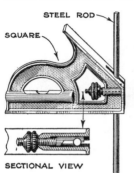

STEEL ROD

SQUARE

SECTIONAL VIEW

ened in position instead of the usual straightedge blade, a pattern-maker doubles the usefulness of this indispensable tool. A hole that will make a sliding fit for the rod is drilled through the head, as shown in the detail, and a semicircular groove is filed in the clamping bolt, just back of the jaw, to allow the rod to pass through it.

This arrangement enables the tool to be used as a depth gauge in small holes or slots where the rule will not enter; by inserting a small steel point near one end of the rod, a good marking gauge is formed.

Improved Centers for Arbors

An improvement on lathe and milling-machine arbors, that overcomes the all too familiar burring of the centers, has

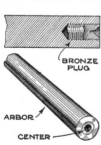

BRONZE PLUG

ARBOR

CENTER

been used by the owner of a general machine shop with satisfactory results. The idea is simplicity itself, and consists in boring out the working end of the arbor to a depth of about 1 in. with a ⁵⁄₁₆-in. drill; this hole is tapped to accommodate a ³⁄₈-in. threaded bronze plug. The plug is screwed in flush and centered in the usual way. The bronze center produces a bearing that is tough, yet not hard enough to burr the lathe centers.—John M. Pipp, Muncie, Ind.

Umbrella Ribs for Welding Rods

I have been using the ribs from old umbrellas in place of welding rods for such work as lengthening twist drills, augers, and for sheet-metal work, with perfectly satisfactory results. On account of the thinness of the ribs a smaller flame

is required to melt them, and no hard spots are apparent in the weld when machining or filing. When the neutral flame strikes the rib, numerous sparks will appear which may cause the operator to believe his torch is not adjusted properly, or that the steel is burning. This is merely the action of the oxygen on the rust and enamel on the rib, and does not interfere with the free flow of metal into the weld.—Fred Brand, Middletown, N. Y.

Cutting Brake-Band Rivets

To cut off the old rivets cleanly, when relining brake, clutch, or transmission

ORDINARY CHISEL

CHISEL GROUND FOR CUTTING BRAKE RIVETS

bands of an automobile, without bending them over, the cold chisel used should have a specially ground edge.

The ordinary cold chisel is beveled on both sides, but, to get the most satisfactory results with the type of rivets generally used for the purpose mentioned, the chisel should be ground with a bevel on but one side and used with the flat side against the band.—J. H. Rouse, San Francisco, California.

Stretching Leather Lagging on Pulleys

When it is desired to stretch a piece of leather over the face of a pulley to increase its diameter, or to reduce slip, and to rivet it in place, the mechanic finds that he does not possess enough

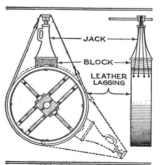

JACK

BLOCK

LEATHER LAGGING

hands and fingers to manipulate the lever that is commonly used, and to insert and head over the rivets while the leather is taut.

The drawing shows how an ordinary screw-jack is used by one old-time mechanic to draw the leather lagging up tight, and hold it thus while the rivets are inserted and headed. Holes are punched through the end of the leather, which should be about 3 in. longer than necessary to reach around the pulley. The ends of the belt are connected by a number of strong wires, twisted together into a single strand and placed over the head of the jack. With a V-block underneath the jack, the screw is turned until the leather, which has been previously soaked in warm water for about 10 minutes, is sufficiently stretched. Rivets are placed in holes drilled through the leather and pulley, except in two near the rim of the pulley on the side opposite the jack. The jack is loosened, the wire removed from one end and this end cut off squarely. The jack is then reset in the position indicated by the dotted lines, the free end of the wire being inserted into the holes in which no rivets were inserted. The leather is again stretched and the rest of the rivets inserted. The jack is then removed, the ends of the lagging scarfed off, and the final rivets inserted where the wires were attached. When the leather becomes dry, as nearly a perfect fit as it is possible to obtain will be the result.—Geo. G. McVicker, North Bend, Neb.

Clamp for Drawing Board

The clamp shown in the drawing eliminates the need of thumbtacks to hold standard-size drawings to the board, and

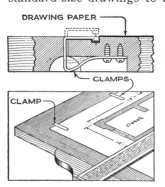

it will not spoil the board for use in making larger drawings, as the clamp is let in flush with the surfaces of the board. Only two clamps are used, and they are located at the top of the board in such a position that they will accommodate the majority of the drawings. The clamps are made from spring wire and fit into mortises of the proper size, cut in the surface of the board. A recess is made for the fingers on the underside of the board, so that the springs can easily be pressed upward.—Geo. Simonson, Cambridge, Mass.

❡The boiler should be set 30 to 42 in. above the fire grate to give room for air and gases to mix.

Truing Small Commutators in a Vise

In truing up the commutator of a small motor generator, such as found in

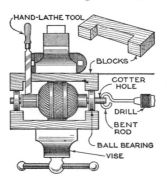

automobile electric systems, when no lathe is available, the vise set-up illustrated can be used. Two wooden blocks, relieved at their centers to clear the winding, are clamped in the vise, the armature being held by its ball bearings, so that it can rotate freely.

At one end of the shaft is a hole for a cotter or taper pin, and this is connected to a drill chuck in the manner shown. Then, while the work is being rotated, a hand lathe tool is brought to bear against the copper and the proper amount of metal removed. Sandpaper is used to smooth the turned work and give a polished finish.

Removing Ball from Check Valve

An ordinary horseshoe magnet, kept around the automobile repair shop, will

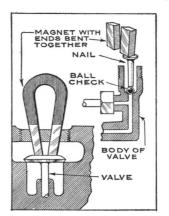

make it possible to remove easily the balls from oil check valves, inaccessible valves, and other parts that it is difficult to get a grip upon with fingers or tools. A magnet from an old magneto, with its ends bent close together, but not in contact with each other, can be found around almost any shop and will give excellent results. In removing the check-valve ball, a nail or similar short piece is inserted into the valve, and nail and ball drawn out together. Brass parts are unaffected by magnetism and therefore cannot be removed in this manner.

A Tap and Reamer-Milling Fixture

By J. V. ROMIG

INEXPENSIVE, yet a useful and time-saving addition to the shop equipment, the tap and reamer-milling fixture described in this article fully justifies the slight cost of its construction. With it, taps and reamers can be milled as quickly and as accurately as when using a large and bulky index head. Furthermore, this fixture permits the work to be done on

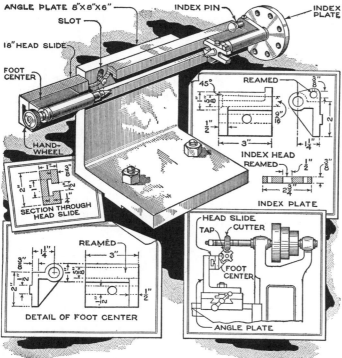

A Tap and Reamer-Milling Fixture That Has Its Index Head Self-Contained: It Accommodates Itself to Tapered Work, and can be Mounted on Small High-Speed Millers

a small miller, thereby saving the larger miller and its index head for larger and possibly more important jobs. Being self-contained in a single unit, much time is saved on the set-up of each job, as the fixture only requires to be clamped to the milling-machine table with two bolts.

The base of the fixture is an angle plate, machined square on its bottom and inside faces and having a tongue on the bottom machined to fit the table slots; to this the head slide is bolted with two capscrews. The capscrew on the index-center end is a turning fit in a hole drilled in the angle plate, while the other, at the foot-center end, slides in a curved slot, so that the slide can be tilted to take care of taper work. The head slide is

machined from cast iron to the form and dimensions shown; it is machined all over and the T-slot is cut throughout its length.

The index head and foot center are cast in soft gray iron from simple patterns, and machined to the dimensions given. The index-head spindle is taper-turned, and should be a snug fit in its bearing. It has a center turned on its front end and is also threaded for the index plate.

The index plates, of which there should be several, say, one of 16 holes and another of 18 holes, give nearly all the spacings needed in the fluting of taps or reamers. The indexing is done by pulling the pin out, rotating the plate by hand, and then inserting the pin to hold the head in position. The foot-center head slides along the front face of the head slide, and can be clamped in any position to suit the length of the work held between the centers. The foot-center spindle should be of hardened tool steel and be fitted with a screw and hand-wheel for advancing the center into the work, as in a lathe tailstock.

By using a fixture of this type, more speed can be made on small work, as it allows the work to be done on a high-speed machine of small size.

Lock and Chain Prevent Accidents

Deaths and accidents are often the direct result of a machine being set in motion by some one who does not know that there is a man working on it. Practically all such accidents can be prevented by providing the men who do work of this kind with a piece of chain and a padlock, and making the use of them compulsory, to lock the starting lever, switch, or whatever it is that makes the machine operative. In the same way, whenever it is necessary for a man to enter a boiler, gasometer, or similar ves sel, he should lock all inlet-control valves, and take the key along with him to prevent the steam or gas from being turned on. Sprinkler-system valves, and other valves that are connected to the fire-protection system, which should be kept open, can also be kept from being closed by the application of a lock and chain.

Cement Bases for Lanterns

Lanterns that are used by contractors and municipalities to warn traffic against obstructions or dangers in the roadway are easily upset and extinguished by the wind, when set on the ground. If suspended from a barricade or stake there is frequently considerable swaying that may dislodge the lantern and extinguish the light. However, by molding a cement base around

CEMENT BASE

the oil reservoir of the lantern it can be set on the ground with every assurance that it will not be blown over or accidentally upset.

Removing "Frozen" Bolts

Owing to rust, or the end of the bolt being riveted over the nut, bolts in the chassis of automobiles frequently resist all

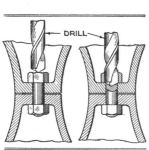

DRILL

efforts to start them with wrenches, and sometimes they are so located as to prevent the use of a chisel or drift on the nut. A simple method for removing such bolts is to drill through the bolt head down into the body of the bolt. Make a punch mark in the center of the head, and using a drill slightly larger than the diameter of the bolt body, drill as shown; if an air or electric drill is used, the bolt will be out in a comparatively short time. In any case the drilling method is better than cutting the head off the bolt, as there is no possibility of a flying bolt head striking and injuring anyone, breaking a window, or doing any other damage.

Wrench for Cylinder-Base Nuts

Cylinder-base nuts are, in many cases, so located that they can only be turned with a chisel. The reason for this is simple; the corners of the hexagon nut being 60° apart, the nut requires to be turned 60° before the wrench can be replaced on it and the turning movement continued; on the other hand, condi-

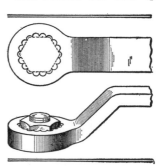

tions usually permit turning the wrench no more than 30°, obviously making it impossible for the common wrench to resume its hold on the nut.

The drawing illustrates the construction of a simple wrench that will grip the hexagon heads of capscrews or nuts in any position so that the wrench can turn the nut as far as possible. A circle of holes is drilled in the wrench, as indicated, and the center piece knocked out; with this arrangement, no matter in what way the wrench is applied, the corners of the nut or bolt head will fit into some of the holes in the manner shown. The wrench head should, of course, be case-hardened.—C. Nye, New York, N. Y.

Dogs Aid in Sawing Wood

Two simple grippers, or dogs, fastened to opposite sides of a sawbuck, as shown in the drawing, will greatly facilitate the work of sawing wood into stove lengths, by holding it so that it cannot move as it is being sawed. The dogs are made of iron and bolted to the buck in the manner shown. In use, the sharp points are pressed into the wood, relieving the sawyer of

all the effort that is generally required to keep the wood from turning a little with each stroke of the saw.—P. T. Williams, Hairoa, N. Z.

Plugs for Radiator Testing

Old automobile valves are utilized for the essential parts of the automobile-radi-ator testing plugs shown in the draw-ing. The end of the stem is threaded and two threaded handles and a conical washer are provided. In assembling the plugs, a number of sections of heavy rubber tubing of dif-ferent diame-ters are slipped over the valve stem, the conical washer ap-plied, and then the two handles, one of which is pinned rigidly to the valve stem, as shown. In use, the plugs are inserted into the openings of the radiator headers and the handle screwed down; this forces the sections of rubber tubing against the valve head and conical washer, causing the rubber to expand and completely fill the opening, so that the radiator can be tested for leaks.

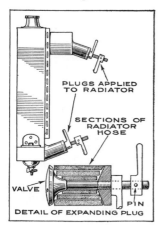

PLUGS APPLIED TO RADIATOR

SECTIONS OF RADIATOR HOSE

VALVE

PIN

DETAIL OF EXPANDING PLUG

A Novel Toolholder

The toolholder shown will be found handy when used on work that requires a frequent changing of tools, as it is self-contained, requires no separate wrench to operate it, and is very quick in action. Very little pressure is re-quired to se-cure or release the tool, as the holder is built to secure extra lever-age.

The body of the holder has a 1-in. hole reamed through it at right angles to the shank, and a 5/16-in. slot is cut in the top. A short piece of drill rod is driven tightly into a disk of 1-in. tool

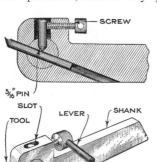

SCREW

5/16" PIN

SLOT

TOOL

LEVER

SHANK

TOOL-STEEL CENTER PIECE

steel, which is made a snug fit in the reamed hole. The holder is drilled and tapped for a tightening screw, the head of which is drilled for a 3-in. length of drill rod that serves as a lever. When the piece has been thus assembled, a hole is drilled, at the proper angle, clear through the holder and the tool-steel disk or cen-terpiece. This hole is afterward broached square to take the tool bit. While the broaching is being done, a piece of pack-ing is placed in the slot, and the screw is tightened on this to hold the centerpiece firm. The lever in the tightening screw should be set in a vertical position when the tool is released, one-quarter turn tightening the tool and bringing the lever down to a horizontal position. It will be immediately apparent that the screw, bearing on the pin driver in the center-piece, forces the latter around and binds the tool on the bottom of the square hole.

Precision Scribing Tool

It is an exceedingly delicate operation to scribe a perfectly true line along the edge of a scale with an ordinary scriber or scratch-awl. Since the scriber is round and ta-pering to a point, and it is almost im-possible to keep the hand in exactly the same position the whole time the line is being drawn, an un-even line us-ually results, which may cut through a fine center on one end of the work and probably be off at the other. If the line is not exactly true, other attempts will be necessary, and this will make other fine lines that will be confusing.

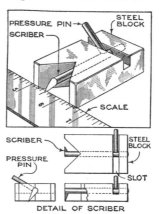

PRESSURE PIN

SCRIBER

STEEL BLOCK

SCALE

SCRIBER

PRESSURE PIN

STEEL BLOCK

SLOT

DETAIL OF SCRIBER

The tool shown in the drawing will draw a dead-straight line exactly between two points, providing, of course, that the scale is accurately placed on the points. The body is a steel block, ground on the base, with a V-cut in the front end. The piece is drilled from the back end clear through to the center of the "V," to take the bent scriber, which is made as shown. A slot, cut across the top of the block, enables a pin to be threaded into the scriber in a position at right angles to the scriber point. When the piece is thus assembled, a light finishing cut, preferably on the grinder, is taken across the front of the block and end of the scriber, insuring that these will form a dead-flat face.

In use, the block is placed close against the edge of the scale, and, with one finger pressing on the pin, the block is drawn along the scale, scribing a light or heavy line according to the pressure exerted.

Auxiliary Automobile Seat

The auxiliary automobile seat illustrated is designed for the use of a child, and is simply constructed of iron rod and a board of suitable size to form the seat. The iron rod is bent to form a hook that fits over the back of the car seat, and the board is attached to the lower ends. Arms for the seat are made from the same material

and fastened to the underside of the seat, which can be upholstered as desired, or, by the exercise of a little more ingenuity, the back and arms may be formed of one length of rod. Completed, the seat is intended to elevate the young passenger so that he can see over the side of the car.—F. C. Davis, St. Joseph, Mo.

An Adjustable Lathe Dog

The drawing shows a lathe dog that is capable of holding various sizes of work.

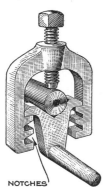

NOTCHES

Merely by releasing the regular binding screw at the top and dropping the lower portion of the dog a notch, larger work can be accommodated. The design is very simple, the parts easily made to suit individual requirements, and considerable time can be saved because a large variety of sizes is not necessary. This dog is driven from a faceplate in the usual manner, the tail being made to fit into the slot in the plate.

Adjustable Parallel Blocks

A very handy and useful parallel block that will save much time, and facilitate setting of work, is made according to the form and dimensions given in the drawing. The vertical adjustment is made by two screws that support the upper member. Such blocks can be used individually, in pairs, or threes, as the job in hand may require, and, by using a mi-

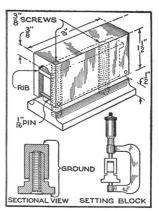

SECTIONAL VIEW   SETTING BLOCK

crometer as in the drawing, the blocks are easily set to the same height. The screws should be threaded with a fine S.A.E. thread, which will permit close adjustment. The base of the block is shaped, drilled, and tapped as shown, and notice should be taken of the retaining rib that keeps the two parts of the block from coming apart. The base is wide enough to furnish a good support, and it, as well as the top, is ground to a flat surface. The upper member slips over the tongue of the base and is countersunk for the points of the adjusting screws. A small pin through each end of the upper member catches against the rib and holds the top and base together.

Blocks of different heights, each set overlapping the other in its limits of adjustability, should be made; one set with a 1-in. adjustment, starting with a height of 2 in. and opening out to 3 in., with the next size opening from 3 to 4 in., and so on.

Gravel in Concrete Mixtures

Most bank-run gravels contain a great deal more sand than is desirable in a concrete mixture. Sometimes this sand is twice as great in quantity as would be best. If about 75 per cent of bank-run gravel were fine material, the proper proportion of cement would vary widely from that required in case only 30 per cent of the gravel were fine material. Only by separating the fine sand from the pebbles can definitely specified concrete mixtures be secured.

Unusual Type of Pattern Construction

It is common practice among pattern-makers to build a cylindrical pattern in segmental courses, in which case it is of

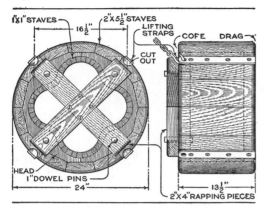

A Method of Building Cylindrical Patterns That Uses Staves Parallel to the Center of the Pattern Instead of Segmental Sections, Makes the Work of the Molder Easier and Prolongs the Life of the Pattern

the utmost importance that the lumber is thoroughly dried and seasoned; that the segments are securely glued and fastened together, and that at least three coats of good varnish are applied to the surfaces of the finished work. If these things are not done carefully, the damp molding sand will loosen the glued joints, causing the segments to warp, twist, and contract or expand, so that the pattern will not be truly cylindrical. This expansion or contraction will cause pockets in the sides of the cylinder, in which one or more segments may overlap slightly. When this occurs, the molder has a troublesome job in extricating the pattern from the sand mold, and the sand that forms the face of the mold is, in many cases, "sheared" away when the pattern is lifted from the mold. A pattern in this condition receives rough treatment at the hands of the molder, as considerable rapping is required to loosen it enough to enable him to extract it from the mold.

The objections above outlined, and others that could also be cited, do not apply to cylindrical patterns of the type shown in the drawing; if they did, very few castings could be produced from it, as it has a rather weak cross section. The pattern is made stave-fashion, with the staves running parallel to the center instead of being built up in segments. The pattern consists of the heads and the outer and inner staves. Contrary to the usual practice of making the heads in

a complete circle and building the staves around them, the heads are made in two pieces that are temporarily held together on a flat board. The body staves are next fitted and fastened to these half heads. The half pattern is now removed from the board, and reinforcing pieces are fastened inside the heads with an overlap at the joints, to which the opposite half of the pattern is fastened. The opposite half heads are put in place and fastened securely with glue and screws. The inside staves are fitted and fastened with glue and finishing nails, and finished with a round-bottom plane to the required shape and dimensions. This is done very simply, if the pattern is laid out and built up correctly. The pattern is now turned and finished in the lathe, sanded, and given three coats of good black varnish. The ³⁄₁₆ by 1¼-in. lifting straps are then fastened to the side of the pattern. The straps are made the same length as the pattern and do not project beyond it, and cup-shaped depressions are cut into the wood to permit the insertion of hooks into the holes in the straps.

A novel feature of this mold is the rapping piece, made from two pieces of 2 by 4-in. lumber, fastened at right angles to each other. This piece has a 1-in. dowel pin at each end which fits into holes in the cope head. Instead of the heavy iron bar that is usually driven into the pattern for rapping purposes, the rapping is done on the rapping piece, which is put on after the cope flask has been lifted, and removed after the rapping has been finished.—M. E. Duggan, Kenosha, Wis.

Marking Off Centers on Shafts

When large numbers of short lengths of round stock require to be marked off at the ends, preparatory to center drilling, much time can be saved by the simple set-up shown in the drawing, together with a special marking-off gauge.

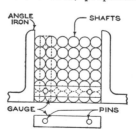

Arrange the shafts, after cutting to the proper length, in layers six wide and six deep, between two angle plates bolted down to a drill-press table, or other plane surface. The gauge can be made from any flat stock, but its width must be the exact diameter of the shafts. A pin is driven into each end of the gauge, their diameter being such as to make them a snug fit into the spaces formed by the junction of four shafts. The distance apart of these pins is the same distance as the first and last spaces in the rows of stock.

When marking off, place the gauge in a horizontal position, with the pins in the spaces, as indicated in the drawing, and scribe a line along the shafts; this will give the center in one direction. After the lot has been scribed horizontally the gauge is placed in a vertical position and lines are scribed perpendicularly, the intersections of the horizontal and perpendicular lines being the centers of the shafts.

Light Reflector for Drafting

Often the light on a drafting board is poor and the shadows of the triangle and T-square are dense enough to cause eye-

strain in detecting the exactness of the lines to be drawn or traced. Under such conditions it is advisable to use a reflector of the type shown in the drawing. Nothing more than a square of white Bristol board is required, with a strip of the same material glued to the back to form an easel. By moving the reflector about so that the shadows are illuminated by the reflected light, the strain on the draftsman's eyes will be considerably lessened.—Truman R. Hart, Ashtabula, Ohio.

Galvanizing Brass and Copper

Copper and brass may be coated with metallic zinc in the following manner: Place finely divided zinc in a nonmetallic vessel, and cover it with a concentrated solution of sal ammoniac. This is heated to the boiling point, and the copper or brass articles are introduced. A few minutes in the boiling bath will suffice to produce a firm and brilliant covering over the surface of the work. The zinc can be reduced to the requisite fineness by pouring the melted metal into an iron mortar and pounding it with an iron pestle until the solid mass has been granulated to the desired fineness.

A Simple Radius Tool

The illustration shows a simple and almost automatic arrangement for cutting radii in a lathe. It only requires that the

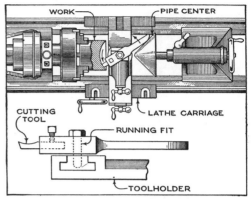

A Simple Radius-Cutting Tool That Is Almost Automatic in Its Operation: The Toolholder is Pivoted, and a Projecting Tail Bears against the Conical Center

tailstock center be fed forward. The tool bit is held in a holder that is pivoted at its center to the cross slide, in the manner shown. The projecting tail of the holder bears against the pipe center held in the tailstock. Consequently, as the conical center is fed forward, the tool is forced to travel in an arc.—Jos. F. Convery, Worcester, Mass.

Grinding Ball-Check Valve Seats

After a considerable period of use, ball-check valve seats will pit and rust, the valve will leak, and it will be found that the trouble cannot be entirely corrected by the insertion of a new ball into the worn seat. It is a simple matter to regrind such a check-valve seat by the method illustrated. The end of a piece of cop-

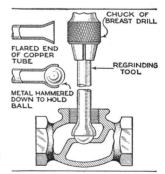

per tubing is flared by driving it over one of the hardened steel or brass balls used. After the end is flared, it is hammered in to hold the ball securely. With this tool, held in the breast drill, and a small amount of valve-grinding compound, the seat of the valve may be quickly reground.

Drain Pit for Filling Stations

A small pit used for draining crankcases, and placed convenient to the filling station, has proved to be a good investment to a number of automobile-filling stations. Once the pit has been installed, there is no operating expense, and the sale of crankcase oil is greatly increased, since

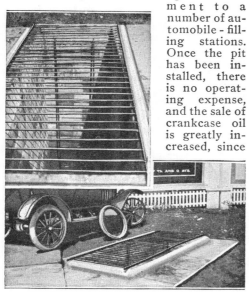

A Concrete Pit for Automobile-Service Stations Facilitates Drainage of Crankcase Oil. A Five-Inch Molded Rim Prevents Cars from Running over the Edge, and the Pit is Covered with an Iron Grating

the draining is not charged for. The stations can afford to do the work of draining the crankcases of their customers' cars free, since it results in the sale of several quarts of oil in each instance.

The pits are of concrete, made with a 5-in. molded rim, to prevent cars from running over the edge. An iron grating is always kept handy, and is put over the opening when the pit is not in use, to prevent accidents. By providing filtering facilities, the oil that is drained from the crankcases can be restored to salable condition, and can be sold for the lubrication of farm machinery and similar purposes.

Preventing Loss of Tracings

The chief draftsman in a large shop uses a very effective method of keeping track of tracings taken from the file by draftsmen for reference, alteration, or other purposes. A draftsman taking any tracing is required to leave with the file clerk a receipt in the form of a card 2 in. wide and 3 in. high, which is then filed by number in a tray. When the tracing is returned, the file clerk destroys the card before filing the tracing. This much of the procedure is very common. The shop referred to had experienced a great deal of trouble because the draftsmen failed to return valuable tracings, and the receipt cards remained forgotten in the file. To prevent this, all the blank cards are now beveled off at the top; one month, cards are used beveled off toward the right side of the card, and the next month's supply of cards are beveled off toward the left. Toward the end of the month the file clerk goes through the card tray and takes out any cards which show by their bevel that they are remaining from the previous month. He then inquires of the writer of each of these receipts why he has not returned the tracing. If there is a good reason for keeping the tracing so long, the old receipt is destroyed, and a new one written on a card beveled to conform to those for the current month. In this way, the receipt file is brought up to date at the first of each month, and cases of "buried" and forgotten tracings are avoided.

Window Box Aids in Filing Band Saws

In pattern shops and other places where band-saw blades are filed frequently, the arrangement shown will facilitate the work of setting and filing the teeth, and keep the saws from getting snarled up on the bench or floor so that there would be—as there generally is in such cases—danger of breakage. A wooden box is permanently

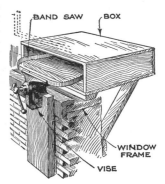

fastened to the outside of a window frame, so that it will clear the sash and not interfere with its operation. The folded saw is inserted in the box, where it is kept coiled throughout the operation. In this manner the saw filer requires but a minimum of room for his work, and he can get his vise as close as possible to the source of light.

¶ In addition to the time-honored expedient of ruling lines for tables on the reverse side of a tracing, this side can be used for inking in temporary details. These can be removed later without affecting the main drawing.

Corners for Log Cabins

By A. NEUMAN

IN building log cabins, the parts that cause the most trouble are the corners, where the logs cross each other at right angles. To get the best and most attractive effect, and to retain the "pioneer" look, the logs should project beyond the corners, but, unless properly done, the effect will not be pleasing. The pictures show how accurately and neatly the logs can be joined at the corners. To make

although, if necessary, it can be done. The logs should be cut about 6 ft. longer than the inside dimensions of the building, and good straight ones should be selected; they should also hold their size well, that is, they should not taper very much.

The notches are marked with a compass with an indelible-lead point, if green timber is used, as an ordinary pencil or

If a Neat and Finished Job is Desired in a Log Building, Particular Pains must be Taken to Fit the Logs Accurately at the Corners. By Marking the Notches According to the Method Described, a Very Neat Corner Is the Result. The Drawings Show the Tools Used and the Method of Marking Off the Logs

this type of corner it is necessary to have made at a blacksmith shop a gouge adz along the lines of the one shown. The cutting edge is ground with an inside bevel and sharpened with a slip stone. The hammer head is to give it the right "heft" and balance, and is useful to drive the timber dogs into the logs to hold the latter while they are being notched. Two of these timber dogs are needed, and they are made and used as shown in the drawing. Peeled logs are best to use, as it is quite difficult to get a distinct pencil mark on the bark of a rough log,

lead will not make a good mark on the surface of freshly peeled logs. Two logs are dogged together at right angles, as shown; the compass is set to a radius of a little less than half the diameter of the log to be cut, then, with the steel point against the lower log and the pencil point against the upper one, it is drawn over the surface of the logs as shown, marking, on the upper log, an accurate representation of the contour of the lower one.

A similar mark is made in the same manner on the opposite side of the upper log, which is then rolled over, dogged again, and the notch cut. It should be noted that the notches are cut in only one side of each log—the underside.

As the logs taper somewhat, the diameter of the notch at the small end must be a trifle smaller than the diameter of the notch at the larger end. If the joints do not fit exactly when first cut, the compass should be set with its points ¼ to ½ in. apart, new marks made, and the notches cut down to these marks. If the work has been carefully done, extra fitting is usually unnecessary; after the first few experiments with the method, neat and accurately fitting notches can be cut, and, where the work is exceptionally well done, it is hard to tell which log is cut.

About an inch of space is left between the logs, and this space is "stuccoed" according to the methods commonly used. Straight logs should be selected for building purposes, but if there should be a slight bend or bow in some of them, they should be placed in the building with the bow up, so that, in time, they will sag and straighten out.

The logs settle a great deal more than is generally thought after being put in place, and it is advisable to allow the building to settle for two or three months before furring in the doors and windows, or trying to stucco the chinks between the logs. If the building is allowed to settle for a while, nails driven close up into the cracks, about 2 or 3 in. apart, and the chinks then filled, the stucco will stay tight for years, as the heads of the nails will be imbedded in it and hold it tightly.

Wrench for Cylinder-Head Bolts

It is difficult to place a straight open-end wrench on the cylinder-head bolts of certain makes of automobile engines, as the nuts are set below the surface in such a manner that a good grip cannot

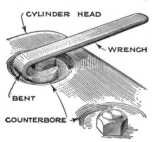

be taken. In such cases a wrench of the type shown in the drawing can be used to considerable advantage. It is only necessary to bend over the open end of the wrench, so that the jaws will fit into the counterbore or depression in the casting.

Cleaning Silver Cathodes

Silver cathodes for use in the electrodeposition of copper are cleaned by placing them in contact with pure tinfoil in a boiling 10-per-cent solution of sodium hydroxide until bright. They are then washed successively with dilute hydrochloric acid, dilute ammonia, and distilled water, rinsed with alcohol, burning off any adhering alcohol by igniting it. The electrolysis is carried out as usual, except that the electrode is not immersed in the solution until the current has been switched on. To remove the copper deposit, after the final weighing, the cathode is placed in a wide-mouthed stoppered bottle, filled with a 10-per-cent solution of trichloroacetic acid in aqueous ammonia (.90 specific gravity), to which an equal volume of water has been added. The copper is removed in about ten minutes and the silver electrode is not attacked. Chloroform or carbon tetrachloride may be substituted for trichloroacetic acid, but in this case the ammonia solution should be made from one part ammonia (.90 specific gravity), and one part alcohol. The reaction is slower, and care must be taken that no sulphur compounds are present in the carbon tetrachloride that is used.

Driving Long, Slender Pins

A very efficient tool for driving long, slender pins that have a tendency to bend when being driven, because their length is so much out of proportion to

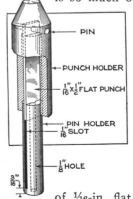

their diameter, and also because they are not always set squarely, is shown in the drawing. The part that holds the pin is made from ½-in. steel, drilled through to accommodate the pins, and a slot is cut through to within ³⁄₁₆ in. of the end. The punch, or driver, is a piece of ¹⁄₁₆-in. flat steel, ½ in. wide, held by means of a pin in the sliding punch holder, which is drilled out, ½ in. in diameter, to within a short distance of the top. Care should be taken in making this tool to see that the flat piece fits the hole in the punch holder neatly, as this supports the driver lengthwise. When the two parts are assembled, the flat punch should slide nicely in the slot of the pin holder.

When driving the pins, they are first placed in the hole and the driver slipped over them; then, taps on the top of the punch holder will drive them home to within 3/16 in., a final tap being sufficient to bring the pin flush with the face of the work. It will be seen that the pin is supported at all times by the holder, and that the punch holder pilots the punch down centrally, thus overcoming the two main difficulties mentioned. — Harry Moore, Montreal, Can.

Shop Uses for Old Razor Blades

Old safety-razor blades can be put to good use on the bench by soldering on

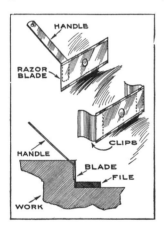

sheet-metal handles, and then using the blade as a guard in filing the corners of dies and castings. Even a safe-edge file will sometimes cut up a finished metal surface badly, and the blade will form a good protection when any file, even a three-cornered one, is used. Instead of a single handle, especially on repetition work, a metal clip can be soldered to each side of a blade to hold it up against the work, so that both hands will be free to use the file.

Sticker Identifies Rush Orders

Small gummed-paper stickers, such as can be bought at any stationery store, are used on the order cards of a large concern to indicate rush orders. A red seal is stuck in the upper left-hand corner of the card, and everyone who gets the shop ticket knows instantly that the order is to be handled with speed. A variation of the same idea makes use of a blue seal, which enjoins everyone to take particular pains in filling the order, or in working to dimensions.

Heating Water with Steam

Heating cold water by steam is accomplished in various ways, the most common method being to insert the end of a steam pipe into a tank of water and turn on the steam. This method, besides being wasteful of steam, produces disagreeable noises. The drawing shows a simple fitting in which the steam is mixed with the cold water, so that this is heated

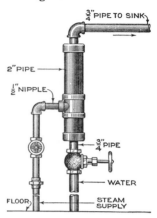

and passes on to an outlet without any fuss. The water and steam-supply pipes are controlled by separate valves, making it possible to regulate the temperature of the heated water very closely. — Earl Stevens, Niagara Falls, N. Y.

Safety Container for Gauge Glasses

In dismantling large ammonia compressors for shipment, most of the small parts are easily disposed of by packing them in a box fastened to the skids. There is one piece, however, that does not mix well with the rest, no matter how carefully it is wrapped in burlap or corrugated cardboard, as it invariably works its way under a heavier piece and is crushed. This is the gauge glass. The difficulty of transporting such glasses, and for that matter all kinds of glass tubing in short

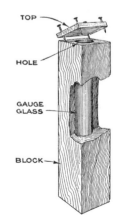

lengths, can be solved by using a block of wood in which a hole, 1 in. longer and about 1/32 in. larger than the glass, is drilled. The tube is inserted in the hole, and a small block, fastened over the opening with four brads, makes it possible for the gauge glass to ride safely along with valves, oil cups, and other small parts.

Automatic Stop for Tumbling Barrel

When tumbling some small castings, to remove the sand and burrs, trouble was experienced when the pieces were tumbled

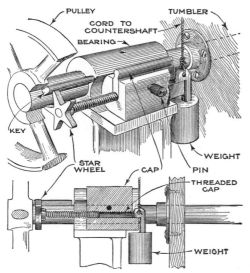

An Automatic Stop for a Tumbling Machine Prevents Injury to Castings by being Tumbled Too Long

too long, the result being that the corners were worn round. The trouble occurred mainly because the operator forgot to stop the tumbler when the work was done.

The result of this experience was that the automatic stop illustrated was devised; this required a new bearing at one end of the machine. The cast-iron bearing supports the tumbler shaft and the threaded stem of the star wheel, a hole being first drilled for the stem, then the hole slotted out on top, and a machine-steel cap fitted. The bearing for the star-wheel stem is tapped to fit the thread on the stem when the cap is in place, as shown. Afterward the thread in the bearing is removed so that the only part having a thread is the movable cap, which is held in place by a pin. A key is driven into the tumbler shaft to operate the star wheel. The end of the star-wheel bearing nearest the tumbler has a weight hooked over it to operate the countershaft, which is not shown.

When the tumbler is ready to start, the attendant takes out the pin, lifts the cap and slides the star wheel out to the position shown; then the cap is secured in place again, the countershaft cord pulled to start the machine, and the weight hooked over the bearing; the tumbler can

then be left to stop itself. As the threaded stem of the star wheel is 3 in. long and makes only one-fifth turn for each revolution of the tumbler, and the stem has a 20-pitch thread, it takes 300 revolutions of the tumbler before the star wheel is fed through enough to push the weight off its bearing, and stop the machine.—S. A. McDonald, Brooklyn, N. Y.

Stencils Made from Old Films

I find that the best material from which to make air-brush stencils is old photographic film, such as can be obtained from any professional negative finisher or photographer, many of whom have discontinued the use of glass plates. Such celluloid masks are much more durable than those of paper, and the alcohol in the colors cannot strike through and stain the work underneath. The designs may be drawn on the rough surface of the stencil directly, then cut out with an old razor blade.—R. E. Deering, Clements, Kan.

Marking Bolt Circles

When turning a cover, flange, gland, or other work that will afterward require a circle of bolt holes drilled in it, it is the usual practice to mark or "strike" the bolt circle, that is, cut a fine tool mark in the face of the work at the required diameter, while the work is held in the chuck or faceplate. This is generally accomplished with a V-shaped tool, held in the toolholder, and the proper radius is obtained by adjusting the tool to a scale held against the lathe center. The drawing shows a special tool for this work, which is simple to make and easily adjusted to the correct radius.

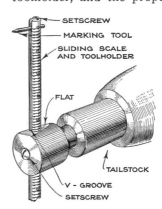

The body is turned on the shank to fit into the tailstock spindle, the front end having a ⅜-in. hole drilled through it at right angles to its center, and a small hole at the center, tapped for a setscrew. A piece of ⅜-in. cold-rolled steel, of suitable length, is centered and placed in the lathe, where a 16-pitch thread is "scratched" on it. The thread is not actually cut, but a fine helical line is made on the rod, which is then grooved on one side to fit the point of the setscrew, and fitted at one end with the marking tool and setscrew. The diameter of the body of the tool should be large enough to permit a flat to be filed on one side, the flat being filed at an angle corresponding with the angle of the thread, and so that when the marking tool is snugly against the flat, the distance from the center of the tool to the center of the body is exactly one inch. When setting the tool, pull out the bar until the measurement of half the diameter of the required circle is obtained, and then tighten the screw. The tool is held in a vertical position so as to clear the toolholder of the lathe, and is fed in by means of the tailstock until a fine line is marked on the work.

Face Milling with Side Mills

A good deal of quick face milling can be done with the ordinary face and side-milling cutter when held in the simple holder illustrated. This is turned, on the shank, to fit the spindle, and on the front

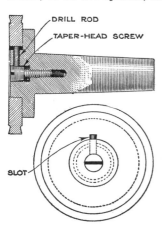

to a snug fit in the bore of the cutter. A shoulder, to take the end thrust of the cut, is left on the holder. The center of the holder is next drilled, tapped, and counterbored for the special screw indicated. This is an ordinary filister-head screw with the head turned to a slight taper. At right angles to this hole is another, drilled to a diameter the same as the width of the keyway in the cutter. A piece of drill rod is inserted in this hole, and the tool is ready for use. It will be seen that when the screw is tightened, the drill-rod pin will be forced out against the cutter and act as a driving key. With a cutter held as shown, and close to the spindle of the machine, face-milling operations can be successfully accomplished.

Rack for Storing Sheet Glass

So-called "country" hardware and paint stores, that carry an extensive assortment of sizes in sheet window glass, realize

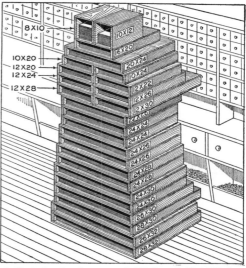

A Rack for the Storage and Display of Flat Window Glass That is Made Up of the Boxes in Which the Stock is Received

how difficult it is to arrange the different-sized boxes to the best advantage and with the least possibility of loss by breakage. The drawing shows an idea that has been worked out by a jobber who is recommending it for the use of his trade. The rack is built up of empty glass boxes, the glass, as received, being removed from its case and placed in the rack.—Arthur Hartley, Fargo, N. D.

Crankshaft-Turning Tool

When an automobile motor is being overhauled and the crankshaft or connecting-rod bearings are being fitted, difficulty is usually experienced in turning the crankshaft, as both the flywheel and starting crank are removed from the engine. Even with these in place, considerable effort is required to turn the shaft in the tightened bearings. A simple tool for turning the shaft can be made from the V-shaped radius rod of a light automobile. The ends of the radius rod are brought within a few inches of each other, the ends ground down to fit into the bolt holes in the flywheel flange, and then bent over. Apart from its simplicity, this tool affords the proper leverage and can be set into any pair of the flange bolt holes.

Correct Design of Movement for Intermittent Motion

Most machine designers and draftsmen have occasion to make use of cams and Geneva movements in their work, and these certainly form two of the principal elements in the study of machine design. Results are obtained by using them which would otherwise be impossible, and upon whether they are correctly or incorrectly used depends the success of the machine in a great many cases. High-speed production is a great factor in present-day machine operation, and it is surprising to find the number of designs which fail to meet this condition, although it should be one of the first things to consider. Harmonic cams, being capable of high speed, should be used whenever possible. When a uniform or constant motion is required for the cam roller, the entire movement cannot, of course, be harmonic, but an effort should be made gradually to accelerate the roller at the start and gradually retard it at the end of its movement; in most cases this can be done, though often neglected.

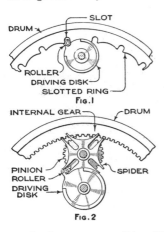

Fig. 1

Fig. 2

In the present example a machine was to be redesigned. The highest possible speed was 15 cycles per minute; it would have broken down at a higher speed, and to make it a commercial success more speed was absolutely necessary. Its various moving elements consisted mainly of abrupt-movement cams and Geneva movements. A close examination revealed the fact that the design of these parts was not based upon the principle of gradual acceleration and retardation. The cams and Geneva parts were redesigned, and in so doing it was found that most of them could be given true harmonic forms, and, in consequence, the machine was operated up to a speed of 90 cycles per minute, without undue vibration, and without exceeding safe stresses.

One of the several sources of trouble in the original design was the Geneva action illustrated in Fig. 1. The drum was driven with an intermittent motion and had a diameter of about 24 in. Attached to it was a slotted ring engaging the driving disk. The drum remained stationary while the disk revolved, excepting when the roller was in engagement with the slot, as shown, when the drum started to revolve at nearly the full speed of the disk. As the parts driving the disk had considerable weight, as had also the drum, their opposing inertia forces caused a shock each time the roller struck the side of the slot. This condition was entirely overcome in the redesigned movement, shown in Fig. 2, in which the slotted ring was replaced by an internal gear, engaging a pinion which was secured to a slotted spider. A driving disk was located so that its roller engaged in the radial slots of the spider, care being taken to have the roller begin to enter the slot in a direction parallel to the slot, or radial to the center of the spider. This arrangement insured the starting of the spider and drum at zero speed, accelerating to full speed, and retarding to zero again. The engaging curved surfaces of the spider and disk were slightly tapered on their faces so that, by axially adjusting the disk, lost motion was easily taken up.—R. E. Bates, Dorchester, Mass.

Lock for Firm-Joint Calipers

Anyone who has used calipers of the firm-jointed type knows how easily the setting may be altered when this kind of tool is being tried on the work. The knowledge of this causes the user to be continually testing the setting with a scale, which, of course, takes much time. The drawing shows a simple lock that will give the user of firm-jointed calipers confidence that the setting will not be disturbed by any ordinary usage. Two disks are bored out, one with a clear hole and the other with a blind one, the diameter of the holes being a snug fit over the joint washers. A piece of drill rod or cold-rolled stock is bent as shown, the two

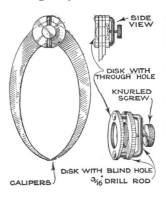

ends entering holes in the through-drilled disk, while the disk with the blind hole has slots cut in the edge to fit the rod. A tapped hole in the center of the bent rod receives a small knurled-head screw for tightening after adjustment. When the attachment is made as described, it is placed on the caliper and the ends of the drill rod riveted over, thus making it a fixture, with no possibility of loss.

It will immediately be apparent that the lock is out of the way and will not interfere with the full capacity of the instrument. When the calipers are set to the required dimensions, a slight turn of the screw tightens the two legs firmly together. The depth of the blind hole should be such that its bottom will not touch the face of the washer, in order that the pressure may fall on the caliper legs only.

Combining Grinder Light and Switch

The usual practice of placing a separately controlled light over the tool grinder results in considerable wasted current, because the person using the machine generally forgets to turn off the light when finished with the grinder. A simpler method, and one which makes it impossible to start or stop the grinder without turning the light on and off, is shown in the drawing. The switch that controls the 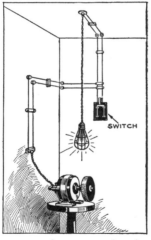 grinding-wheel motor also controls the lamp, as the light circuit is tapped into the one supplying current to the motor. When the user throws the switch to stop the grinding wheel, the light is extinguished.—G. A. Luers, Washington, D. C.

❡No plates or bars of steel or iron should be worked at a blue or black heat; the material will stand far more strain worked either red-hot or cold. At an intermediate point, great risk is run, as strains will probably be induced that will produce rupture later on.

Making Stereotype Matrices from Type Forms

Country newspapers equipped with plate-casting boxes can make their own stereotype matrices by a simple method that has been worked out with satisfactory results in the composing room of a Minnesota paper.

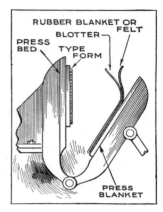

Lock up the type in any job or cylinder-press form. Cut a piece of medium-weight blotting paper to the exact size of the casting box. Place the blotting paper on a felt or rubber blanket, blotter on top. Take an impression and the type form will be pressed into the blotter in the form of a matrix.

Too much pressure will crack the blotter and spoil it, and too light an impression will leave the matrix too shallow for the casting of a good plate. Strips of strawboard, pasted behind the places on the matrix that correspond to white portions in print, will keep the open parts of the plate from being too shallow and smudging up on the impressions made from the plate.

Composing-room foremen will find it possible and profitable to set up in this way business cards, small advertisements, and similar matter that run for considerable periods without change.—J. Harold Curtis, Columbia, Mo.

Cutting Glass with a Soldering Bit

For cutting glass when there is no glass cutter at hand, a heated soldering bit or any other piece of heated brass or copper can be used. The edge of the glass to be cut is nicked, and the soldering copper, very hot, is passed above the section of the glass to be cut. Then, starting at the notch, the bit should be drawn slowly across, keeping just ahead of the crack that will follow the hot iron. With practice, fairly accurate cuts can be made, but it is advisable to practice the method on a worthless piece of glass before undertaking to cut an expensive sheet.

Two Simple Machine Guards

Anything that protects the operator of a machine from injury without interfering with production is well worth while, and

flying into the operator's face, but the hands are kept from contact with the revolving cutters. The other picture shows a small wire guard which is so placed around the die of a punch press that the

Left, Guard for a Milling Machine That Prevents Chips from being Projected into the Operator's Face and Keeps His Hands from Contact with the Cutters; Right, a Safety Guard for Punch Presses That Prevents the Operator from Getting His Fingers under the Descending Ram

the photographs illustrate two such safety devices that have been found quite efficient.

The first picture shows how the cutters on a milling machine have been covered so that not only are chips prevented from

operator cannot possibly get his hand underneath, and, of course, he would never want to put it over the top. This particular type of guard saved so many fingers that it was installed on all the punch presses of the firm using it.

Sponging Wood before Staining

There are a number of advantages to be claimed for sponging wood before it is stained. First, the action of the water, which should preferably be cold, raises the grain of the wood, so that after subsequent drying, this raised grain may be leveled off with sandpaper, thus doing away with its recurrence upon application of the stain. Hot water should not be used on veneer work, since it may strike through and loosen the glue on the cross-banding. With any work, it is best to play safe and use cold water. The second advantage in sponging lies in the fact that the water opens the pores of the wood, relieving them of the clogged condition resulting from previous sandings, and so enables the staining material to be drawn deeply into the wood, thereby producing a very even color, which is capable of withstanding light sanding

with fine sandpaper, if such should be necessary to produce that perfect smoothness of surface upon which the subsequent varnish coats depend for their beauty.

The last big advantage is also the result of opening the pores, and this has to do with the use of a filler previous to varnishing. If the wood is filled without sponging and sandpapering previous to staining, the old sandpaper dust and other material which clog the pores will absorb water from the stain and remain in a condition considerably more damp than that portion of the wood in direct contact with the air. When filling is now attempted upon such a foundation, this material in the pores dries out through the absorption of the water by the surrounding wood, with the result that shrinkage and settling develop, causing the varnish coat to be pulled down into the pores.

On the other hand, the same moist condition in the pores of the wood may result, in some cases, in the varnish being forced out in small spots, due to expansion of the moisture if the varnish work is done in an excessively warm room.

Why Pumps Become Air-Bound

Under atmospheric conditions water contains about two per cent of air. When subject to a lower pressure than that of the atmosphere, the air expands, and when given sufficient time, as while the water is flowing through a long suction pipe, the air will escape from the water in small bubbles. These bubbles will stick to the pipe or pump surfaces, or the air will gather in the pockets of the pump spaces. The trouble can largely be prevented by increasing the head of the suction supply and by operating the pump more slowly, so that the pressure of the suction water in the pump cylinder will be higher.

Driving Unit for Banding Motor Generators

Having experienced a great deal of difficulty in turning over large motor-generator armatures for banding, a western electric railway built the device shown in the photograph. The driving unit, a 600-volt variable-speed motor, is controlled by a portable rheostat. Connected to the motor is a three-speed

A Western Electric Railway Uses the Portable Arrangement Illustrated to Turn Motor-Generator Armatures for Banding. It Consists of a 600-Volt Motor Connected to a Three-Speed Transmission

transmission, the lowest ratio being slow enough to turn the heaviest armature over for banding. The entire arrangement is mounted on a wheeled truck so that it can easily be pulled to any part of the shop where its services may be needed.—Hyman M. Fink, Los Angeles, California.

Safety Attachment for Printing Press

A common accident in printing shops where platen job presses are used is the crushing of a feeder's fingers between

A Safety Device for Platen Printing Presses That Forces Out the Pressman's Hand Before It is Caught between the Platen and Type Form

the chase and platen, because he did not withdraw his hand fast enough. A Pennsylvania concern has equipped a press with a safety device that prevents accidents of this character.

A wooden bar is mounted outside the upper platen band, on adjustable metal strips. These strips are attached to rods at the side and are adjustable vertically. The side rods are provided with cam rollers, and attached to the sides of the press in such a manner that, just before the platen closes on the type form, the connecting rods between the platen and gears that operate it, strike the cams and elevate the wooden bar. The pressman's arm and hand, if not previously removed, will be forced out of the press before they can be caught between the form and platen.—Armstrong Perry, New York City.

Carburetor Leakage

That dirt and grease on the outside of some types of automobile carburetors may cause leakage and dripping is rarely suspected. However, this is possible, and occurs in numerous cases. At the top of the float chamber of the carburetor is a small vent that must be kept open in order to permit the escape of air, and so allow the incoming gasoline to raise the float. When this vent is closed, the air is trapped in the upper part of the chamber, and as the air pressure will not allow the float to rise and shut the needle valve, the gasoline will continue to flow. When the carburetor develops flooding, before replacing or overhauling, inspect this vent for dirt, as, in many cases, nothing more than this is wrong.

TESTING MOTORS, GENERATORS, and TRANSFORMERS

By KENNETH C. COGGESHALL

Part II—Generators and Transformers

TO determine what is known as the external characteristics of a generator, that is, the variation in terminal voltage with an increase or decrease in load, connections are made as in Fig. 8, which shows a shunt-wound dynamo under test. The generator must be driven at constant speed during the test, and this should be the speed shown on the nameplate. The field rheostat, once adjusted, should not be touched again during the test. A water rheostat, lamp bank, or other device capable of being adjusted, should be used to vary the load by steps, from 0 to 150-per-cent load. At each step, readings of the meters should be made, recorded, and plotted graphically, as shown in Fig. 9. The line drawn through the points representing the readings indicates the trend of the terminal voltage under varying loads. The characteristic curve of a series-wound or over-compounded dynamo will rise above that of a shunt-wound dynamo.

The power necessary to drive the generator is:

$$Hp. = \frac{E \times I}{746 \times \text{Efficiency}}.$$

If the efficiency is not known, but the power necessary to drive the dynamo is, then

$$\text{Efficiency} = \frac{E \times I}{746 \times Hp.}.$$

Figure 10 shows the connections for testing the output of a three-phase a.-c. generator. Only one set of instruments need be used, if a switching system is used to connect the meters in the various phases in quick rotation. During the test the field current should be kept constant. An external characteristic curve should be plotted, as in Fig. 9, from the data recorded during the test. The load, if the test is conducted in the laboratory, may be a water rheostat or lamp bank; if the regular commercial load is used, the test may be of longer duration. The average current flowing in each phase is:

$$I = \frac{I_1 + I_2 + I_3}{3},$$

that is, the average value, I, is obtained by adding the readings of the three am-

meters and dividing by 3. Similarly, for the average value of E,

$$E = \frac{E_1 + E_2 + E_3}{3}.$$

The power output is:

$$P = E \times I \times 1.73 \times Pf.$$

The horsepower required to drive the generator, when the efficiency of the machine is known, is:

$$Hp. = \frac{E \times I \times 1.73 \times Pf.}{746 \times \text{Efficiency}};$$

and, consequently,

$$Pf. = \frac{Hp. \times \text{Efficiency} \times 746}{E \times I \times 1.73}, \text{ or, } \frac{P}{E \times I \times 1.73};$$

and

$$\text{Efficiency} = \frac{E \times I \times 1.73 \times Pf.}{746 \times Hp.} = \frac{P}{746 \times Hp.}.$$

It is a good plan to measure the operating temperature of a motor or generator, to make sure that the insulation is not in danger of injury by heat. Place the bulb of a thermometer in the hottest available spot on the machine, and take temperature readings while the machine is running. Continue the test until the thermometer indicates no further increase in temperature. Compare the reading with the room temperature; the difference, or temperature rise, should not exceed 50° C. (90° F.). In no case, regardless of surrounding conditions, should the thermometer show a temperature of more than 90° C. (194° F.).

As intimated in the preceding paragraph, the capacity of a machine depends, to a large extent, upon the temperature at which it operates. This is especially true of transformers. Insulation breaks down very rapidly at high temperatures, and weakened insulation materially shortens the life of a transformer.

To test the capacity of a transformer, suspend a thermometer in the oil in the case, placing the bulb as near to the coils as possible. An ammeter connected in the low-tension side indicates the load current, while a voltmeter shows the line voltage, as shown in Fig. 11. If the load consists only of lamps, as is preferable, then the product of the volts and amperes approximates the output. Temperature readings of the surrounding air should

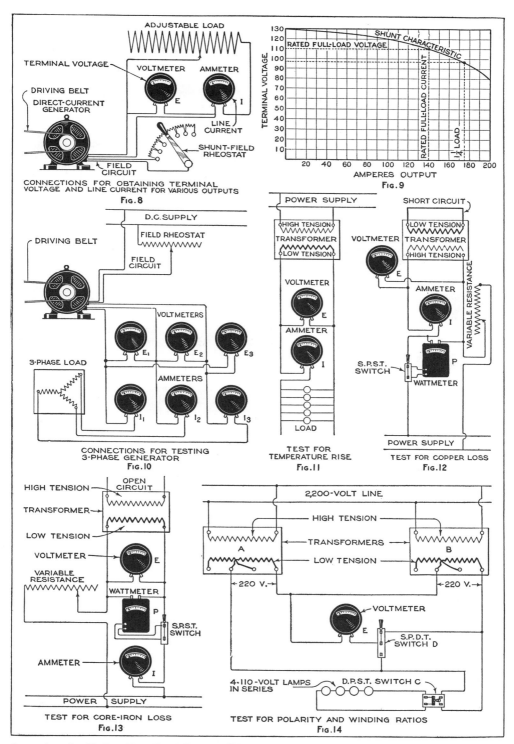

CONNECTIONS FOR OBTAINING TERMINAL VOLTAGE AND LINE CURRENT FOR VARIOUS OUTPUTS
Fig. 8

Fig. 9

CONNECTIONS FOR TESTING 3-PHASE GENERATOR
Fig. 10

TEST FOR TEMPERATURE RISE
Fig. 11

TEST FOR COPPER LOSS
Fig. 12

TEST FOR CORE-IRON LOSS
Fig. 13

TEST FOR POLARITY AND WINDING RATIOS
Fig. 14

Connections for Making Most Usual Tests on Direct-Current and Alternating-Current Generators and Transformers: Figure 8 Shows Connections for Direct-Current Generators; Figure 9, External-Characteristic Graph for a Direct-Current Shunt-Wound Generator; Figure 10, Connections for Testing Alternating-Current Dynamos, and Figures 11 to 14, Connections for Various Tests on Transformers

also be taken so that the temperature rise may be determined. This difference should not exceed 50° C. (90°F.) nor should the temperature of the oil rise above 90° C. (194° F.).

It is both difficult and dangerous to obtain the current and voltage values of the high-tension circuit without special testing apparatus. The efficiency of a transformer is, therefore, determined by finding the copper and iron losses; the input is, then, the output plus the iron or core loss plus the copper loss.

To make the copper-loss test, short-circuit the low-voltage windings and place a voltmeter, an ammeter, and a watt-meter in the high-tension circuit, as in Fig. 12. Connections are made through a rheostat to a low-voltage power supply. Manipulate the rheostat until the full-load current, the value of which will be found on the nameplate, flows in the windings. The wattmeter will then indicate the copper loss of the transformer—since the transformer is doing no outside work and the power consumed is that due to the heat loss in the windings. Take other readings at various loads, and record the readings graphically.

The test for iron loss is somewhat similar to the copper-loss test, as indicated in Fig. 13. In this instance, the high-voltage winding is left open-circuited, and the instruments are connected in the low-tension side. Since no current flows in the high-voltage winding, the watt-meter shows the power consumed in exciting the iron. The wattmeter reading also includes the potential coil losses in both voltmeter and wattmeter, but unless very accurate tests are being made, these losses can be disregarded.

If possible, an auto transformer should be used instead of the rheostat for varying the testing voltage.

Knowing, now, the copper and iron losses, the efficiency of the transformer under test is:

$$\text{Efficiency} = \frac{P}{P + \text{copper loss} + \text{iron loss}}.$$

Should it be necessary to change the transformer leads, or should there be any question as to whether the connections are correct, a polarity test is advisable. Such a test requires a transformer of equal rating for comparison. Make the connections as indicated in Fig. 14, which shows a relative-polarity test on a 2,200 to 220-440-volt transformer. The high-tension windings of both A and B are connected to a 2,200-volt power-supply circuit. Four 110-volt lamps are connected in series through a double-pole single-throw switch, C, with leads from the low-tension side of both A and B. A voltmeter is connected through a single-pole double-throw switch, D, in such manner that the voltage of either transformer may be read as desired.

When all is ready for the test, throw switch C and note if the lamps light brightly. If they do, the leads are brought out correctly; if not, the leads are reversed. The latter case indicates that the transformers are opposing each other. Repeat this test on all leads until every connection is known to be correct.

The ratio between the windings of a transformer may be found by making the same connections as for the polarity test. Transformer B must, however, be of a known ratio. Leaving switch C open, quickly throw switch D from one contact to the other. If the transformers have similar windings, and similar ratios, the two readings should be identical.

In making transformer tests, high voltages are sometimes encountered and great care must therefore be exercised to insure personal safety.

Using Drawing Pencils

Always sharpen a drawing pencil at both ends; the ordinary round point at one end and a knife-edge at the other. Use the knife-edge whenever a long line is to be drawn, as it will do much more work than the round point before resharpening is necessary.

In forming a knife-edge on a drawing pencil, always hold the pencil so that the edge will be made parallel with one of the six flats on the hexagon pencil—preferably the one on which the name and grade of the pencil are stamped. This makes it easy to form the second side of the edge, for it is simply made parallel with the opposite flat of the "hex," and the edge thus comes out straight, instead of on a slant. Thus, when the pencil is gripped by the fingers, the edge will always have the proper angular relation to the hexagon, bringing it instantly parallel with the edge of the T-square.

Since sharpening a pencil in this way soon removes the maker's mark, it is necessary to mark the pencil near the middle; this is done by cutting the required number of notches near the center of the flat; that is, two notches for a 2H pencil, three for a 3H, and so forth.—Curtis Ralston, Chicago, Ill.

Lubricating Broaches

Square broaches should be pulled with a corner upward. The cutting lubricant then flows down around both sides, and does not spatter off, as would be the case were a flat surface used upward. Spline broaches should be so slotted that a channel between two of the splines will be on top; the channel then serves to conduct the lubricant into the hole.

Wick-Feed Oiler Made from Grease Cup

A satisfactory homemade wick-feed oiler can be applied to the bearings of a dynamo or similar mechanism, so that the necessity of constant hand oiling, with the attendant possibility of flooding, are eliminated. A large grease cup is screwed to the underside of the bearing, with a piece of wicking extending through it and touching the revolving shaft. The cap of the grease cup serves as a reservoir for a liberal supply of oil. This is a simple method, for use where small quantities of oil are required, and where excess oiling is to be avoided.

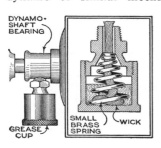

Special Trowel for Concrete-Road Work

Concrete workers on road-paving contracts are familiar with those jobs in which a groove, or flangeway, must be molded on the inside of street-car or railway tracks, in order to provide clearance for the flanges on the car wheels. The drawing shows a type of trowel used on one such contract, for forming the

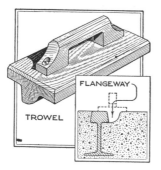

flangeways. A single block of wood is used for the trowel, which can be cut out on a bandsaw or formed in a pattern shop on a shaper.

Lifting Check-Valve Balls

The drawing shows clearly how a small metal ball can be removed from its position in a ball-check valve, or other position where it is inaccessible to the fingers or ordinary tools. Nothing more than a piece of rubber tubing, such as can be bought at any drug store, is needed. The rubber tube can be used alone or it

can be fitted with a small piece of metal tubing in each end, as shown in the drawing, for handling balls smaller than the diameter of the rubber tube. In use, the operator places one end of the tube in his mouth, the other end being in firm contact against the surface of the ball, which is drawn up and held tightly against the tube by suction.—C. A. Clark, Miyazaki, Japan.

Drilling Tempered Springs

After attempting to drill a ⅜-in. hole through a number of tempered springs with no better success than a number of broken drills, an observant mechanic noticed that the lips of the drill would still cut, even when the center was dulled, and an idea being suggested by this, he proceeded to put it into execution, with satisfactory results. In order

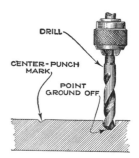

to bring the lips of the drill into contact with the metal, the point of the drill was ground off square so that when set into the punch mark the drill immediately began to cut. The drill was run at slow speed, and, when it stopped cutting, was raised from the work, a heavy center punch used to make another depression in the center of the hole, and the drill fed down again. By alternately punching and drilling in this manner, the steel was finally drilled through.—E. K. Wehry, Cedar Rapids, Ia.

An Improved Blueprint Washer

The washing of large blueprints is always an awkward job because of the splashing and mess, which is impossible

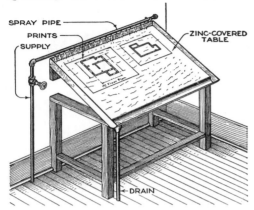

A Blueprint Washer That Uses Nothing but Clean Water to Develop the Exposed Prints, and Eliminates the Need of Using Trays and Sinks

to avoid when large trays are used. Also, owing to the size of some of the trays and the inconvenience of emptying them, they are not uncommonly left for a long time full of dirty greenish-yellow water.

The washing device illustrated does away with the tray or sink, as the washing is done entirely by a flow of clean water over the print. An inclined table, which is built in any convenient location, is provided with raised sides and a trough at the bottom for carrying off the excess water, the whole being covered with sheet zinc or lead. A water pipe, which is drilled with a series of small holes, is arranged parallel with the top of the table so that there will be a uniform flow of water over the surface of the prints.—B. Francis Dashiell, Dunkirk, Md.

Testing for Vibration in Buildings

In a western city, a reinforced-concrete building had but recently been completed when the plastering began to fall from the ceilings. The owner claimed that work was not according to specifications, and the contractor asserted that the trouble was the result of vibrations, which were caused by trolley cars crossing a frog in the street just in front of the building. As none of the vibrations were heavy enough to be seen or felt in the four-story building, an engineer solved the problem and traced down the trouble in a novel manner. A shallow bowl of me-

tallic mercury was placed on the floor of the top story, in such a manner that the mercury would be in direct sunlight. Those interested in the result of the test stationed themselves at a window and watched. A reflection from the sun was thrown onto the ceiling by the mercury and as the street cars passed, it was noticed that the reflection on the ceiling moved several inches, thus greatly magnifying the movement of the building and vindicating the contractor.—J. R. Linton, Sioux City, Ia.

Curing Slapping Exhaust Valves

Sometimes, when a Corliss engine is running under a light load, a slapping noise will be heard from the exhaust valves. Examination of the indicator diagrams will usually show that, under light load, the cut-off is very short, and expansion is carried to a pressure below that of the atmosphere. The exhaust valves are then forced from their seats, causing the slapping or chattering noise.

The steam should be throttled, or the boiler pressure lowered, and the cut-off made later in the stroke, so that the steam will not be expanded below atmospheric pressure.

An Adjustable Bench Stop

A bench stop, which can be adjusted to any height, or lowered so as to be flush with the top of the bench, is quite easily

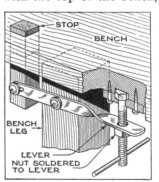

installed on any bench in the manner illustrated. A square hole is cut through the bench, in line with one of the legs; this hole is for the piece of oak that forms the stop proper. A flat-iron lever is next made; twist one end of this to lie flat, drill a hole for a capscrew, and solder or braze a nut underneath. Drill two other holes in the lever—one to pivot it to the bench leg and the other to fasten it to the lower end of the stop. This latter hole should be slotted, so that the stop will be moved upward in a straight line. Fit a bolt into the nut on the lever, then bore a blind hole in the underside of the bench, to receive the capscrew head, and screw a wooden block, with a hole for the screw shank, below it. Drill a small hole through the bottom end of the bolt for a turning lever, which may be a piece of stiff wire or a nail. To raise or lower the stop, it is only necessary to turn the screw either to the right or left.—L. B. Robbins, Harwich, Mass.

Polishing the Ends of Pins

The appearance of pins with round or spherical ends will be greatly improved if the ends are well polished. It is a difficult matter to get a good polish by holding the emery cloth with the fingers while the work is revolved, because it is impossible to hold the cloth perfectly steady, with the result that fine grains of the abrasive cross and recross the surface, producing a scratchy appearance. To obtain the best re-

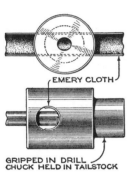

EMERY CLOTH

GRIPPED IN DRILL
CHUCK HELD IN TAILSTOCK

sults when using emery cloth, it should be held, if at all possible, in some kind of rigid holder of the type illustrated. A holder of this kind is merely a piece of cold-rolled steel which is turned down to a handy diameter to fit into a drill chuck. A hole of the same diameter as the work is drilled in the center, and another hole, of a diameter that will conform to the radius of the end of the pin, is drilled at right angles to and intersecting the first hole, as shown. A strip of emery cloth is inserted into the side hole and moved along as it becomes worn. This method gives a very high polish quickly and easily, and is well worth the trouble when a quantity of work is to be finished.

Presses for Straightening Bent Fenders

The drawing shows two devices that can be used to advantage for the quick and easy removal of dents from fenders, or any other sheet-metal work to which they can be applied.

The upper tool is made entirely of ¼-in. flat iron to the dimensions shown. The tight joint indicated should be very solid and should be riveted, although a nut

and bolt will hold it sufficiently tight. Downward pressure on the hand lever gives a powerful compression at the ends of the jaws. Any width of fender or any curve can be restored to its original shape

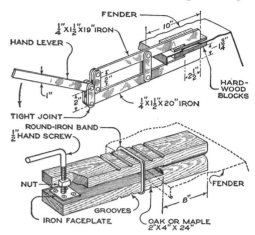

Two Convenient and Simple Tools for Pressing Out Bumps and Dents in the Fenders and Bodies of Automobiles and Similar Sheet-Metal Work

by inserting hardwood blocks of the proper size and shape between the jaws and the work.

The lower tool is made from hardwood, with a handscrew at one end which serves to press the outer ends of the members together with sufficient force to flatten out practically any dent. Notches are cut in both members, to permit changing the position of the round iron band holding them together, so that the tool can be adjusted to fenders of different widths. The thrust of the screw is taken by an iron plate, screwed to the lower member.

Size for Porous Walls

A good size for preparing walls for papering or calcimining may be made by dissolving 1 lb. of glue in 1 gal. of boiling water, as in making ordinary size; dissolve also 1 lb. resin soap (yellow laundry soap), cut in thin slices, in 1 gal. of boiling water; then 2 lb. of alum in 2 qt. water. Thoroughly stir together the glue and soap solutions, then add the dissolved alum. This makes about 3 gal., which will require 2 gal. of water to thin to the proper consistency for a porous wall, and still more water for a hard surface. One or more applications should be put on, as hot as possible. This size is more resistant to moisture than ordinary size.—A. MacCullough, Chicago, Ill.

Adjustable Planer Vises

Many jobs that are machined on the planer could be done better, and in less

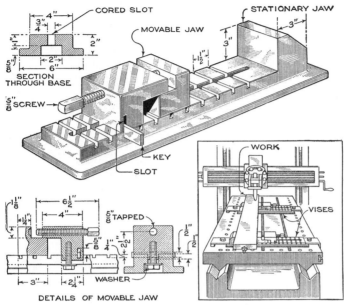

Adjustable Vises for the Planer, That Make It Possible to Set Up and Remove the Work Quickly with a Considerable Saving in Time, Particularly on Repetition Work

time, if the work were held in vises instead of being bolted to the planer table. The work is generally bolted to the table because suitable vises are lacking, the only ones available being generally of too limited capacity for wide work.

The drawing shows a type of planer vise that permits rapid set-up, which is an advantage when several pieces of the same kind are to be worked. For a planer having an 8-ft. stroke, three or more of these vises should be used, depending

upon the thickness and length of the work; they can be bolted anywhere on the table so as to hold odd-shaped work at any angle. The length of these vises is left entirely to the requirements of the user; some will prefer them made to the width of the table, and others will not want them quite so long.

The body and stationary jaw are cast in one piece from a simple pattern, the resulting casting being machined on the top, bottom, and face of the jaw. On the top face of the jaw slide, a number of key slots, $\frac{1}{4}$ by $\frac{1}{4}$ in., are cut, $1\frac{1}{2}$ in. apart.

The sliding, or movable, jaw is built up in two parts, the front member being the real jaw, while the rear piece serves as a buttress, and as a nut for the clamping screws. The rear block is shaped so as to overhang and slide on the tongue of the front member, and serves to hold the latter down to the slide. The countersunk screw seat is the only means used to hold this loose jaw centrally, which is free to float, to adjust itself to the face of the work. The rear part of the sliding jaw has a tongue that fits into the slot in the base, to which it is loosely clamped by a screw or bolt, as shown.

The key, which fits loosely, is used to form an absolute buttress and prevents the jaw from sliding backward while the clamping screw is tightened.—J. V. Romig, Allentown, Pa.

Testing New Refrigerating System

When testing a new installation of coils in a refrigerating system, a small, portable, air-cooled, motor-driven air compressor is used to provide the necessary test pressure, which, depending upon the contract specifications, runs up to 200 lb. and over. A suitable connection is made between the coils and pump for the insertion of a high-pressure gauge, and also an ammonia-charging valve. Pressure is pumped into the coils, using fresh air, for the first test. If there are any serious leaks, they will be detected immediately

by the hissing of escaping air. Should there be no such leaks, watch the pressure gauge and see whether the pressure falls very much, remembering, however, that a slight fall in pressure will accompany the cooling of the highly compressed air. After this slight drop, which should take place within a half hour, the pressure should remain constant. If this test is satisfactory and the pressure stands up well, discharge the air, and connect a drum of ammonia to the ammonia valve between the air pump and the coils, and allow a small amount of the ammonia to escape into the closed-up system, enough to raise the pressure to about 10 lb. This amount of ammonia will be sufficient to make the detection of any leaks, no matter how small, possible. Now, pump the system to 200-lb. pressure again and go over all the joints, smelling for the sharp ammonia odor, which will escape through any porous or leaky spots.

Leaks come from badly cut pipe threads, poorly cemented joints, bad seams in the piping, porous and honeycombed spots in the fittings, and from cracked fittings.

If the second test is successful, discharge the ammonia-laden air into the open, and pump a vacuum in the coils, before filling the system with the full ammonia charge.

Small leaks are sometimes closed by peening the metal with small punches and ball-peen hammers. Another way consists in pumping a strong vacuum and smearing the leaky spots with a thin mixture of glycerin and litharge, which has a tendency to be sucked into the holes and porous parts, closing them when the litharge sets. Soldering may also be resorted to, but never with the system under pressure.

A Novel Scale for Machinists

A new die, having 16 threads per inch, was being tested out on some ¼-in. drill rod, the result being an exceptionally fine-cut thread. A few of these threaded rods were made into 6-in. scales by one of the machinists in the shop in the following manner: Two steel blocks were drilled and tapped for a ¼-16 screw and then cut down at the ends, as

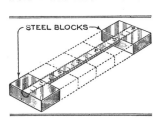

shown in the drawing, to about half the diameter of the rod. The threaded rod, resting on the steel half-blocks, was placed on the magnetic chuck of a surface grinder, and faced down flat. After grinding, the rod was removed from the grinder, graduated with a very sharp chisel, and marked with small figures. The half-blocks were moved along, as indicated by the dotted lines, to serve as anvils for the rod during the graduating. The threads, being 16 to the inch, take the place of ¹⁄₁₆-in. graduations, and the chisel marks are ¼-in. apart.—M. E. Duggan, Kenosha, Wis.

Ball-Bearing Puller

A puller for inner races of ball bearings, that is different from the usual device, is built on about the same principle

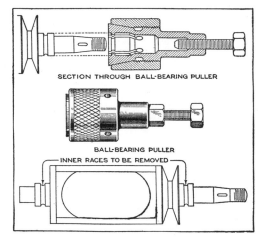

SECTION THROUGH BALL-BEARING PULLER

BALL-BEARING PULLER
INNER RACES TO BE REMOVED

A Ball-Bearing Puller That Embodies the Principle of a Lathe Collet, Holding the Inner Race While the Screw is Turned, to Force the Shaft Out

as a lathe collet. As the puller can be made for use on bearings of different sizes, no dimensions are given in the drawing, which clearly shows the constructional details.

The inner part is machined, as shown, with split jaws. The largest diameter of this part is tapered so that the similarly tapered and threaded sleeve can be screwed down to tighten the jaws of the puller on the bearing race. A long screw at one end of the puller bears against the end of the shaft; when this is tightened the race is pulled off.—J. Magis-Frankart, Ouffet, Belgium.

Belt-Loop Hammer Holder

Carpenters, and others who must always have their hammers within easy reach, or those who work with two styles of hammers, will find the hanger shown in the drawing to be of great utility. All that is required to make such a holder is a piece of leather, about 3 by 4 in., which is pierced with a hole for the hammer handle and slitted to fit over the belt.—A. C. Cole, Chicago, Ill.

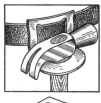

Planer-Tool Lifter

When a machinist is working at piece rates on duplicate production work, every little trick to preserve the cutting edge

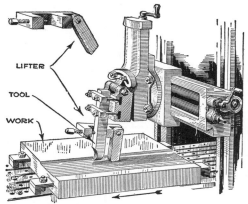

LIFTER

TOOL

WORK

A Lifter for Planer Tools That Prevents the Tool from Rubbing on the Work on the Backstroke, Thus Preserving the Cutting Edge of the Tool

of his tools helps to put money in his pocket. As everyone knows who is familiar with planer tools, the rubbing of the cutting edge on the return stroke soon makes resharpening necessary, and many operators lift their tools on the backstroke by hand, just to eliminate this dulling action.

While there are many devices for the automatic elevation of the tool above the surface of the work, the one shown in the drawing is among the simplest and most effective, as it is easily made and quickly clamped to any cutting tool. The body is made from a piece of flat steel; it is fitted with a latch, which has a form somewhat similar to that of the cutting tool and is held to the body by a bolt or rivet. By rounding off the top corner, this latch will drag behind the tool on the forward or cutting stroke, but will fall in a vertical position on the return stroke. When the lifter has been adjusted to the proper height, it will cause the tool to rise on the return stroke, as shown.

Making Good Brazed Joints

A method which adds strength to a brazed joint, in either tubular or plate work, consists in drilling one of the parts with a series of holes, at the point where the braze is to be made. Ordinarily the practice is to apply the spelter and flux to the pieces and then heat until the spelter flows and runs into the joint. Lack of heat, or dirt in the joint, will cause an imperfect union, that cannot be detected from the outside. Drilling the holes, as suggested, and applying the spelter to this portion of the joint, causes the melted brass to enter between the surfaces where it is desired. The size of the holes depends, of course, upon the size of the job, but ordinarily holes not larger than ¼ in. should be used; these can be filled with spelter and finished to present a smooth job. This method has been satisfactorily used in brazing automobile-axle housings.

Beveling Edges of Wallboard

In working with wallboard, it is sometimes desirable to bevel the edges to form a neat joint; this can be done without sawing, which generally leaves ragged edges, by means of a simple device that uses sandpaper for forming the bevel. A piece of wood, about 6 in. square, is cut diagonally to make two 45° triangles, and these are fastened together by two braces, as shown, a handle also being provided. A piece of wallboard is nailed to the hypotenuses of the triangles, and the sandpaper is fastened to this with thumbtacks. In use, the sanding device is moved back and forth across the edge of the panel, and, by raising or lowering the panel, the whole surface of the sandpaper can be used.—Karl L. Martin, Cleveland, Ohio.

WALLBOARD BEING BEVELED

HANDLE

WALLBOARD COVERED WITH LAYER OF SANDPAPER

Spring Circular-Saw Guide

When the circular saw is used to split narrow stock, the simple spring holder shown in the drawing will enable the operator to do his work faster and without danger of having a finger cut off. Such a holder is made by bolting a piece of ⅛ by ⅝-in. spring steel between blocks of hardwood. The length of the spring will vary with different saw tables, but 12 in. is about the average.

A piece of stock is set against the saw guide, and the spring holder is clamped in

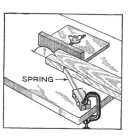

SPRING

place on the saw table with a C-clamp, in such a manner that the spring presses firmly against the stock. Make certain that the extreme point of the spring cannot come into contact with the saw itself. A similar spring can be used to press downward on the stock, in which case the holder would be clamped to the saw guide, and the steel spring would be adjusted to press on the wood between guide and saw. With two such guides in position, the stock can be sent through the saw from one end to the other without carrying the hands beyond a safe distance from the saw. Once started, the man "taking away" can pull the stock toward him and at the same time be certain that the wood is bearing hard against the saw guide.—E. L. Bragdon, New York City.

Rustproofing Iron

A new method of rustproofing, which has been applied especially to small automobile parts, consists in boiling the articles in a solution of hydrophosphate of iron. An attractive dark-gray finish is produced, and this is practically proof against all attacks of rust. The process is more rapid than others, and there is no effect upon the strength or temper of the metal.

Artist's Magnifying-Glass Holder

An artist's ability to do fine work on a drawing, such as producing a fine stipple with pen or pencil, can be greatly in-

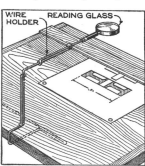

creased by using a 3-in. reading glass. Besides, the eyes are relieved of a great deal of strain, and the pen can be more accurately guided.

The drawing shows a wire support for the magnifying glass, which is slipped underneath the edge of the drawing board and can be instantly removed. The support can be made to any suitable measurements from stiff wire, and is adjustable horizontally and vertically. The magnifying glass has a hole drilled in its handle to make a tight fit over the wire, as shown in the drawing.

Discarded Vise Makes Arbor Press

Scrapped on account of a broken jaw, an old vise was made to serve in the capacity of an arbor press, the device

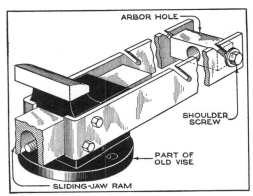

Discarded Because of a Broken Jaw, This Vise was Made into a Substantial and Quick-Acting Arbor Press for Work within Its Capacity

proving very quick and solid. Two pieces of ¾ by 2½-in. flat steel are used for the sidepieces, which are fastened to the fixed part of the vise by screws. One end of each piece is bent at right angles and fits around the vise, to give extra strength and rigidity. Next, a piece is made that serves as the arbor plate of the fixture; this is a 3 by 3-in. piece of machine steel, the length of which is such as to fit easily between the sidepieces. It is bored in the center for the arbors to slip through, and each end is drilled and tapped for ¾-in. bolts. To make the press quick-acting, holes are drilled in the sidepieces at intervals of about 2 in., and slots are cut at an angle, as shown. From the drawing it will be seen that the part bored to take the arbors is free to revolve, and that, consequently, the arbor can be inserted in the hole while in an upright position, thus lessening the distance necessary between this part and the end of the vise ram. This feature, in conjunction with the freedom with which the piece can be dropped into any convenient slot that the length of the arbor may call for, makes this press quite rapid. For small arbors, a bushing is made to fit the hole. When the whole fixture is assembled, it should be bolted securely to a bench, preferably one mounted on wheels, so that it can be moved around the shop.

⁌Nails and screws dipped in grease, wax, or soap will drive more easily, particularly in hardwood.

Truss Stiffens a Long Ladder

The use of long ladders, such as fire ladders, is only made possible because of a system of trussing, which can be

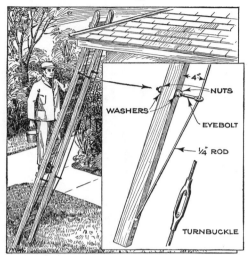

Trusses on the Underside of a Long Ladder Prevent It from Swaying and Swinging and Give a Sense of Safety to the Worker

adopted, in a modified form, for stiffening other long ladders and preventing them from swaying. Four eyebolts are made, large enough to permit a ¼-in. rod to be inserted through the eye, which should be about 4 in. away from the underside of the ladder. Four pieces of ¼-in. mild steel are used for the trusses, and each of these is about half the length of the ladder itself; one end of each is flattened and drilled for heavy screws, the other ends of two lengths are threaded with left-hand threads, the other two being threaded right-hand. Turnbuckles are fitted to each truss after the ends have been passed through the eyebolts. With each side of a long ladder braced as shown, practically all spring will be eliminated, and it will be sufficiently strong to be used in many places where otherwise it could not be considered.—Lowell R. Butcher, Ames, Ia.

A Cheap Board for Large Drawings

The high price of a large drawing board and the still higher price demanded for a large-size drawing table are items that must be seriously considered when the board is required only for some special piece of work. An idea that represents an economical and practical solution makes use of a variety of wallboard that can be obtained in panels of almost any dimensions up to 4 by 12 ft. The type of wallboard best suited for the purpose is that which is built up of wooden strips, cemented together to make a continuous board, with a smooth surface of tough brown paper. The cost of this material is but a few cents per square foot. Wallboard of this kind is made ¼ in. thick, and the large panels are therefore flexible and should be well supported when used horizontally; when used vertically, this is unnecessary. A standard ¼-in. metal channel, fitted to the edges of the board, makes a fine sliding edge for the T-square.—C. Nye, New York City.

Making Smooth Joints in Large Tile

Where firmly cemented joints are required in lines of large sewer tile, several difficulties are encountered unless an unnecessarily large quantity of cement mixture is used. If a dry, coarse mixture is used, it will be hard to make an absolutely tight joint, and if a thin, rich mixture is used it will flow through the joints. The latter is, of course, the better mixture, as it will flow and fill in below the tile without

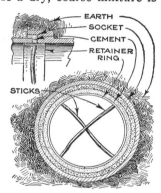

tamping or the use of a great amount of the cement mixture, and will make a good joint if some means of confining it is used. This is easily done. Having placed a new section of tile in position and centered it by means of small bits of stone or like objects, placed between the socket of one pipe and the end of the other, take a narrow strip of some thin springy material—wallboard is excellent—and shape it to the inner curve of the joint to be cemented. The ends of the strip should butt closely together; if this retainer ring is correctly made, it will hold itself in place, but light sticks, a trifle longer than the diameter of the pipe can be sprung into place to help retain it. With the aid of this device, a very thin cement mixture can be poured about the joint, into which it will flow, filling it completely and showing a smooth inner bore when set.—Louis Schneider, Clinton, Mo.

A Power Hammer for Farm Shops

By L. B. ROBBINS

A BLACKSMITH shop is a necessity on the modern farm, and where heavy work must occasionally be handled, a simple power hammer, built of material found around any farm, will prove of great value.

The site selected for the erection of the hammer should be close to the forge; the foundation should be solid, and there should be a good ceiling, or heavy roof beams, against which to butt the hammer guides.

To construct the hammer, first obtain a discarded lightweight-automobile or carriage spring, full-elliptical type, and be

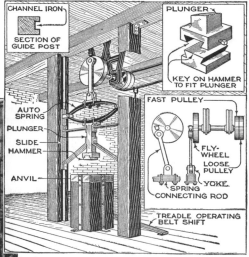

A Power Hammer for the Farm, Built of Materials Picked Up around the Shop, or Easily Obtained from Any Junk Dealer: It will Save Much Time and Hard Labor Where Any Heavy Forging is Done, Especially on an Out-of-the-Way Farm, Where Any Breakdown of the Farm Machinery Means a Long Wait for New Parts

sure that it is quite springy. Two heavy posts, of a size suitable for the hammer to be built, say about 12 by 12 in. in cross section, are then cut to length, and a rectangular groove cut along the center of one face of each. A length of channel iron is fastened in each groove, to serve as guides for the plunger or head of the hammer.

The plunger can be forged to the shape

indicated from a piece of heavy steel; a wide dovetail groove is cut in the bottom, to accommodate hammers of various depths, thus altering the distance between hammer face and anvil, and consequently the force of the blow. A dovetailed key on the top of each hammer fits in the groove in the plunger, and is tightly locked in place with a setscrew.

Horizontal and angular braces, of heavy flat iron, are bolted to the sides of the plunger, and to lengths of rectangular steel, sliding in the guides. These should be so fitted that the plunger will slide easily, and yet have no undue sideplay. The ends of the spring are yoked to the sliding pieces in the same manner as they were fitted to the auto or carriage. The upper side of the spring is bolted to a yoke, in which the connecting rod is pivoted. The latter is a forging, and is attached to a disk crank mounted on a shaft on the end of which are fast and loose pulleys. The crankpin should be set 3 in. from the center, giving the hammer a 6-in. stroke. The bottom of the spring is fastened to the top of the plunger by U-bolts.

The belt shifter should be operated by a foot treadle, working through a bell crank, and should be so arranged that the belt is on the fast pulley when the treadle is down, while the bell crank should have a spring attached to it, so that when pressure is taken off the treadle, the belt will automatically be shifted to the loose pulley. The crankshaft should be driven at a speed sufficient to operate the hammer at about 40 strokes a minute. The anvil consists of a heavy iron block, fastened to a wooden block by flat-iron straps, which hold the whole to the floor.

It is obviously impossible to give any dimensions, or lay down any hard and fast rules for constructing a machine that is to be made of any material at hand. These instructions, however, should enable anyone to build a hammer that will save much heavy hand forging.

Ladder for Work on Shafting

An ordinary ladder is more or less un-suited for such work as oiling lineshaft hangers, repairing belts, and the like. The

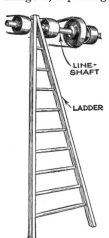

ladder shown in the drawing has many advantages for work of this kind, as it is not top-heavy, and can be rested against the shafting when the pulleys are but a few inches apart. The top of the ladder should be as narrow as possible, while the bottom should be at least 3 ft. wide, so that it can be rested on a minimum of space and yet not slip to one side when the workman leans to one side or tugs at a pulley or belt. A hook at the top to fit over the shaft and spikes at the bottom are suggested as measures for reducing the possibility of accident.

Action of Metallic Salts on Aluminum

Aluminum utensils should not be used as containers for certain solutions of metallic salts, such as copper sulphate and mercuric chloride (bichloride of mercury). The reason for this is, that aluminum is higher in the electrochemical series than mercury or copper and will displace mercury or copper from their salts when the latter are in contact with it. The same thing happens when aluminum is in contact with the salt of any other metal that is below it in the electrochemical series. In the case of a piece of aluminum being placed in a solution of copper sulphate, aluminum will go into solution and copper will be forced out in the metallic form. When mercuric chloride is in contact with aluminum, the latter goes into solution as aluminum chloride and metallic mercury will be deposited on the aluminum surface. Metallic mercury in contact with aluminum forms an amalgam that is oxidized, with the formation of aluminum oxide. This process goes on until the aluminum is eaten away. Consequently, aluminum utensils should not be used for antiseptic mercurial solutions, or for the mercury intensifier used in photography. Also, medical instruments that are made entirely, or in part, of aluminum should not be sterilized in bichloride solutions.

Gauge for Laying Out Square Holes

To inclose a circle accurately in a square requires considerable time and care, and when a number of squares are

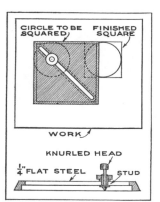

to be laid out, the job becomes very tedious. The tool shown in the drawing, if accurately made, will greatly simplify the squaring of circles of any diameter within its capacity. The body is made from ¼-in. flat steel, ground square and beveled on the edges. A slot is cut diagonally through the piece and then milled out to a slightly greater width for about two-thirds of the thickness of the stock. A center, made of tool steel, has a knurled head pinned or riveted to it after final assembly, as indicated by the drawing. To enable this center to slide up and down in the slot, a stud is made with a head of the same diameter as the greatest width of the slot, with a shank which is a sliding fit in the smallest width. A knurled nut, fitting the threaded stud, completes the tool.

To square a circle, push down the center and place it in a punch mark made in the exact center of the circle, the nut on the stud being loose; let the body of the tool rest flat on the work and slide it gently until the two edges coincide exactly with the scribed circumference of the circle; then tighten the nut. After lines have been scribed along the two sides, turn the tool around on its center and repeat the operation to form the other two sides of the square.

An Improvised Valve-Seat Reamer

In a small shop, not provided with too many tools, a machinist was working on the cylinder head of a stationary gasoline engine, on which one of the valve seats was so badly pitted that it would have been impossible to make a good face by the ordinary process of "grinding in."

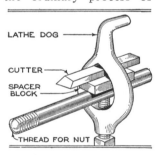

The shop had no reamer that would fit, and it seemed that the whole head would have to be swung in a lathe just to remove less than an ounce of metal. The mechanic, however, found an easier way. A piece of cold-rolled steel, the same size as the valve stem, and about 1 ft. long, was cut and threaded on one end. An ordinary tool bit was then ground with a bevel on one end, to correspond to the angle of the seat. A lathe dog and a spacer block completed the outfit. The tool bit was clamped against the rod with the dog, the spacer block holding the cutting tool just far enough away from the rod to face the seat. The rod was inserted through the guide hole, a nut run on, and screwed up just tight enough so that, when the tool was turned with the dog, the cutter would scrape the seat. As the seat was trued up, the nut was tightened until the seat was free from pits.—James Ellis, Memphis, Tenn.

Drilling Holes in Porcelain

The mechanic who undertakes to drill holes through porcelain bathroom fittings, and other expensive equipment of the same material, is quite likely to break the article unless considerable care is used. Although brittle and hard, glazed porcelain can be drilled easily if properly handled. The main difficulty lies in getting the drill properly sharpened; the proper way is to grind the point of the drill perfectly square and then,

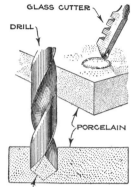

holding it on one edge of the wheel, to grind the cutting edges as shown in the drawing. To start the drill through the vitreous glaze, cut a circle, the same diameter as the hole, at the proper location, with a glass cutter, the cut being carried through the glaze; the drill will then enter easily. As soon as the drill stops cutting take it out and carefully chip off the triangular peak in the center of the hole with a narrow chisel, nailset, or similar tool. This operation is repeated until the hole has been drilled through.—W. Norman Fox, Atlantic City, New Jersey.

A Clamping Kink

It frequently happens, when clamping a piece of work to the bed of a machine, that there are no bolts of sufficient length on hand. The drawing illustrates a method of clamping that will be found useful in such cases. Two short bolts are necessary;

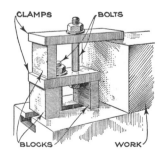

one is set in a T-slot, and used to clamp a plate and blocks to the table. The plate is provided with a second hole, through which the other bolt is passed, clamping the work as shown.—Chas. Homewood, Ontario, Calif.

Homemade Gas Blowpipe

A small blowpipe, suitable for soldering or light brazing, can be made almost entirely of pipe fittings; it is used with illu-

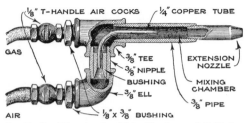

An Air-Gas Blowpipe for Light Brazing and Soldering Jobs That Uses Illuminating Gas, under the Usual City Pressure, and Light Air Pressure from a Blower, Bellows, or Compressor

minating gas at the usual city pressure, and air from a small compressor, blower, or foot-operated bellows. Only a few pounds' air pressure are needed. Most soldering jobs can be better done with this apparatus than with a soldering iron, as the heat is applied directly to the work, and the size of the flame may be regulated by varying the size of the nozzle, as well as from the valves. For very fine work, a small-diameter nozzle, giving a thin, pointed flame, is attached.

The body of the blowpipe is made from $\frac{3}{8}$-in. pipe and fittings, then reduced down to $\frac{1}{8}$ or $\frac{1}{4}$ in. for the cocks. An interior air nozzle is made by filling a piece of $\frac{1}{4}$-in. (outside diameter) copper tube with melted lead, giving it a short right-angled bend and then melting out the lead. Then, a fiber, brass, or iron bushing is driven into a $\frac{3}{8}$-in. pipe nipple and drilled out to a close fit for the copper tube, one arm of which is pushed into it and the whole screwed into a $\frac{3}{8}$-in. tee. A brass or iron nipple, about 5 in. long, is then screwed into the tee, the outer end tapped to $\frac{1}{4}$-in. pipe size, and a smaller extension nozzle screwed in. Several different sizes of these tips or nozzles are made up for light or heavy work. An elbow is screwed onto the lower end of the nipple, both tee and ell are reduced to $\frac{1}{8}$ or $\frac{1}{4}$-in. pipe size, and two ground-in brass T-handle air cocks attached. The blowpipe is connected to the gas and air supply by means of rubber tubes.

Cold-Tinning of Metals

Finely divided block tin is mixed with metallic mercury to form an amalgam having the consistency of soft paste, and, of course, the finer the tin is divided, the easier it will be to amalgamate the two

metals. The work to be tinned is cleaned thoroughly so that it will be free from all greasiness. Then the area to be tinned is rubbed with a rag moistened with muriatic acid. Immediately after, a little of the amalgam is applied to the surface and rubbed with the same rag, the amalgam adhering to the surface of the work and thoroughly tinning it. Cast and wrought iron, steel, copper, and other metals, can be tinned by this process. In case it is found difficult, if not impossible, to make soft solder adhere to iron when using sal ammoniac as a flux, no trouble will be experienced in soldering if the surfaces to be joined are first tinned as described and then the same procedure as in soldering tin is followed.

Safeguarding Price Marks on Stock Drawers

The owner of a hardware store was greatly bothered by the price marks, which were written on stickers gummed on the side of the drawers, becoming rubbed and torn off after the drawers had been opened and closed a few times. This meant that the office force had to prepare

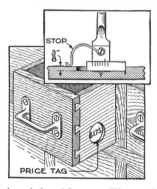

a new set of tags every few weeks, and with nearly 2,000 drawers to be marked, this meant considerable extra work. The problem was solved by the store's carpenter. He removed each drawer and turned it with its right side up. Then with an expansion bit, he drilled a depression in the side of the drawer about $\frac{3}{8}$ in. deep and $1\frac{1}{2}$ in. in diameter. The depth of the depression was made uniform by means of a stop made from steel wire, which was fastened to the setscrew of the bit. Circular gummed price stickers, with the price of the article contained in the drawer written on them, were then pasted against the bottom of the depression, and as prices were changed or the contents of the drawer altered, new stickers were pasted over the old ones. No amount of chafing against the sides of the drawers can damage the price marks thus protected, and the system has proved to be a great labor saver.

Action of Grease in Boilers

The action of grease in a steam boiler is peculiar. Grease does not dissolve or decompose in water, nor does it remain on the surface. Heat in the water and its violent boiling cause the grease to form in sticky drops which adhere to and varnish the metal surfaces of the boiler. The varnish, by preventing the water from coming into contact with the metal, prevents the water from absorbing heat, and this causes a blister or burning of the plates that often results in a serious rupture or violent explosion.

Stand for Painting Auto Hoods

When painting the automobile, best results on the hood are obtained by remov-

ing it and treating it as a separate job, as, aside from the body, it is the most conspicuous part of the car and should be treated accordingly. By building a simple stand of the type shown, the hood is supported in a manner that makes all parts of it conveniently reached with the brush. While the paint on the hood is still wet, the whole thing can be pushed into a room or inclosure that is free from dust.

A Special Slotting Hacksaw

A common operation in most small shops is the slotting of odd screws, the slitting of bushings, and similar work. The device illustrated will be found a convenient aid whenever a saw slot is desired in the center or along the axis of a piece of circular work. While it may not be necessary, for example, in the case of a screw, that the slot be exactly in the center, it will be agreed that nothing looks worse on a finished article than screws that have their slots cut on one side. Trusting entirely to the eye in such cases, often results in the slot being far enough off center to be unsightly. The tool shown in the drawing is made after

the manner of an ordinary saw frame, but fitted with a V-guide. The frame is bent or forged, as indicated, with one end

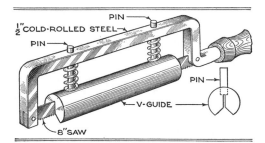

A Special Hacksaw for Slotting Heads of Machine Screws, Slitting Round Stock Parallel to the Axis, and Similar Work

drawn to a tang to fit the handle. The V-guide is a piece of 1-in. cold-rolled steel with a "V" cut in the bottom, the center of the cut being slotted or sawed to accommodate the saw blade. Holes are drilled in the top of the guide, to take two pins that pass through two clear holes drilled in the frame. When the whole is assembled, two light springs are slipped over the pins between the guide and the saw frame; the tool has a 6-in. guide when used with an 8-in. saw.

When slotting work, the guide is placed on it, and the operator saws in the usual manner, the guide moving along with the saw and keeping it centered on, and in close contact with, the work.

Dust Guards on Eccentric Straps

The sliding and revolving parts of machinery used for coal, ashes, and sand, are continually exposed to more or less gritty dust, which quickly destroys the reciprocating and revolving parts and their bearings. The drawing shows an eccentric for an automatic boiler stoker,

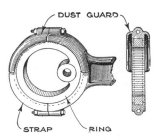

which has been fitted with a dust guard to prevent coal dust from shortening the life of the eccentric straps. The dust guard, or cover, is cast on both sides of the upper strap, deflecting the dust that would otherwise fall directly onto the revolving sheave.—M. E. Duggan, Kenosha, Wis.

Keying Small Pulley to Motor

After buying a ¼-hp. electric motor to operate a small lathe, it was found that the 2-in. grooved pulley with which the motor was equipped was unsuited to the work. This pulley was secured to the

KEY
SHAFT
TOOLREST
WOODEN PULLEY

armature shaft with a setscrew. The shaft was filed flat as shown. As a flat-face pulley was necessary and an iron one could not be obtained, a wooden pulley, of 2½-in. diameter and 1½-in. face, was cut from a 2½-in. square of maple plank. A ½-in. hole was drilled through the center, and a key was cut from thin sheet metal. One end of the key was slightly tapered for easy insertion, and it was then driven in on the flat side of the shaft. The key was about ¹⁄₃₂ in. wider than the flat, so that it took good hold in the wooden pulley. The motor was then set up, and a simple toolrest made as shown; then, by connecting the motor to the current and using a wood-turning gouge, the face of the pulley was crowned as well as it could have been done on the lathe.—Edwin J. Bachman, Fullerton, Pa.

Mounting Knife Switches in a Safe Position

By removing the unprotected knife switches from the front of the back of the lathes, a large manufacturing concern has,

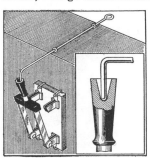

at small expense, done away with a constant source of danger to its workmen. Mounted on the back of the tool-cabinet end of the lathe, as indicated in the drawing, the switch is out of reach of the operator and is operated by means of a rod over the top of the cabinet. This rod is fastened by ordinary staples, or screweyes,

so that it may slide freely. The end of the rod behind the cabinet is bent at right angles and fits loosely into a hole drilled in the end of the switch handle. The end of the rod that projects in front of the cabinet is bent into a ring, or fitted with a convenient knob or handle.—Clementine Paddleford, New York City.

Gauge for Grinding Milling Cutters

To grind the tooth face of formed milling cutters, the work is, as a rule, held on a stud fastened to the grinder table. In order to keep the form of the cutter true, it is necessary to set the stud central with the face of the grinding wheel. The gauge shown in the drawing forms a handy means of alining the stud; it is made from flat steel, cut to form a "V,"

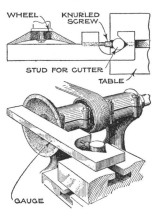

WHEEL
KNURLED SCREW
STUD FOR CUTTER
TABLE
GAUGE

with the flat face that touches the wheel in line with the apex of the angle. The gauge is drilled from the V-end and tapped for a knurled screw which holds the device to the stud. As studs of different diameters are required to accommodate different cutters, the V-construction referred to automatically takes care of this. In use, the gauge is slipped over the stud, and the screw is turned out until it grips the latter lightly. This leaves the operator's hands free to adjust the table, which, of course, is set correctly when the face of the gauge is touching both sides of the grinding wheel. Stock about ⅜ in. thick will be found best for a gauge of this type.—Harry Moore, Montreal, Can.

Sunken Joints in Furniture Panels

A defect in manufacture known as a sunken joint is sometimes noticeable in thick panels, especially tops of tables, desks, and other pieces of furniture. This defect appears as a long shallow depression in the surface, and may be very conspicuous when viewed at certain angles.

In modern practice, furniture tops are

generally built up of five plies of wood, consisting of a thick core, cross-banding, and faces. The core is usually made of a number of pieces of lumber glued together, and investigation proves that the defect in question occurs over the joints in the core stock.

It has been found that too rapid progress in the preparation of the core is the basic cause of sunken joints. The wood next the joint absorbs moisture from the glue and swells. If insufficient time is allowed between the gluing of the joints and the surfacing of the core, which is the next step in manufacture, more wood will be removed at the joints, because of the greater swelling there than at intermediate points. During subsequent drying and seasoning, greater shrinkage takes place at the joints, causing permanent depressions.

The remedy for sunken joints is an extension of the seasoning period between gluing and planing. The proper length of this period will vary with the thickness and species of wood, and with atmospheric conditions, but it should be long enough to allow the moisture added by the glue to evaporate, or to distribute itself through the wood.—U. S. Forest Products Laboratory, Madison, Wis.

Ball-Check Valve Made from Screw

There are many cases in which a small ball-check valve could be used to advantage in experimental work, or even for constant service. Such an article is carried in stock by but a few dealers, and

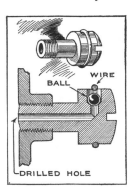

BALL
WIRE
DRILLED HOLE

it is consequently more or less difficult to obtain. The drawing shows how an ordinary machine screw can be made into a thoroughly serviceable check valve, with a minimum of trouble, by drilling a small hole along the axis of the screw body, to the center of the head, where it intersects a similar hole drilled at right angles. The latter hole is counterbored to take a steel ball of the right size, and this is prevented from coming out by means of a wire ring which fits into a groove filed or turned in the circumference of the head.—G. A. Luers, Washington, D. C.

Universal Soldering Copper

The trouble with the ordinary fixed-handle soldering copper is that it is impossible to use it to the best advantage in cramped places and corners, this shortcoming being most apparent in soldering the seams of tanks and similar work. For this particular class of work, the flat, broad point shown in the drawing will be

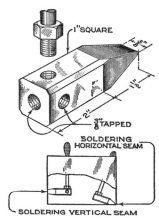

1" SQUARE
2"
3/8 TAPPED
SOLDERING HORIZONTAL SEAM
SOLDERING VERTICAL SEAM

found the best. By drilling the rear end as shown, and tapping it to fit a threaded 3/8-in. handle, three different positions of the head are obtainable, and by tightening the locknut, the head is held firmly. The sizes given in the drawing are for a general-utility copper, one that will hold its heat for a long time. One such universal tool will take the place of three of the solid type, and will reduce the weight of the journeyman tinsmith's tool kit.

Locking Cotter Pins

Link connections on the carburetor and spark-lever controls of an automobile are usually held in place and prevented from becoming loose by cotter pins. However, as these parts are often disconnected, which requires that the ends of the cotters be bent back and forth, the result is that the ends break off after using a few

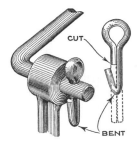

CUT
BENT

times. The modified cotter pin shown in the drawing avoids the necessity of bending the points for insertion or removal, yet provides a perfect lock. These pins are made by cutting off one end of the cotter and bending the other back, as shown in the drawing. The bent end is sprung out enough to catch against the link, so that the cotter cannot come out.

Holding Round Stock in Vise

A handy fixture for the shop holds round stock in the vise at any angle, so that the work cannot slip. The body of the device is made from a 3-in. disk of cold - rolled steel. This disk is drilled and counterbored in the center for a fillister-head screw, and V-grooves are cut across the face, starting with a deep groove and finishing with a shallow one suitable for holding very small pieces of drill rod and similar work. To complete the attachment, a piece of ½-in. flat stock is bent to the shape of the vise jaw, and drilled and tapped to take the screw that holds the revolving disk. The opposite jaw of the vise can be covered with an ordinary copper clamp, if it is desired to avoid marring the work.

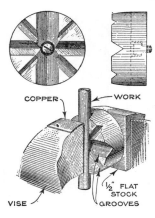

COPPER — WORK
VISE — ½" FLAT STOCK GROOVES

Ball-Grip Drill Chuck

A drill chuck for holding small drills up to ⅛ in. in diameter is a convenient article of shop equipment, but one not always at hand. The chuck shown in the drawing can easily be produced in the average small shop, as it has no intricately shaped parts.

The body is made of ¾-in. cold-rolled round stock, is turned on the shank to suit the drill-press spindle, threaded, drilled with a long-pointed ⅛-in. drill, and drilled for a stop pin, then beveled as shown, the completed piece being case-hardened. Three ³⁄₁₆-in. steel balls are required, as well as a disk with three radial grooves, about ¹⁄₁₆ in. deep, for the balls to rest in, and to keep them equally

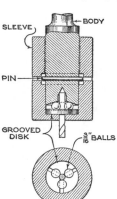

SLEEVE — BODY
PIN
GROOVED DISK — ³⁄₁₆ BALLS

spaced. The sleeve is bored out to accommodate the grooved disk, which has the same outside diameter as the body, is tapped to fit the threaded portion of the body, and recessed to clear the stop pin. This pin is necessary to prevent the sleeve from being screwed too far down, and allowing the balls to slip out of their grooves.

Soap as a Lubricant for Drilling

A bar of common laundry soap makes a good lubricant for the drill when cutting holes in fibrous materials, such as red or black fiber, and similar substances. The soap is held against the drill point occasionally, and prevents the chips from packing around the drill, which would cause heating and binding. With soap as a lubricant, the chips feed readily up the flutes of the drill, regardless of the depth of the hole. The same lubricant can be used when tapping.

Stop for Taper Reamers

When using taper reamers with a stop attached to the reamer itself, a solid stop consisting of a metal ring reamed out to the size required is generally used. This makes a good stop, but it has the distinct disadvantage of being useful for but one particular size or depth of cut, and if a cut even ¹⁄₁₆-in. deeper is to be taken, it is necessary to use another stop, or ream out the first one. Various depths are required on one reamer, and the adjustable stop illustrated was designed to meet such requirements. The main part of the attachment is made from a block of tool steel, drilled at one end to fit over the shank of the reamer, the opposite end being slotted

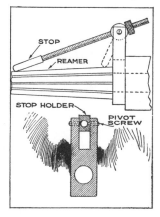

STOP
REAMER
STOP HOLDER
PIVOT SCREW

to take the stop holder, which is a small steel disk, with small centers on its sides, and a hole drilled and tapped through its center for the threaded stop. The stop holder is held in place by two screws, the pointed ends of which fit into the centers.

The stop proper is made from a piece of 5/16-in. drill rod, rounded at one end, threaded to fit the tapped hole in the stop-holder block, and fitted with a knurled locknut.

When in use, the device is slipped over the reamer shank, which is then inserted in its holder, or wrench, the attachment being held tightly between the reamer and face of the holder. To set the reamer for any desired depth of cut, the stop is screwed in or out, and the adjustment held by screwing down the knurled nut. The single round end of the stop makes an ideal stop, as the cuttings do not collect around it as in a solid stop, and when correctly set, the rounded end will lie snugly in one of the reamer flutes.

Making Special Sewer-Cap Castings

A change from the standard in the curbing and paving of a certain street

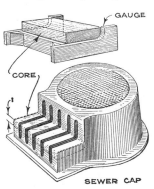

GAUGE

CORE

SEWER CAP

called for an alteration in the standard sewer-cap casting; 10 of the altered caps were needed. The road step was to be 1 in. lower than in the original pattern. There were two patterns made for this job, a wooden master pattern and a cast-iron working pattern. The patternmaker suggested that the wooden pattern be altered to correspond to the change in requirements, but to do so meant quite an expense, and besides, the covers made from the metal pattern would not fit the holes in the castings produced from the altered pattern.

Instead of altering the pattern, the job was taken in hand by the foundry foreman who made the castings with a minimum of trouble. A frame of 1-in. lumber was made to fit the ends and front of the mold 1 in. below the top. This frame formed a guide in cutting 1 in. off the top of the mold along the dotted lines. Then 1-in. slab cores, taken from stock, were cut and filed to the required shape. These cores were placed in the molds in place of the material previously removed.

With a correctly made gauge, and a core box to produce the cores, the making of the castings was very simple.

Fixture for Relining Brake Bands

The fixture shown in the drawing, which is of particular usefulness for relining the brake and transmission bands of automobiles, consists of a piece of shafting on which brake and transmission drums of the commonest sizes are mounted. Brackets at the ends support the shaft, and make it possible to revolve the drums. In use, the brake

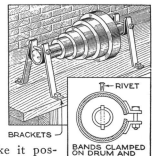

RIVET

BRACKETS

BANDS CLAMPED ON DRUM AND RIVETED

band to be relined, together with the strip of new brake lining, is placed over a drum of the proper size, and clamped. The split rivets, after penetrating the brake lining, strike the face of the drums and spread, clinching the lining tightly to the brake band.

Micrometer Lock for Repetition Work

When gauging repetition work, or finishing work that requires constant testing with a micrometer, it is necessary to have some means of locking the sleeve of the instrument, else the setting must be examined and perhaps adjusted every time it is picked up. Large numbers of micrometers are not provided with locknuts, and the simple device shown in the drawing is designed for use in such cases.

An L-shaped piece of cold-rolled steel stock, 1/8 by 1/2 in., is slotted at one end to fit the frame of the micrometer very closely, and bored at the opposite end to make a

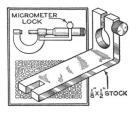

MICROMETER LOCK

1/8"x1/2" STOCK

neat fit for the sleeve. A slot is sawed through the hole, and a hole drilled and tapped to take a 1/16-in. knurled-head screw. The lock is placed on the micrometer as shown in the drawing, and tightened in position when the sleeve is adjusted to the proper measurement. On some micrometers the knurl on the sleeve extends down almost to the graduations; in this case, of course, the hole in the clamp is bored to fit the outer diameter of the knurls.

Homemade Cylinder-Reaming Machines

By L. R. PERRY

THE owner of any auto-repair shop can easily and cheaply build a cylinder-reaming machine from parts rescued from the junk pile, or obtained from the automobile "graveyards" of the larger communities. Practically any make of engine cylinder can be reamed with these devices, using stock reamers of the expanding type.

In Fig. 1 is shown one of the simplest

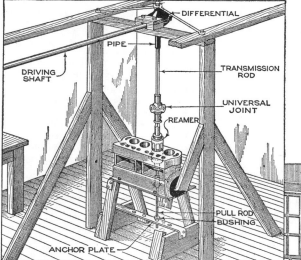

machines, the important features of which are the universal joint and the pull rod. A wood-and-steel horse is first built, along the lines indicated, to support the cylinder block while being reamed; the block is bolted down to the flat-steel bars forming the top of the horse, or stand. The short bars at the ends may be given a downward curve between the legs of the stand so that the crankshaft can be swung into place, if desired. An anchor plate, of 5/8 by 2-in. stock, is bolted or screwed to the stand as shown, and drilled with four holes, each accurately centered under one cylinder. These holes are tapped to receive a 1/2 by 1/8-in. pipe bushing, which serves as a feed nut, and causes the threaded pull rod to draw the

3786

reamer into the work. It is important that the thread on the pull rod be quite fine, such as the 1/8-in. standard pipe thread. The pull rod itself may be a piece of 1/8-in. pipe threaded for the proper distance, but a piece of cold-rolled steel, with a 1/8-in. pipe thread cut in the lathe, would be better. Another piece of 1/8-in. pipe, 5 in. long, and threaded at both ends, is screwed into the lower end of the reamer. This is connected to the pull rod by means of a sleeve, which is screwed to the reamer pipe; the lower half of the sleeve is reamed out to make a free fit over the end of the pull rod, and the latter is held in place in the sleeve by a heavy cotter pin. The reamers used are tools of standard manufacture, and are obtainable in various sizes. The guides furnished with most cylinder reamers of this type must always be inserted in the top and bottom

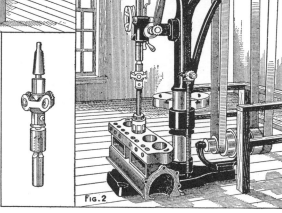

Above: The Simplest Type of Cylinder-Reaming Machine. The Feed is Obtained by the Pull Rod, Working through a Bushing Screwed into the Anchor Plate. Right: Reaming Cylinders in the Drill Press. The Insert Shows How the Reamer is Connected to the Drill-Press Spindle

of the cylinder before starting to ream. An interesting feature of this machine is the driving mechanism. The source of power is optional, but the speed should be uniform, and should be such that the reamer will not make more than 15 or 20 revolutions per minute. The builder of the original machine used a 4-hp. gas engine to drive it, clamping a small pulley to the side of the flywheel, and running a belt from this to a large pulley on a countershaft. Another belt conveyed the power from a small pulley on this shaft

being bolted to the bed of an ordinary drill press. A standard taper shank, fitting the drill-press spindle, is connected

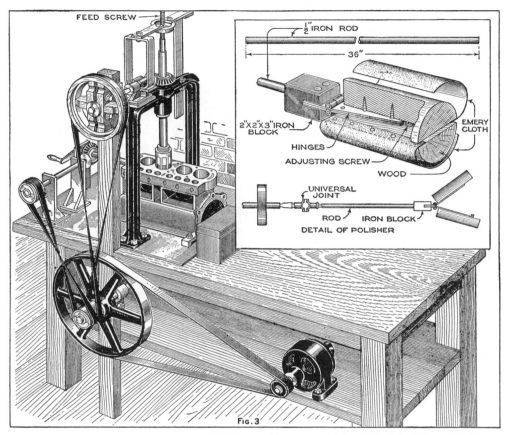

FEED SCREW

1½" IRON ROD

36"

2"x2"x3" IRON BLOCK

HINGES

ADJUSTING SCREW

EMERY CLOTH

WOOD

UNIVERSAL JOINT

ROD   IRON BLOCK

DETAIL OF POLISHER

FIG. 3

Assembly View of a More Elaborate Homemade Reamer: No Universal Joint is Used in This, as the Frame is Alined Accurately with the Block. The Insert Shows a Cylinder Polisher That may be Used in Any Type of Machine; It is Provided with a Universal Joint, to Allow It to Float in the Bore

to a large pulley clamped to a discarded motorcycle wheel, which was fastened to the driveshaft. The drawing shows how the power from the driveshaft is transmitted to the reamer through the differential of a light automobile, with a universal joint between the vertical shaft and reamer, to take up any inequalities of alinement. The differential end of a left-axle shaft is cut off short, and a 12-in. length of 1½-in. pipe is brazed onto it; the lower end of the pipe has one of the square-socket ends of a universal joint brazed into it. This arrangement permits vertical movement of the square transmission rod, and makes it possible to feed the reamer down through the cylinder.

Another method of using the same type of reamer is shown in Fig. 2, the work

to one end of a universal joint in any desirable manner; the square end of the reamer shank can be fitted directly into the universal-joint socket, as shown. It is advisable that some form of universal joint be used when cylinders are reamed out in the drill press, as the spindles of many repair-shop drill presses are badly out of line, and the results depend altogether upon how well the drill spindle lines up with the cylinder bore. Slow speed and hand feed should be used.

A more elaborate machine, built by another auto repairman, is illustrated in Fig. 3. In this machine a casting is used for the frame bedplate and some other parts, but there is no reason why they could not be made from built-up parts. The work is bolted to a heavy cast-iron bedplate, 2 in. thick, to which also the cast frame, which supports the reamer feed and drive gear, is fastened. No uni-

of the photographs gives a view of the cylinder reamer from a different angle, and also the method of reaming out

Left: Another View of the Machine Shown in Figure 3. The Connecting-Rod Reaming Fixture is Not Shown in This View, for the Sake of Clearness, but is Shown on the Right, with a Connecting Rod Mounted on the Angle Plate in Process of Reaming

versal joint is needed in this design, as the casting and cylinder may be accurately alined. The reamer-spindle sleeve is splined so that it can be moved vertically, a key in the bevel gear causing it to revolve. The motor driving the machine is a 1½-hp. unit, running at 1,800 r.p.m. The motor pulley is 1⅜ in. diameter by 2½ in. face; this drives a 26-in. pulley, keyed to a countershaft running in boxes under the bench. On the same shaft is a 4-in. pulley, and a belt from this runs to a 16-in. pulley on the bevel-gear shaft; the bevel gears are taken from the differential of a light car. The reamer is fed into the work by a handle, mounted on a threaded extension of the spindle; this is ¾ in. in diameter and is cut with a ⅟₁₆-in. pitch thread. Another feature of this particular device is a connecting-rod reaming fixture, which is partially illustrated in the drawing, and more fully in one of the photos. The connecting rod is merely slipped onto a stationary wristpin or stud in the vertical face of the angle plate of the fixture, and the reamer is inserted through the crankpin end. The connecting-rod reamer is fed into the work by a hand feed, identical with the one used with the cylinder reamer. One

the crankpin bearings of connecting rods, with a rod in place on the fixture.

The insert in Fig. 3 illustrates a polisher for finishing the reamed cylinders, and giving them a perfectly smooth surface. The iron rod is threaded at one end and screwed into an iron block, and a pair of hinges are riveted into a slot cut in the opposite face of the block. A wooden cylinder, turned to fit loosely in the cylinder bore, is cut in two, and the separate halves are fastened to the free ends of the hinges. Sheets of very fine-grained emery cloth are attached to the blocks, as shown, so that the whole can be inserted into the cylinder and turned in one direction without doubling up the cloth. The blocks are made adjustable for cylinders of slightly varying diameters by an adjusting screw in the flat face of one of the blocks. While primarily designed for use with the device shown in Fig. 1, the polisher can be adapted for use with the other designs, and can also be used horizontally.

¶A convenient anvil, horse, or trestle for many uses is made by using a suitable length of old steel rail to form the top crosspiece.

Multicolored Printing

Some very pretty multicolored printing can be done on an ordinary platen job press without any expensive attachments. In the first place, the ink platen must be fixed so that it does not move when the press is in motion; this is accomplished by tying the pawl that revolves the platen at each impression. Then inks of different colors are put on the platen in the form of dots running in a row parallel with the top of the chase. Care must be taken not to put too much ink on the platen at one time, or it will spread too far and spoil the effect. By starting the press and letting the rollers work over the platen, the ink will be distributed over it in parallel columns running at right angles to the top of the chase. As the ink is used up, a little more of the same color must be put on, care being taken to guard against using too much. The printing done by this method will have a rainbow effect that is quite pleasing.—Russel Raymond Voorhees, West Hoboken, N. J.

Old Fork Places Small Screws

Some useful and labor-saving tools can be made from old table forks, the photograph showing such a tool that facilitates replacing of 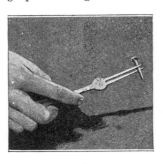 small screws and bolts in positions that would be practically inaccessible by other means. A fork that has seen better days will make just as good a tool as a new one, when it is flattened out and the outside tines ground off, leaving just two at the center, as in the picture.—John H. Schalek, Pittsburgh, Pa.

Blower Reduces Cost of Concrete Aggregate

A western roadbuilder has devised a simple attachment for a gravel screen that enables him to get a uniformly fine aggregate from near-by gravel banks, thus saving the cost of transporting a higher-grade material from a distance, as was at first thought necessary. The equipment is so simple that the same idea can doubtless be used in many similar situations.

The apparatus consists of an ordinary bucket conveyor that elevates the sand

Blowing the Light Material from Sand and Gravel, as It is Screened, by an Air Blast to Make It Conform to Certain Specifications

and gravel to a revolving cylindrical screen, through which the material that will pass through a $\frac{1}{4}$-in. mesh is discharged into a hopper. This hopper, placed under the screen, collects the screened gravel, and passes it, through a slot, 2 in. wide and 13 in. long, into a bin underneath. As the material pours into the bin in a stream of uniform width and thickness it is met by a blast of air from a centrifugal blower.

The exact amount of fine material that is thus separated from the coarser can be accurately controlled by a pressure regulator. A few tests will demonstrate the proper amount of pressure to use for the air blast.

The blower is installed at the base of the elevator, and is operated by a belt from the gas engine that drives the latter. One point must be borne in mind if satisfactory results are to be obtained: The gravel must be dry. In many cases the cost of drying the gravel can be kept so low that the use of this simple arrangement is highly desirable.

A Simple Scale Holder

When laying out work set up on the surface plate, some kind of scale holder is usually employed to hold the scale in a vertical position, with its end resting on the plate, so that measurements may be transferred from it to the work by means of the surface gauge. While the combination-square head is generally used for this purpose, homemade holders are also popular, but since in most cases the scale is not adjustable, it often happens that the first mark scribed on the work is not an even number of inches above the plate, but is a mixed number, say $5\frac{17}{32}$ in. If other lines are to be scribed above and below this line, and located from it, it is very easy to make a mistake in setting the scriber to a fixed scale. A better way is to mark the first line with the end of the scale resting on the plate, and then set the scale to some even inch, corresponding to the height of the surface-gauge scriber. Then it is only necessary to take dimensions from this inch mark, thus avoiding confusion.

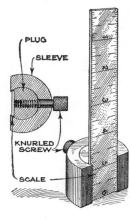

The scale holder illustrated herewith holds the scale securely at right angles to the plate, allows the scale to be adjusted vertically, and, moreover, is easily made, as no delicate machining, to get a correct line-up when assembled, is required. The holder is made in two pieces, a plug, 1 in. in diameter, and a sleeve or collar that fits neatly around it, the latter having an outside diameter of about 2 in. The plug is then machined flat on one side, until the scale will just slip between it and the sleeve, in the manner shown. The sleeve is also cut away to expose the scale. The two parts are then clamped together, and a hole is drilled and tapped for the knurled tightening screw. A holder made to the dimensions given will be heavy enough to hold a 12 or 24-in. scale solidly. A small brass plug is placed in the tapped hole in front of the tightening screw, so that the scale will not be injured; little pressure is required to hold the scale in any position.

Repairing an Engine Water Jacket

Many gasoline engines, upon the water jacket becoming cracked, have been put out of commission for indefinite periods, until a new casting could be obtained from the factory, or the broken one welded. There is a simple method of making a repair, however, that will put the engine back into commission in a short time.

Take a narrow square-pointed chisel, and cut along the crack to make a narrow channel in the casting. Fill this channel with a little white lead and then lay in a piece of copper wire, a little larger in diameter than the width, and slightly longer than the length of the channel. The wire is forced into the channel by means of hammer and punch, completely filling it and making a smooth job.—Wm. J. Douglas, Missouri Valley, Ia.

Keyway Re-Dressing Broach

When repairing or overhauling old or secondhand machinery one generally finds that the keyways are more or less banged up, and to put them into proper shape for further use they must be straightened up on the sides and fitted with new and wider keys. To dress up a damaged keyway is quite a job, and to do it properly, without taking the work to a machine shop, re-

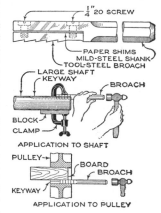

quires some fine, accurate handwork. To eliminate this handwork, yet obtain a perfect-fitting job, the broach illustrated was designed. The broach proper is made of good tool steel and has teeth cut on one face, as shown, $\frac{1}{4}$-in. screws holding it tightly against a mild-steel shank. The proper adjustment is obtained by the insertion of paper shims between shank and tool. The broach should be hardened and drawn to a straw color, care being taken when hardening to pack the holes in order to prevent cracking.

In actual use, select the good side of the keyway, place the face of the shank against this side, and set up the broach with paper shims until it takes a light cut. Oil the cutting as well as the rear sliding surfaces and drive it through the keyway with a hammer. If the broach has a tendency to rise, hold it down with a C-clamp, which will follow along if not screwed too tightly. Internal keyways are treated in the same manner, using a block to keep the broach down in the keyway. When fitting a key, care should be taken to have it fit well on the sides as this is more important than having it fit at top and bottom. Rather than depend on the taper for holding the key, use a setscrew and get a good side fit.

Straightening Heavy Springs

After the loop has been bent, on heavy spiral springs made by hand, it is generally found that the spring is bent, and to straighten it by hand is often impossible owing to the great strength of the wire. A good way to do this job is to use a cross-peen hammer. The spring is laid on an anvil, or plate,

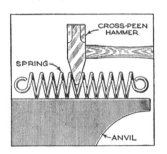

convex side down, and the wedge-shaped hammer is driven between the separate coils, as shown in the drawing. This will open up each coil just a trifle so that the spring can be easily straightened. If a spring has been wound too closely, it can be opened up by peening all around until the desired tension is obtained.

Cleaning Belts of Oil

Leather belts can be cleaned of an accumulation of machine oil and grease by first scraping off all gum and glaze from the belt with a putty knife, or other scraper, the edges of which have been rounded off to prevent cutting or scratching the leather. Then the belt is spread on a flat surface and first one side, then the other, cleaned by the vigorous application of clean, dry sawdust with a clean, stiff broom, or brush, whereupon it is packed in fuller's earth, fine sawdust, or powdered chalk, and allowed to remain for several days in a warm room. Practically all of the oil and grease in the belt will be absorbed by the packing material.

Sawhorse for Uneven Floors

Frequently the woodworker finds it necessary to work in a shop with a rough or uneven floor, where it is almost impossible to locate a sawhorse so that all four feet will bear solidly on the ground. A convenient method of overcoming this difficulty is to use a three-legged

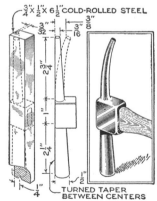

horse of the type shown in the drawing. This sawhorse will stand solidly on a very uneven surface, and all rocking and swaying are eliminated. For the craftsman working on small jobs, in which a great part of the sawing is done on one horse, it is well to use a solid top piece, 5 or 6 in. wide, as shown.— Geo. N. Weaver, Indianapolis, Ind.

A Patternmaker's Hammer

A patternmaker's hammer is always admired by woodworkers, and justly so, as it is a very sensible and well-balanced tool. The small end is just the thing for setting sprigs and small nails, while the large end is heavy enough to drive them home. The hammers are generally homemade, in two sizes, small and large; the small one, be-

ing the most popular, is the one described, and is very easily made from a piece of cold-rolled steel. The piece is centered as in the drawing and turned up in the lathe, throwing the tailstock over to get the correct taper, and polishing all over. The head is then drilled and the slot cut for the handle. After this is done, the hammer is bent, making the drop of the small end about $\frac{3}{8}$ in.

The hammer is finished by heating it to a cherry red and sprinkling powdered cyanide of potassium (poison) over the whole surface. Sprinkle the head and rear tip most, as these must be the hardest, and quench in cold water. The cyanide will melt and run over the whole surface, giving the head a very beautiful mottled finish that also prevents rust.

A Simple Tool Handle or Pin Vise

The drawing shows a simple form of tool handle suitable for holding files,

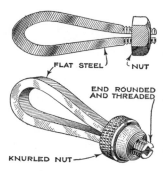

FLAT STEEL — NUT

END ROUNDED AND THREADED

KNURLED NUT

screwdriver blades, drills, and similar tools, or, used as a hand vise, for holding small pins, screws, or other parts. It is made in two pieces and consists of a clamping nut and a handle. The clamping nut is made with a taper thread, and the handle is formed from flat-steel stock, bent as shown and ground down sufficiently to permit threading with a pipe-threading die. Two different styles are shown, one involving the use of a lathe to produce the knurled and turned nut, while the other uses an ordinary hexagonal nut to clamp the jaws.

Stresses in Laminated Wood Construction

The use of heavy and light material of the same species in laminated or glued-up wood construction has less injurious effect than has been generally supposed. Laminated-wood specimens under observation at the Forest Products Laboratory, at Madison, Wis., show little weakening or tendency to warp from this cause. Most warping and checking in laminated construction can be traced to one of two causes. The first is the use of plain-sawed and quarter-sawed lumber in the same construction, and the second is the combination of material of different moisture content.

Plain-sawed lumber of any species shrinks and swells more than quarter-sawed lumber; and when the two kinds are glued together, they pull against each other with every change in moisture content. If the block containing such a combination is kept for a long time in the same atmospheric conditions, the stresses die out, because the block checks or changes shape more or less to relieve the stretched condition of its fibers. As soon as the atmospheric conditions change, new stresses will be set up.

If boards of different moisture contents are glued together, internal stresses will result from unequal shrinkage of the boards, as their moisture contents equalize through seasoning. In some blocks made at the laboratory, these stresses were great enough to rupture the wood. If the wood is not ruptured, the stresses will in time permanently disappear, but the block will have changed its shape somewhat in getting rid of them.

From these facts it becomes apparent that for laminated-wood articles, where strength and accurate shape are required, it is desirable to use all plain-sawed or all quarter-sawed material, to have all pieces of a uniform moisture content when glued, and to prevent, as far as possible, subsequent moisture changes by means of moisture-resistant coatings. For the manufacture of rougher articles, where slight changes in form are of no consequence, these precautions are of less importance, although, by paying some attention to them, a better product will result.

Preventing Breakage of Milling Saws

When cutting stock clamped to the table of a milling machine, the burr caused by the saw has a tendency, when the cut is completed, to catch and draw the cut stock under the saw, with the result that the saw is broken. The attachment shown in the drawing consists of a flat-spring finger, inserted into a steel block,

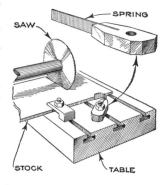

SPRING
SAW
STOCK
TABLE

which is bolted to the table of the machine. When the stock has been set, ready for cutting, the spring is adjusted against the work in such a manner that, as soon as the saw completes the cut, the spring will straighten out and push the cut-off piece clear of the saw.

White Lead Locks Nuts

Many machines, notably agricultural implements, are not fitted with cotter pins to prevent bolts and nuts from loosening. Under continued use, the nut loosens and drops off, or rusts solidly in place, making it difficult to remove. A liberal coating of white lead applied to the threads before screwing on the nuts, prevents each of these conditions. The white lead will harden and lock the nuts, rust is prevented, and the nut can be removed with a wrench. The white lead is also effective as a lock washer when the face of a nut is in contact with wood.

Gauge for Dividing Circles

A novel gauge, designed to divide a circle into equally spaced parts, for drilling or other operations, is shown in the drawing. A disk of ¼-in. iron plate is drilled and reamed at the center for a

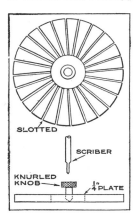

knurled-head centerpiece, the bottom of which is pointed, and cut down on the outside to any diameter desired. Mounted on a short arbor, the plate is next slotted in the milling machine, 24 slots being milled with a ⅟₁₆-in. saw. A special scriber or scratch awl is required for use with the gauge; the point of this should be filed flat near the end to fit into the slots. With the centerpiece of the gauge in the center of the circle to be divided, press the gauge down firmly and run the scriber through the desired slots. If the circumference is to be divided into, say, eight equal spaces, make a fine chalk line across every third slot to avoid confusion. If the circumference required to be divided is larger than the gauge, proceed as above and then extend the lines with a scale until they intersect the periphery of the circle.

⁌Boiler feed water should always be preheated, not only because it saves expense, but because it causes much of the scale-forming material to be deposited in the heater instead of in the boiler.

Repairing a Worn Stuffing Box

As the end of the threshing season drew near, the valve-rod packing of a 20-hp. steam engine refused to remain in place, regardless of the kind of packing used or the method of using it. The reason for this was found to be that the gland and rod had become worn to such an extent that even a new gland would have afforded but little improvement. The worn condition of rod and gland left an opening between them, as shown at A in the drawing.

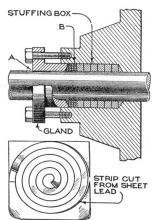

To remedy the trouble without removing the rod, a spiral strip was cut from a piece of ⅟₁₆-in. sheet lead. This strip was then formed around the rod in a continuous helix inside the gland, as at B, in such a manner that when forced up against the packing a tight solid-lead packing was obtained, which fitted the rod so snugly that the season's work was finished without further trouble.

A Taper-Turning Gauge

To make a good job of taper turning, the work should be completed to a gauge, or template. A taper-turning template that has some novel and unusual features is shown in the drawing. As will be noted, the device is provided with a movable blade, which makes it possible

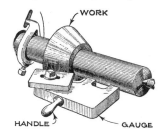

to use the same gauge for various tapers. This blade is held to the body by a square-headed setscrew and a washer. The body of the gauge is not solid, but is relieved at the center; this makes allowance for any slight inaccuracy in the mandrel or work. The handle makes the gauge very convenient to use.

Overhead Drive for Lathe Attachments

By H. H. PARKER

UNLESS a small independent electric motor is available, some sort of overhead belt drive is required for the small lathe equipped with a tool-slide grinding head and milling or drilling attachments. Once such an installation is made, the range of the work that may be done on the lathe is greatly increased, and the time and labor spent in making it will be well repaid. As the overhead belt drive should be available for the whole length of the lathe bed, or the travel of the rest, a long straight drum pulley on the overhead shaft will be needed, but one running on a fixed shaft would be im-

scheme is to mount a pulley on the projecting end of the lathe countershaft extending toward the tailstock end of the machine. Then another shaft is installed in boxes on a line with the countershaft, but independent of it and extending the length of the lathe bed; this shaft does not rotate but only rocks, and has two swinging arms setscrewed, or pinned, to it. These must be well secured to the rocker shaft, and the shaft itself must be large enough in diameter not to twist under the tension of the drive belt when near the end of the drum. The countershaft and rocker shaft need only be in approximate alinement; not lined up as though they were to be coupled together. Probably iron pipe and fittings will be the most available material for making the arms and other parts, the bearing housings being either tees or crosses filled with babbitt or bronze-bushed. Steel tubing, if obtainable, would be stronger and lighter. Castings, as shown in the drawing, could be used, or the arms might be built up of bar stock, with the bearing hubs bolted or riveted in place. For light work, the arms might even be made of hardwood. One arm is extended back, and an iron counterweight slides along this extension, or, if there is room, two arms and two counterweights would be better, owing to the more equal distribution of strain thus obtained. The distance between the rocker and drum shafts should be as short as practicable.

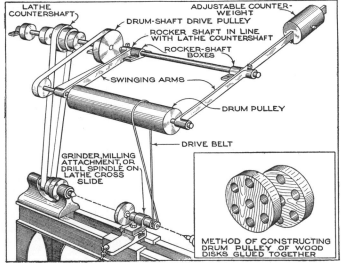

LATHE COUNTERSHAFT
ADJUSTABLE COUNTER-WEIGHT
DRUM-SHAFT DRIVE PULLEY
ROCKER SHAFT IN LINE WITH LATHE COUNTERSHAFT
ROCKER-SHAFT BOXES
SWINGING ARMS
DRUM PULLEY
DRIVE BELT
GRINDER, MILLING ATTACHMENT, OR DRILL SPINDLE ON LATHE CROSS SLIDE
METHOD OF CONSTRUCTING DRUM PULLEY OF WOOD DISKS GLUED TOGETHER

An Overhead Belt Arrangement for the Lathe Which Permits the Operation of Grinding and Milling Attachments throughout the Length of the Machine Bed. The Belt is Kept at a Uniform Tension by a Counterweight

practicable without some form of belt tightener to maintain an even tension on the belt, to allow the use of different lathe attachments, or when one is used that must be moved in and out laterally on the cross slide. The best way is to have the drum-pulley shaft swing up and down, with a constant upward tension on the drive belt furnished by an adjustable counterweight, thus doing away with an extra pulley as a belt tightener, which would require means for shifting it along with the lathe carriage.

The layout shown is merely suggestive, as the actual details of construction will necessarily be regulated by the lathe-countershaft installation, the type of lathe used, and the material and equipment at hand with which to do the work. The

A pulley is placed on the projecting end of the drum shaft, and is driven by a belt from the pulley on the end of the countershaft. As the drum shaft swings up and down, the belt tension will be constant, since the counter and rocker shafts are in line. If these two pulleys are of the stepped type, the drum can be driven at varying speeds. One way of building up the drum from disks, turned from plank and bored with lightening holes, is shown. These disks are glued and nailed together with the grain of adjacent disks at right angles, assembled on the shaft, and turned to the finished diameter as a whole, a blank disk being used at each end. Another way is to saw off a length of old spar or house-moving roller, bore a shaft hole for the full length, mount it on the shaft, and turn to size. Or a section of large pipe or well casing could be plugged with hardwood heads, then accurately bored and turned.

In case it is desired to operate the tool-slide attachment without rotating the lathe spindle, the headstock cone on the lathe should be set free, the back gears thrown out, and the cone allowed to run idly without moving the spindle. Either a round belt on a grooved pulley, or a flat one, running on a straight-faced flanged pulley on the driven apparatus, may be run over the drum. If a drive entirely independent of the lathe countershaft is desired, another countershaft in line with the rocker shaft and driven by a belt from the lineshaft, or from a separate motor, can be installed.

Countersunk Thumbtacks

T-squares have a disagreeable habit of catching and holding on the thumbtack heads. Besides being a nuisance, this

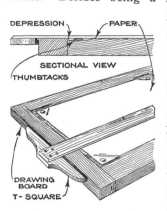

DEPRESSION PAPER

SECTIONAL VIEW

THUMBTACKS

DRAWING BOARD

T-SQUARE

slows up the worker's production. Students, and in many cases professionals as well, use standard-sized sheets of drawing paper. The drawing shows a method by means of which the heads of the thumbtacks are brought below the surface of the board or at least flush with it. V-shaped notches, about ⅛ in. deep and placed at the corners of a standard sheet, are cut into one or both ends of the board, as shown.

Removing Stiff Tires

A useful and inexpensive article of equipment for the garage and tire-repair shop, for removing tires that have rusted onto the rims, or that, for other reasons, are found difficult to remove, consists of

nothing more than an ordinary barrel. The barrel should be a tight one, that is, one that has contained vinegar, oil, or other liquids. One of the heads is removed, and a slot is cut out with a saw to accommodate the tire valve, after the hoops have been secured on each side of the slot. In use, the tire,

SLOT FOR VALVE STEM

on its rim, is slipped over the barrel, with the valve in the slot. At one point on the bilge the diameter of the barrel will be greater than that of the rim, and the latter will be firmly held at such a height that the work of removing the tire can be done conveniently and with comparative ease. It may be found desirable to ballast the barrel by filling the bottom with several inches of cement, or old iron, to prevent it from being tipped over easily.—C. C. Spreen, Birmingham, Mich.

A Reamer Protector

Reamers that are allowed to lie around the bench or in the tool box together with other tools soon have their cutting teeth nicked and dulled, so that they become practically worthless for fine work, or at least would require regrinding to make them serviceable. The drawing shows a simple and inex-

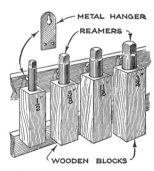

METAL HANGER

REAMERS

WOODEN BLOCKS

pensive method of protecting each reamer in an individual case, which consists simply of a square block of wood, bored out large enough to accommodate the reamer, and marked with the size of the tool on the outside. A small metal hanger of the type shown is fastened to the top of each case so that it can be hung over a screw in the wall, or on a special rack.—E. N. Davey, Montreal, Canada.

Substitute for Beam Compasses

A handy substitute for the draftsman's beam compasses, on large work, is obtained by equipping the T-square with a

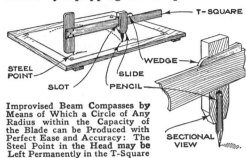

Improvised Beam Compasses by Means of Which a Circle of Any Radius within the Capacity of the Blade can be Produced with Perfect Ease and Accuracy: The Steel Point in the Head may be Left Permanently in the T-Square

pencil slide, and inserting a point into the head, in the manner illustrated. The slide that holds the pencil is made by gluing two pieces of hardwood together, half of the slot for the blade being cut in each, thus making it possible to work out the slot in an easy manner. The bottom end of the slide is drilled to fit the regular drawing pencil tightly. A hardwood wedge, pushed into the slot between the T-square blade and the slide, holds the pencil at the proper radius. The steel needle in the head of the T-square need not be removed, as it is never in the way. A circle of any radius up to the capacity of the blade can be produced by these improvised compasses with perfect ease and accuracy.

Repairing Worn Eccentrics

There is a great deal of wear on the circumference of the eccentric sheaves of any engine using the Stephenson valve gear, and a large number of eccentrics are scrapped annually on account of this wear. Railway shops are now using a system that will also appeal to the users of traction and similar reversing-geared engines, who find it necessary to re-turn their eccentrics and rebabbitt the straps. Just as soon as the blocks must

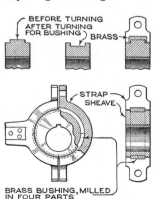

be re-turned, they should be grooved as in the drawing. A brass shoe or bushing, cut into four sectors, is made to fit the sheaves and strap; as the brass will wear faster than the sheaves or straps, they can be run much longer without re-turning, by renewing the brass bushing when necessary. If the eccentric sheave is so made that it cannot be grooved as shown, it may be reduced in size, still keeping the original shape, and the bushing made to fit both it and the strap, as shown in the upper right-hand detail.—A. A. Stafford, Reno, Nev.

An Adjustable Machine Strap

When strapping work down to machine tables, it is very convenient to have a little "adjustability" in the strap. If the work is of slight thickness, the strap alone may be sufficient without packing, but the principal object of the strap shown in the drawing is to facilitate setting it at the correct height without the usual bother of looking around for washers or pieces of scrap. The ordinary heel-type strap of the drawing has a hole drilled in the back, to which the angular machine-steel piece illustrated is riveted. The distances of the faces of

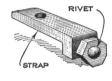

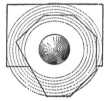

these angles should vary by about $\frac{1}{32}$ in., measured from the center. When in use, packing is put underneath the strap to approximately the right height, the final setting being obtained by turning the hexagon-shaped piece that raises or lowers the strap.

Cleaning Brass Parts

The small brass fittings of an automobile, or other mechanism, such as petcocks, carburetor parts, and the like, can be made to look like new by dipping them into a pickle composed of 75 parts nitric acid, 100 parts sulphuric acid, 2 parts lampblack, and 1 part salt. This solution should be mixed and kept in an earthenware or glass jar, and the parts should be thoroughly rinsed and dried after dipping. When dried, the work should be lacquered or given a thin coating of some light grease.—D. V. Wilson, Houston, Tex.

Blueprints for Notebooks

Drawings, diagrams, or similar information that the reader would like to transfer to a notebook, are often found in technical books or magazines. When such matter is contained in the books of a reference library, from which they cannot be removed, the transfer must be made in the library. To make a sketch and finish it at home is tedious, and some of the finer details are likely to be lost or misdrawn. This is particularly true of dimensions.

To overcome these difficulties, I take some tracing cloth or paper to the library; this is fastened with paper clips to the page on which the drawing appears. Then, with drawing ink, a straight-edge, ruling pen, and bow pen, I trace the drawing in ink, just as one would trace an original drawing. If one takes time, it is not necessary to use the pencil first. Blueprints are made from the tracing and pasted in the notebook, or the tracing itself may be pasted in.—R. E. Deering, Clements, Kan.

Easily Made Drawers

An extra drawer is often needed on the drawing board or table, for small instruments, thumbtacks, and the like, and such a drawer can be provided in a few minutes' time from an ordinary slide-cover box. The sliding cover of the box is fastened to the underside of the table or board with small screws, and the box is then slid onto it. A screweye or small knob can be fastened to one end of the box to serve as a handle.—Chas. I. Reid, Millersburg, Pa.

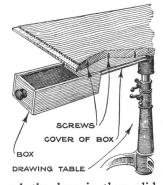

SCREWS
COVER OF BOX
BOX
DRAWING TABLE

Attachments for Gas-Engine Hoppers

The hopper-type water jacket is a convenient design for portable gasoline engines, and those located where a supply of running water is not available are familiar with its merit. But there is the disadvantage of the water boiling and slopping over the top, very often causing a short circuit in the ignition system. One way to overcome this objection is to

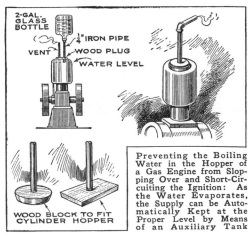

2-GAL. GLASS BOTTLE
VENT
¼" IRON PIPE
WOOD PLUG
WATER LEVEL

WOOD BLOCK TO FIT CYLINDER HOPPER

Preventing the Boiling Water in the Hopper of a Gas Engine from Slopping Over and Short-Circuiting the Ignition: As the Water Evaporates, the Supply can be Automatically Kept at the Proper Level by Means of an Auxiliary Tank

fit a thick wooden plug in the hopper opening. It should be tapered enough to permit its being driven to a fairly tight fit, allowance, of course, being made for the wood swelling when steamed. In the center of the plug a hole is drilled, and a length of pipe screwed in for a vent. This prevents the water from slopping or boiling over, when the engine is being moved from one location to another or when it is in use. An elbow and short length of pipe may be fitted to carry the steam off to one side of the spark plug and wiring.

The water in the hopper needs to be replenished frequently as it is evaporated. One of the drawings shows how an auxiliary water tank may be made from a large glass bottle, or similar container. A metal container would work as well, but by using the bottle the operator can always tell just how much water is left. A plug is fitted into the hopper opening, as mentioned before, although this is not necessary if the pipe is otherwise well supported. The vessel is filled with water, fitted with a stopper into which a pipe fits tightly, then inverted over the hopper. The lower end of the pipe should be at the high-water level of the hopper and be kept in that position. Then, as soon as enough water evaporates to uncover the end of the pipe, more will flow in from the bottle. If the stopper is airtight, the hopper will be automatically kept filled until the bottle is empty.

¶ Be sure there are no sags or pockets in steam mains that would allow water to accumulate and be carried over to the engine in "slugs."

Shoenails a Peril to Electrical Workers

Electrical workers should accept the dictum that all shoes worn by them must have the soles fastened to the uppers by

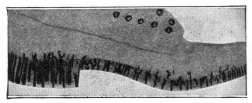

The X-Ray Photo Shows How Nails in the Shoes Form a Metal Path for an Electrical Current to the Ground

wooden pegs, for the life of a worker may depend upon the absence of metal nails.

The X-ray photograph gives a view of the nails in the shoe of an electrical worker who was killed by a heavy current. Everyone of the dozens of deadly little things is just waiting for the chance of being turned into a live wire, and to carry the current to the ground, as soon as the wearer of such shoes comes into contact with an electrical potential.—Geo. F. Paul, Chicago, Ill.

Drinking Fountain Attached to Fire Hydrant

In many instances the cost of installing drinking fountains and connecting them to underground supply and drain pipes, is higher than the authorities of a municipality or village care to pay; in such cases, the arrangement shown in the illustration can be used in conjunction with the fire hydrants, without in the least interfering with their regular use. The hand-controlled

bubbling drinking cup, a short length of pipe, and a shut-off cock are the only materials to be bought, and the assembly is screwed into a hole drilled in the top of the hydrant in the manner illustrated, the excess water simply running off into the gutter. The same idea can be applied to fire hydrants of other types, by making the tapped hole on the side and bringing the bubble cup up to a proper height by means of a nipple and elbow.

Improved Resist for Etching

When using beeswax as a resist for etching tools, the beeswax sometimes breaks away from the metal, causing much trouble. When this happens, a neat job is impossible, as the etching solution will leave a ragged edge wherever the wax is raised off the steel. If one-tenth part of powdered resin is thoroughly mixed with the melted beeswax before being applied, this trouble will not occur.—Louis M. Steffen, Dayton, Ohio.

Increasing Ice-Machine Condenser Efficiency

A large ice-cream factory was suddenly and severely handicapped in the rush of its summer production by the inefficiency of the condensing system and the extremely high pressure which it was forced to maintain. The pressure had to be run up to 250 lb. and higher, the normal pressure being 180 lb. This condition, besides creating a dangerous situation, also meant extra cost for power. On investigation, it was found that the trouble lay in the warm city water which was used for cooling the condenser. The condenser was 20 pipes high, and had a water inlet at the bottom and an outlet into a drain at the top. The water entered the inlet at a temperature of about 70°F. and circulated through the pipes, coming out at the top with a temperature of from 150 to 160°. It was suggested that the water-supply system of the condenser be cut in two, cutting the supply piping in the center of the condenser, and fitting it with a new inlet and discharge. When this had been done, the high pressure dropped immediately to 190 lb., and the temperature of the discharge water fell to around 100 to 110°. This change was effected without any increase in the quantity of water used. By creating two circulating systems in this manner, a quicker absorption of heat from the hot ammonia liquid took place.

¶ Powdered resin, mixed with denatured alcohol to form a thick paste, makes a soldering flux that is free from the objections inherent in most fluxes, as it does not corrode the work.

An Arbor Press of Large Capacity

By J. V. ROMIG

EVERY machine shop or garage doing any considerable repair work has an arbor press as part of its equipment. Most of those that I have seen and used, however, have been small, and of very little, if any, use for long work. The press described herein was designed and built by the writer with this in view, and the result is a press of large capacity, adjustable over a wide range, but not too clumsy.

The main member is a length of 3½-in. pipe, which has an outside diameter of 4 in.; it is drilled with a row of ½-in. holes, 2 in. apart, and fitted with a floor flange at each end, the over-all length being the same as the height of the ceiling from the floor. The upper and lower arms are castings, made from simple patterns; the upper arm is bored to fit the rack and gear. The rack and gear are eight-pitch,

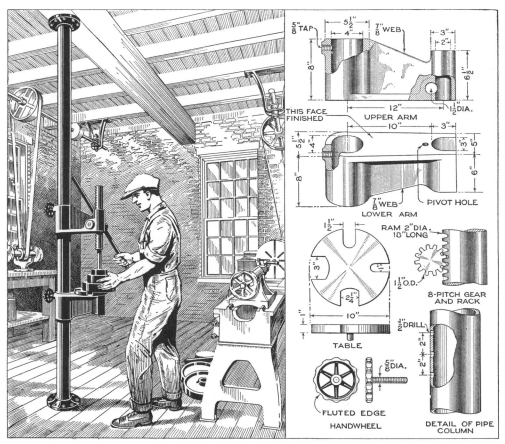

An Arbor Press Suitable for Any Shop or Garage Where a Wide Range of Work is Handled: The Upper and Lower Arms may be Clamped Anywhere on the Column, to Suit the Work or the Operator

and are made and assembled as for any ordinary press. They should be of a good tough grade of steel. The gear may be fitted with a two or four-spoke handle, as desired. Care should be taken, when boring the rack and gear holes, to bore them so that the teeth will mesh correctly. The lower arm is faced on the upper surface, and drilled for the pivot on the table. The table is also a casting, or may be made of steel plate, if a large enough piece is available; it is slotted, as shown, for

An Improvised Crane

In loading some heavy barrels of kerosene, the driver of a truck used a simple method of elevating them to a height

Loading Filled Oil Drums into a Truck without Manual Effort by Means of an Improvised Crane: The Same Idea can be Adapted to Other Work Where a Vertical Pull or Lift is Required

where it was possible to back the truck underneath them. Two long sticks were fastened together, near one end, with a rope, and the opposite ends were placed on the ground about 3 ft. apart. A rope was slung around the oil barrel, passed over the crotch of the sticks, and fastened to the rear axle of a second truck. By moving the second truck forward in low gear for a few feet, the barrels were lifted to a corresponding height, when the truck that was to carry them was backed underneath and the load lowered. The same method can be applied to lifting heavy stones, or other work.—G. A. Luers, Washington, D. C.

Care of Wheel-Truing Diamonds

Take only light cuts with the diamond, and as the stone wears, turn the nib in the holder to insure uniform wear; then when the stone wears down to the metal setting, reset the stone so as to expose a new cutting surface. When the diamond is worn down to a small size, reset it in

work of varying diameters. The clamping screws are made with a pointed end; by means of these, both upper and lower arms can be clamped in the most suitable working positions.

If the height from floor to ceiling is too great for a column, or if overhead cranes are used in the shop, a base of large diameter can be substituted for the lower floor flange, and the pipe column cut off and braced at a height that may be most convenient.

a holder, and use it in the tool room. Be careful not to jam the diamond into the wheel, and instruct operators not to allow the stone to get any violent knocks, as it is very hard and therefore brittle. Never use a diamond dry, except on small wheels for internal grinding, or on tool or cutter wheels; on large wheels for cylindrical or surface grinding, direct a copious stream of water on the diamond at the point of contact with the wheel.

Work Gauged Automatically

The gauge shown in the drawing will be found applicable to many classes of work and will save the time necessarily required for a separate gauging operation; in addition, it prevents the machine hand from turning out work that is afterward found to be incorrect.

The work shown is a sleeve with beveled ends, the outer diameter being held within limits of plus or minus .01 in. The gauge is made of 3/8-in. flat steel, the first operation being to bend it into the form shown, the angle being about 45°. The slots are next milled, the high limit or "go" slot being milled so that the ends, when the gauge is fixed in place, stand in a vertical position, to prevent the work from falling through, back end first, and probably sticking. The low limit or "not go" slot is milled in the bottom portion. It may be as well to say that in cutting the slots, the gauge should be strapped on the table, on its side, and both slots milled with an end mill. The same method is used in grinding the slots to the finished size.

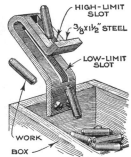

Two holes, drilled and countersunk, accommodate screws that hold the gauge to a wooden box. As the operator cuts off the pieces in a screw machine, he catches them in one hand and places them in the top of the gauge. If the work is below the high-limit size it drops through the slot, and if above the low limit, slides down the slot into the box. If above the high limit, the piece will not drop through the first slot, while if below the low limit, it drops through that slot and onto a piece of tin, where it immediately attracts the operator's attention.

Punch Made from Letter Press

The letter press illustrated was used to good effect in an emergency when it was required to punch ¹⁄₁₆-in. cold-rolled stock with holes up to ½ in. in diameter. In drilling the holes in the base of the

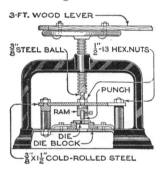

3-FT. WOOD LEVER
⅜"STEEL BALL
½"-13 HEX.NUTS
PUNCH
RAM
DIE
DIE BLOCK
⅜"x1½"COLD-ROLLED STEEL

press, the yoke was removed; holes were cut underneath the die and in one side of the bed so that the punchings could be removed. The die is held to the bed by clamps, while the ram is bolted to a strip of thin steel supported at the proper height at each end. The punch and die being in line with the screw, a cavity is made in the upper end of the ram screw for a steel ball, which furnishes a hardened bearing and reduces the friction. After extensive use, the horizontal piece of steel holding the ram and forming a spring was not permanently bent, as the amount of deflection was not more than ³⁄₁₆ in. The extra leverage required to force the punch through the work was obtained by bolting a wooden lever to the handwheel of the letter press.—Dexter W. Allis, Whitman, Mass.

⁋A "circular mil" is a term used in electrical wire measurements and is the area of a circle .001 in. in diameter. The expression "circular inch" is also met with in electrical measurements and is the area of a circle 1 in. in diameter. Hence a circular inch is equal to 1,000,000 circular mils. The circular inch is equal to .7854 sq. in., and a square inch equals 1.2732 circular inches or 1,273,239 circular mils.

Rubber Stamps for Floor Layouts

Frequently, in engineering offices, it is desirable to make preliminary plans in order to show officials or clients a sug-

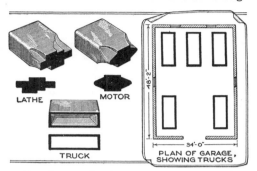

LATHE   MOTOR
TRUCK
48'-2"
34'-0"
PLAN OF GARAGE, SHOWING TRUCKS

Rubber Stamps Cut from Erasers Prove Useful in Laying Out Floor Plans

gested floor layout. For example, a garage of certain dimensions is proposed; this can be outlined in a few minutes, but then the inevitable question, "How many automobiles will it accommodate?" is asked. An ordinary pencil eraser is cut to represent the space that will be occupied by the car on the scale drawing, and, using it as a rubber stamp, the entire available area may be stamped quickly to show its car capacity. In a similar manner, stamps to indicate electric motors, grinders, planers, or other tools and machines, can be made and used to indicate, on the floor plan of a factory, various arrangements to obtain the greatest economy of space.—Robert W. Shelmire, Chicago, Ill.

Clamp for Welding and Brazing Tees

A clamping tool that consists of an eyebolt, rod, and strap is of special service in holding two sections of pipe together at right angles for welding, soldering, or brazing. All parts of the clamp are generally available, and it is applied to the work as shown in the drawing. This type of clamp is of particular ad-

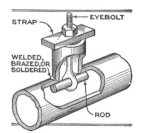

STRAP   EYEBOLT
WELDED, BRAZED,OR SOLDERED
ROD

vantage in brazing, where the main requirement is to hold the parts without the least movement until the molten spelter sets, since otherwise the joint is invariably a failure.

FAULTS IN CONCRETE-SIDEWALK CONSTRUCTION

By A. J. R. CURTIS

ONE of the greatest factors in the tremendously increased use of Portland cement in the last 40 years has been the concrete sidewalk. Although the concrete walk took the country by storm about the time Dewey fought the battle of Manila, and has maintained first place ever since in popular favor, a number of ordinary errors in construction still persist. Some of these mistakes are serious in their consequences, as shown in Fig. 2, endangering life and limb, and causing much needless expense. All, however, are easy to avoid, as the principles involved in laying sidewalks are simple, and the technique easy to acquire.

A concrete sidewalk should be merely a collection of independent concrete slabs, laid one beside another on a firm, well-drained subgrade. In locations where surface water disappears quickly and cannot become trapped under slabs, walks are frequently placed directly on the ground. If the slabs are laid where water is likely to become pocketed under them, either a subgrade, consisting of a 6-in. layer of cinders or gravel, or tile drainage, must be used to prevent possible heaving from frost. Where the walk is placed on an earth fill or elevation, the latter must be thoroughly compacted, and in the case of clay, or other water-bearing soil, the use of a cinder or gravel subgrade under the concrete is a wise precaution. Fills should extend at least 1 ft. beyond the walk on either side and the edges should slope off at an angle of 30°. The finished subgrade should slope toward one side at a pitch of ⅛ in. to the foot, and the finished walk is usually given a corresponding pitch.

Some of the common mistakes in sidewalk construction are shown in the accompanying illustrations. Failures due to disregard, or ignorance, of the law of expansion and contraction, as illustrated in Figs. 1 and 2, and of proper concreting methods, as in Fig. 6, are the most common. Concrete has an expansion coefficient of about .00001, which means that for every degree Fahrenheit in temperature change a piece of concrete will expand or contract approximately one hundred-thousandth of its length. As a

practical illustration, a sidewalk 100 ft. long has an actual variation in length of about 1.2 in. between the extreme temperatures of zero and 100° F. If this walk were put down when the temperature was at 50°, it might be expected to expand one-half of the above amount if the thermometer reached 100°, and to contract as much from its original length if the temperature reached zero. Expansion in sidewalks may be provided for in ordinary straightaway work by leaving a space of from ⅜ in. to ½ in. between slabs every 50 feet.

If a long piece of sidewalk is constructed in the summer, without dividing it into separate slabs, the contraction in cold weather will be sufficient to make the walk tear itself apart at one or more places, and the opening thus formed will continue to widen as the sections continue to shrink. The remedy for this, as well as for several other sidewalk difficulties, lies in making the walk a series of disconnected slabs, usually not more than 6 ft. in each surface dimension, no slab to have a greater length than twice the width. Such slabs can take whatever little movement may be required without affecting adjoining slabs. A very effective method of producing a positive division between the slabs is illustrated in Fig. 7, which shows how the slabs are laid alternately.

The need for efficient concreting methods has always been apparent in our sidewalks. Slipshod methods have been due largely to a failure to realize that the sidewalk really constitutes a very exacting use of concrete. The apparent simplicity of the thing invites careless methods. Sidewalk slabs are quite thin for their size, probably averaging less than 4 in. in thickness, exposing large areas to extreme conditions and often hard use without any protection whatever.

In starting to lay the walk, 2 by 4-in. forms are staked firmly to the desired level, the subgrade having been properly leveled, with its surface 4 in. below the grade of the finished walk. Concrete, made of approximately 1 part cement to 2½ parts torpedo sand, and 5 parts of gravel or crushed stone, all pieces of the

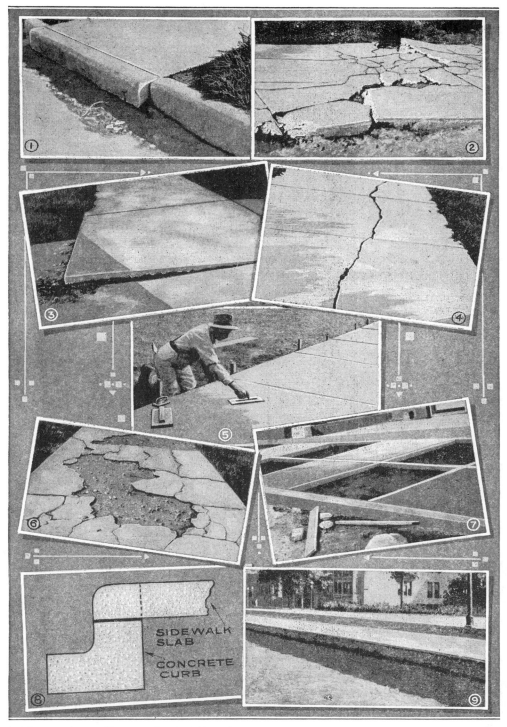

In Figs. 1 and 2 are Shown the Result of Expansion; Fig. 3, a Sidewalk Slab Forced Out of Place by Tree Roots; the Sidewalk in Fig. 4 Failed Because of a Poor Subgrade, While That in Fig. 6 was Made of Weak Concrete, with Dirty Materials, and in Fig. 9 the Subgrade has been Undermined. Fig. 5 Shows the Use of the Trowel, and Fig. 7 the Proper Method of Laying the Walk. Curbs should be Cast as Shown in Fig. 8, to Prevent Their being Pushed Outward by the Expansion of the Walk

latter above ¼ in. in size, is then deposited to a depth of at least 3¼ in. This concrete should be sufficiently wet so that water will flush the surface under light tamping, and should be no wetter. The surface is struck off exactly ¾ in. below the top of the forms by means of a notched straightedge.

The surfacing course, composed of a mortar made of 1 part cement to 2 parts sand, is placed on the base course, usually within an hour, and always before the surface of the base has dried out. The mortar is mixed wet enough to be readily workable, but not sufficient for water to flush to the surface when troweled. The surface grade is obtained by working a straightedge across the top of the forms with a zigzag motion, removing the excess material and filling the depressions.

After the straightedge has brought the surface to a practically true grade, the wooden float, shown in the lower left-hand corner of Fig. 5, and later the steel trowel, are used to produce a true, even surface of smooth texture. The float is merely a flat wooden trowel, the surface of which is 5 by 15 in., with the corners slightly rounded. The steel trowel has the property of drawing the fine particles to the top very readily, and for that reason should be used as sparingly as possible, as excessive troweling will, as a rule, produce slippery surfaces and hairline checks.

Single-course sidewalks are made throughout their entire thickness of a single mixture—usually 1 part cement to 2 parts sand and 3 parts gravel or broken stone—and are usually 4 in. thick. It is not possible to produce as smooth a surface as in two-course work, but less material is required, and quite a little less labor. In practice, the two-course construction described above requires about 1 bbl. or 4 sacks of cement for 45 sq. ft. of surface, while for the one-course construction the same quantity produces about 47 sq. ft. of surface. Metal division plates or wooden partitions provide the most convenient means of dividing the forms to produce independent slabs. The metal plates are better because they can be kept in position a few hours, and then, if kept clean and well oiled, can be withdrawn without difficulty. The slabs are frequently laid alternately, as in Fig. 7, to secure positive division. In such cases heavy paper is inserted between the slabs previously and latterly placed.

The walk is by no means finished until the slabs have been cured. As soon as the surface is sufficiently hard to resist damage by a fine spray from a hose or sprinkling can, it should be wetted, and kept continually moist for four or five days at least. Failure to cure properly, and overtroweling, are the chief causes of "dusting," and the former often leads to definite loss in strength.

Some other faults in sidewalk construction are well illustrated by the photographs. In Fig. 3, the sidewalk was placed too close to a large tree, the roots of which raised the slab shown in the foreground. The sidewalk shown in Fig. 6 was a failure because of the use of poor, weak concrete, made of dirty materials, insufficient cement, and the poor bond between the base course and the surfacing. In Fig. 4 is shown the effect of a poor subgrade, which has sunk away on both sides, failing to support the walk properly, and causing a "broken back." The displacement of the curb, shown in Fig. 1, could have been avoided, had the slab been laid over the curb section, as shown in Fig. 8; the expansion of the slab would not then have damaged the curb. In Fig. 9, the subgrade of the walk has been undermined, and may cause eventual failure of the walk.

Shortening Rivets in Quantities

We needed some rivets, ½ in. long and ⅛ in. thick, but found that the stock of this size was exhausted. There was a large supply of longer rivets on hand, however, and rather than wait for a stock of rivets of the proper size, it was decided to cut down the long ones. A number of ⅛-in. holes were drilled in a ½-in. steel plate, and another and thinner steel plate of the same length and width was also provided. In use, the rivets were inserted in the holes in the drilled plate and the second plate placed over the rivet heads. The assembly was then turned over and clamped in a vise, with the heads of the rivets down. A cold chisel was sharpened on one side only, and used to cut the rivet ends flush with the plate. In using this method, precaution should be taken to prevent injury from the flying ends.—Frank Jablecnik, Chicago, Ill.

¶The average consumption of coal in steam boilers is 12 lb. per hour per sq. ft. of grate surface; there are 9 sq. ft. of heating surface to each square foot of grate surface.

Forms for Concrete Gateposts

The drawings illustrate two designs of concrete gateposts that can be made from easily constructed forms; the latter are put together on the job, and may be used repeatedly.

The style illustrated in Fig. 1 is about the simplest it is possible to build, but the severity of a plain post is relieved by the grooves, which are formed by cleats nailed to the four faces of the form. For either of these types, a footing is sunk 3½ ft. below grade, using alternate layers of field stone and concrete, mixed in the proportion of 1 part cement, 2 parts sand, and 4 parts crushed stone or gravel. Very heavy iron rods are imbedded in the footing with their ends projecting above the ground to serve as an anchorage for the posts. The face forms are made of ⅞-in. pine or spruce, and are crossed at intervals by ½-in. cleats of dressed pine. The front and back faces of the forms should lap the sides, and, when finished, the inside surfaces of all four pieces should be painted with dropblack, which, when dry, is coated with shellac. When set up, the forms should be held together by bolt

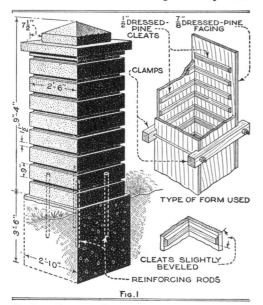

Fig. 1

Simplest Type of Gatepost and Form: Note the Reinforcing Rods Extending into the Footing

clamps, spaced vertically at intervals of about 2 ft. The pyramidal tops of the posts are trowel-finished.

In general, the construction of the type illustrated in Fig. 2 is the same as the

other except that it is paneled. If a light is desired, center the pipe or conduit, and allow plenty of the thread to project above the form, for attaching the lighting fixture, before the concrete mixture is poured. In all cases, the forms should be plumb, securely braced, and tight, so that no cement will run out with

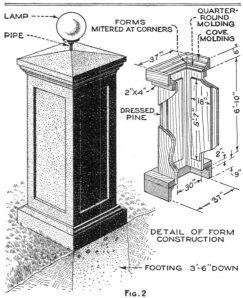

Fig. 2

Form Construction for Paneled Type of Gatepost: The Pipe or Conduit for a Lamp may be Cast in Place and the Top Finished with the Trowel

the water and leave unsightly voids on the outside surfaces.

The cement mixture used for both posts should consist of about 1 part cement, 2 parts sand, and 3 parts of fine aggregate, either in the form of crushed stone or gravel. By using white cement, white sand, and white stone or gravel, a practically pure-white effect is obtained instead of the usually objectionable tone of gray or brown. The concrete should be poured into the forms a little at a time, and should be thoroughly rammed so that it will come into contact with all parts of the mold and fill all corners completely. For convenience in removing the forms, the edges of the cleats and panels should be beveled slightly. The bevel shown on the cleats in Fig. 1 is exaggerated so as to illustrate it better.

❰To fit sheet metal over rivets, hammer the metal over the rivets with a short piece of iron pipe of a diameter suited to the rivets used.

Cutting Sheet Metal with a Handsaw

A simple method of cutting sheet-metal roofing with a handsaw without injury to the latter can be used by carpenters and

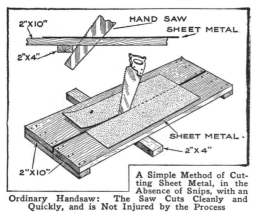

A Simple Method of Cutting Sheet Metal, in the Absence of Snips, with an Ordinary Handsaw: The Saw Cuts Cleanly and Quickly, and is Not Injured by the Process

others if a pair of snips is not available. Two planks are supported by horses at each end. A space just wide enough to permit insertion of the saw blade, is left between the planks. To cut the sheet metal, it is laid on the planks, the line along which the cut is to be made being directly over the space between the boards. The back edge of the saw is placed in the space, against the end of the metal. A piece of two by four is then placed against the underside of the planks and the toothed edge of the saw, as shown in the upper drawing. With the saw held in this manner, a backward pull on the handle starts the cut. This operation is repeated until the sheet has been cut across.—Irl R. Hicks, Centralia, Mo.

Tapped Holes in Thin Tubing

In making an overhead irrigation sprinkler, some of the pipes were found too thin to hold threads into which the

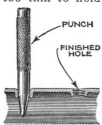

sprinkler jets could be screwed. The difficulty was overcome by using a center punch to make the holes, and to pull the metal into a long neck, which could then readily be tapped. In this manner the whole of the thin-walled pipe was made to take the sprinkler jets, without the delay that would have been caused in obtaining heavier pipe.—John Gormly, Norristown, Pa.

Silent-Chain Sprockets as Belt Pulleys

Small electrical generators for automobile use are almost invariably driven by silent chains running over sprockets. A fact not very generally known is that such a sprocket can be used without alteration to carry a belt when necessary for testing the generator, or even for regular operation on a car in emergency. Many mechanics would suppose that a flat belt would not stay on the sprocket, since it is not crowned like a belt pulley. A test will convince, however, that there is no danger of the belt coming off unless it slips or breaks. The greatest objection to running a belt on a silent-chain sprocket is that it is very hard on the belt and its coupling. The drive should therefore never be used except for a test or when a broken chain, which cannot be immediately replaced, makes the use of the belt necessary.—Curtis Ralston, Chicago, Ill.

Repairing Pump Jack for Engine Drive

A deep-well pump was fitted with a jack geared to a 1½-hp. engine, pumping water through a 1¼-in. pipe against a 200-ft. head. The jack was of the ordinary commercial type, consisting of a cast-iron yoke through which the pump rod fitted and to which it was clamped, and two hardwood arms, drilled with a series of holes and bearing on crankpins on

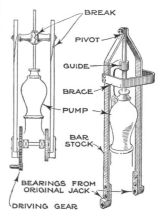

the gears. The yoke broke in the middle, causing the wooden arms to break also, but without damaging the pump rod, guide, or the cast-iron bearing boxes bolted to the lower ends of the wooden members. As it was thought that a new yoke of the same pattern would soon break also, a new rib consisting of two arms of 1½ by ½-in. iron was made. The upper ends were bent inward to meet the pump rod, and were bolted to it with a bolt and locknuts, thus eliminating the yoke. The original cast-iron boxes were bolted to the lower ends of the iron arms. When tried out, the arms were found to bend outward, and to overcome this, an iron brace of ½ by 2-in. stock was bolted across them. As the thrust on the brace was outward, 5/16-in. bolts were found large enough to hold it, although rivets could also have been used. The brace was offset enough to clear the pump-rod guide casting; its corners were forged round instead of square for additional strength.

Gauge for Milling Hexagons

Those who have occasion to mill hexagonal shapes from round stock will find the gauge illustrated a valuable assistant. In order to avoid cutting one side too deeply and thus spoiling the work, it is usual to fall back on the cut-and-try method, whereby it may be necessary to revolve the work in the dividing head several times before a full hexagon is cut. The depth of cut can also, of course, be figured out, but this method is avoided by many on account of the liability of errors creeping into the calculation. The body of the gauge is 3/8 in. thick, with the end cut to a "V," of 120°, included angle, the center of which is filed away or a hole drilled to admit light. A slot is cut along the length of the body, one side of the slot being exactly in line with the center of the V. Next, a piece is made to slide in the slot with a 30° angle on the end, the angular portion fitting a clearance slot cut in the body. A slight bevel is filed on one side of the sliding piece, and a flat-head screw and knurled nut, used as shown, complete the device. To prevent the screw from turning when the nut is tightened, a flat is filed on the underside of the head, to fit against the bevel on the sliding piece.

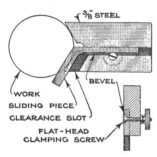

To use the gauge, the sliding piece is pushed forward until the corner is in line with the edge of the shaft, as shown. The nut is then tightened, and a line is scribed on the work along the angular part of the sliding piece. This line is then clearly defined with punch marks, and the cutter set to split these in two. The work can then be milled to this depth on six sides, and a perfect hexagon, for the size of stock used, will result.

Handy Combination Tool

A handy combination tool that will find many uses in the hands of the automotive repairman or in the repair shop, is easily

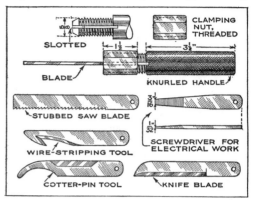

A Handy Toolholder and Outfit of Tools, Made from Pieces of Hacksaw Blades, That will Find Many Uses in the Hands of the Repairman and Auto Owner

made from a piece of round steel, about 7/8 in. in diameter. One end of the stock is turned, threaded, the end beveled, and slotted to take the tools. A nut, with an interior bevel corresponding to that on the screw, is provided to screw over the threaded portion of the holder, so that, when in place and screwed tight, the tools will be firmly held. A set of tools for use in a holder of the type described may easily be made from pieces of hacksaw blades, a few suggestions being shown in the drawing. These, and others that will suggest themselves, can easily be shaped on a grinding wheel.

Improving the Pipe Cutter

A boiler maker found that boiler tubes cut off at the ends with the revolving-wheel type of pipe cutter cracked when the bead was being turned over. To overcome this difficulty, the movable wheel was removed, and for it a cutter similar to a lathe tool was substituted, with results that were entirely satisfactory. The cutter need not be turned down against the work so hard as is the case when the wheel cutter is used.—Irwin T. Fox, Richmond, Ind.

Lathe Used as Milling Machine

With the simple addition of a vertical feed to raise and lower the work, a lathe makes a first-class milling machine. There are various attachments manufactured for this purpose, but all that is necessary

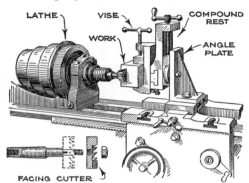

Compound Slide Rest, Mounted on an Angle Plate, Converts the Lathe into a Milling Machine. The Work is Held in a Tool Vise, and Standard Milling Cutters are Mounted on a Taper-Turned Arbor, Fitting into Headstock Spindle

for a small lathe is an angle plate to change the compound slide from the horizontal to the perpendicular. This angle plate, faced on both sides, has holes drilled in it to match the circular groove in the compound swivel. The toolpost slot may be used to hold the work by tapping the casting to receive setscrews. A small tool vise can be clamped to the toolrest, or if a clamping table is preferred, it may be used in the same manner. The attachment is universal, as the plate may be swiveled on the carriage or the compound slide may be swiveled on the plate, to give any desired angle. The cutters are carried on a taper-turned arbor, fitting the lathe spindle. If heavy cutting is to be done, this arbor should be tapped to receive a long stud, passing through the headstock spindle, whereby the arbor can be drawn up tightly. Standard facing, side, or end-milling cutters may be used.—Edwin J. Bachman, Fullerton, Pa.

Creosoted-Wood Silos

Wood-preservation studies have shown that the value of wood silos can be greatly increased by proper treatment with coal-tar creosote. A good creosote treatment will not only increase the durability of the wood, but will reduce the tendency of the staves to shrink when the silo is empty. A creosoted silo cannot be painted afterward; however, it does not need

painting, for the creosote protects the wood, and its color is very pleasing. Highly durable woods, such as heart cypress or redwood, do not need protection against decay so much as the nondurable woods, but a thorough creosote treatment will make the nondurable woods, such as sap pine, last longer than durable species will without treatment.

Contamination of the silage by creosote from the staves need not be feared. This is borne out by experiments and inquiry among the many farmers who have used creosoted silos. In order to be quite sure, it is well to allow the creosoted staves, or the finished silo, to stand a few weeks before filling.

The most thorough creosote treatment can be given by pressure methods. If pressure-treated wood is not available, very good results will be obtained by the hot and cold-bath treatment. If a good penetration of coal-tar creosote is obtained by either of these processes, it is not too much to expect the silo staves to resist decay for from 25 to 30 years.

A Simple Internal Gauge

When used on collars or other work of short length, the adjustable internal gauge illustrated will easily take the place of a number of solid plug gauges. The minimum diameter of the one shown is 1 in., this being the size to which the head is finished. Two 3/16-in. holes are first drilled and reamed in the side to take round-ended pins. Next, a quadrant is milled out as shown, and a clamping plate, with two grooves to fit over the pins, is made. A hole is drilled and tapped in the gauge, between the two pin holes, and a square-headed collar screw, that passes through a hole in the clamp,

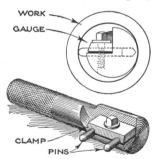

completes the assembly. The first pin is used for the low-limit setting, and the second for the high, the pins being set by measuring over all with a micrometer. When setting, it is convenient to have the clamp tightened on the pins just enough to hold them in place; then the micrometer can be brought down to the size required, pushing the pin in at the same time.

Veterinary Capsules for Small Parts

Empty veterinary capsules make excellent receptacles for holding very small parts and pieces in such a manner that the quantity and condition of the contents can be told at any time, as the capsules are transparent, and, unlike glass, practically unbreakable. Used in series, the capsules, which can be obtained in different sizes, can be used to hold beads, paint or bronze colors, pins, tiny buttons, small screws, graphite, or leads. These capsules, being made of gelatin, must not be allowed to become wet. A simple rack for holding such receptacles in either a horizontal or perpendicular position can easily be made.—C. Nye, New York City.

Connecting-Rod Wrench

An offset made on the end of an open-end wrench, as shown in the drawing, will be found of service in removing the capscrew from the wristpin-end of connecting rods.

The wrench is bent in such a way that the handle will clear the piston skirt. Working with the hands alone, this tool makes it possible to take out or replace the capscrew without requiring any clamping arrangement to prevent the piston from turning.

A Feed-Water Filter

A rather novel filter, made from Turkish towels and marsh hay, was used in connection with the Dayton river-channel improvement work, for removing sediment from the river water in order to have available at all times an adequate supply of clear water for the steamboat boilers.

The construction of the filter is clearly shown in the drawing. It consists primarily of a long rectangular wooden tank, divided into compartments by partitions, through which the feed water is caused to circulate, entering at one end and leaving at the other and passing through consecutive filters of hay and toweling in the course of its journey. The water enters, yellow or brown with unsettled river mud, and leaves ready to enter the boilers, clear enough to drink.

Five compartments are shown in the drawing, but a greater or smaller number may be used, depending on the amount of sediment to be removed. The compartments are separated by double baffle boards set about 3 in. apart, the water

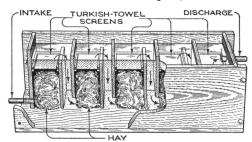

A Simple Filter for Removing Mud from River Water, to Provide Clear Water for Steamboat Boilers, Uses Hay and Turkish Toweling as Filtering Materials

passing, in all cases, over the top of the one nearest the inlet and under the bottom of the next, thus always entering a compartment at the bottom and passing upward through the filter. Each compartment is filled with hay to the level of the cross cleats near the top. Finer screens, made by tacking Turkish toweling onto rectangular frames, are placed on top of the hay and held in place by the cross cleats. The water passing through the compartments, always in an upward direction, leaves its burden of sediment in the hay and under the toweling, thus preventing the rapid clogging of the filter which would result if the water passed downward. With this arrangement, it was necessary to clean the filter only twice a week—a very simple operation, consisting in removing the towels, washing them with a hose and replacing them. It was not found necessary to remove the hay except at long intervals. The simplicity and efficiency of the device, which can easily be built by any carpenter, adapt it to many different situations. It must be remembered, however, that it is for sediment only; lime and other soluble ingredients are, of course, not removed.—Ivan E. Houk, City Engineer, Dayton, Ohio.

Painting on Old Walls

Old walls, especially of kitchens, have a thin layer of grease and smoke upon them that may not be perceptible, but which will prevent paint from adhering properly. Before being repainted, they should be washed thoroughly with soap and water, to which a little ammonia may be added, and finally rinsed with water.

Spindle-Straightening Fixture

Often, in the course of the manufacture of articles of standard design, small shafts or spindles are used; these are

For Straightening Light Shafts or Spindles, in Quantity, a Fixture of This Type Has Much to Commend It. The Centers Holding the Work Are Adjustable Horizontally So That Any Part of the Work can be Reached

usually made from a good grade of tool steel, centered and turned to the form required. After centering a great quantity of such spindles on small turret lathes, it was found, after they had been cut off, that quite a few had been cut from stock that had been slightly bent, and while they would run fairly well at the ends, due to close chucking, the center would run out so badly that they would not clean up on the machining cuts. It was decided that the common method of straightening the stock would be too slow and unprofitable, and the fixture shown in the drawing was made. The body of the device is made of square steel and is bolted to a bench so that the slotted end projects over the edge. A ½-in. slot, cut in one end, receives a movable swinging jaw. Mounted on the top side of the base is a swivel jaw having two extending lugs, the metal between them having been removed on a shaper; this block is fastened loosely to the base by a ⅝-in. capscrew. A ½-in. hole is drilled and reamed horizontally through the iron base, just behind the slot, to take the centering attachment upon which the work to be straightened is supported.

The centering attachment is made from a piece of steel rod, which is flattened at one end and threaded at the other. On the threaded end is screwed a stationary center, which is held tightly by a locknut. A swinging center is pivoted to the flat end of the rod, thus permitting quick positioning of the work between the centers. Also, the weighted end of the swinging center keeps it pressed against the end of the work, and keeps the centering fixture normally in a vertical position.

When the operator has placed a spindle between the centers, he will first revolve it with his fingers, and, by sighting, detect the point at which the work runs out. He now brings the high spot toward himself and by pressing down on the toggle handle, exerts pressure against the work, bending it in the opposite direction. The work is again tested, and the operation repeated as may be necessary.

Stripping Films from Cracked Negatives

To strip the film from cracked glass photographic negatives, so that the film can be placed on another piece of glass and prints made from it in the regular manner, the film is first hardened in a three-per-cent solution of chrome alum, washed for five minutes, and then dried. Next, a 20-per-cent solution of white gelatin is made and filtered while hot. A liberal quantity of this is poured over the negative, which has previously been warmed and placed as level as possible. When the gelatin has hardened, the negative is again placed in the chrome-alum solution, washed for five minutes, and placed in denatured alcohol for a half hour, after which it is dried again.

To strip the negative from the glass, use a mixture of 2 oz. water, 1 oz. denatured alcohol, and 1 dr. of commercial hydrofluoric acid. After a few minutes' immersion in this bath the film can be loosened around the edges with a small stick of wood, cut to a chisel point. When this stage is reached, the negative is transferred to a tray of clean water for a minute or two and then to another; the actual stripping is done in the latter tray, by means of the stick. After removing the film, it is washed in two or three changes of clean water, then laid out smoothly on a ferrotype plate to dry. The fingers should not be allowed to touch the hydrofluoric-acid solution, which is very corrosive and poisonous. Usually it is not advisable to place the film on glass, as there is considerable risk of distortion in drying, but, if necessary, it can be done. A good method is to fix out an unexposed plate, and harden in formalin the layer of clean gelatin left. This is slipped underneath the stripped film while the latter is lying in water. The plate is then raised until the film rests on the glass securely. Finally, it is drained and allowed to dry in contact with the gelatin.

Cutting Torch Produces Ornamental Ironwork

What can be done in the way of producing ornamental hinges from sheet metal

with an oxy-acetylene cutting torch is clearly shown in the photograph. The intense heat developed makes it possible to cut the metal as easily as wood is cut with a band saw. Practically any metal can be worked by this means, the hinges shown having been cut from bronze.—Harold C. Ridgely, New York City.

Balancing Polishing Wheels

It is highly important that polishing wheels be in balance. Balancing ways are made for this special purpose, and the balancing itself is usually done by nailing pieces of sheet lead on the light side of the wheel, until the wheel remains at rest in any position on the ways. It is also important that the wheel run absolutely true. The wheel is not necessarily true, however, even if in balance. By the use of an old file or buff stick, supported by a temporary rest, the wheel can be made to run so that every portion of its circumference will come in contact with the work.

Scaffold That need Not be Fastened to Building

When reshingling or repairing a building, it is quite necessary to have a scaffold to work from, as a ladder does not give the proper er freedom of movement or stability for the worker, and, unlike new construction, it is not usually possible to nail blocking to the sides of the house for supports. The drawing shows how a scaffold can be erected

without marring the surface of the building, and yet be substantial enough for all work. A piece of 2 by 4 or 2 by 6-in. stuff is placed at an angle to the building, and as close up under the eaves as possible, as this saves side bracing. Another piece is placed in a vertical position, and crossing the first, and the two are spiked together where they cross. This is done at each end of the building, and in the middle if necessary; then short pieces of similar lumber are nailed across the long pieces to form supports for the staging.

A Small Bolt Cutter

Sawing off the ends of bolts is slow and tedious work, and it is not always possible to use the hacksaw, because space is lacking. The drawing shows a clipper that can be made from two flat files, the arrangement being such that a powerful leverage is obtained. Four 12-in. files are used, their ends being annealed so that they may be drilled and

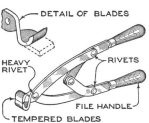

the cutting lips forged. When assembled with bolts or rivets, two ordinary file handles are fitted to the tangs of the files forming the handles. The cutting edges should be tempered to the same hardness as that generally used for lathe tools, that is, to a light-yellow color.

Driving Pipe Underground

It is often possible, when laying iron pipe of small diameter, to drive the pipe through the earth and save the cost and trouble of digging a trench, with the aid of a specially constructed point, something after the style of a well point. One trouble that is common to this method is

CHAIN AND WEDGE

that the outer end of the pipe must be protected against the blows of the hammer or maul used. Wooden blocks offer slight protection and damage to the threads is likely to result in spite of them. A much better method is to use a steel wedge secured to the pipe by a length of chain in the manner shown. The blows of the hammer on the wedge tighten the chain and afford sufficient grip, and the heaviest blow will not damage the pipe.

Punching in the Lathe

The drawing shows a rather novel fixture used for cutting cardboard disks in a lathe. There are three main parts, the punchholder, punch, and operating shaft. The holder is made of any convenient size, to the shape shown, the back end fitting in the toolpost. Near the front, a hole is bored to take the milled bar that operates the punch, and tangent to this hole a small hole is drilled from top to bottom. This is counterbored, the size of the punch to be used, down to the center of the larger hole, and a tapered groove is milled from the counterbore to the front of the holder, on the top face. The punch is made to fit the counterbored hole, as shown, and fitted with a coil spring, washer, and pin, to keep it down on its seat. A narrow slot is

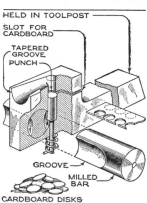

HELD IN TOOLPOST
SLOT FOR CARDBOARD
TAPERED GROOVE
PUNCH
GROOVE
MILLED BAR
CARDBOARD DISKS

cut in the top of the holder, in the position shown, to take the cardboard from which the disks are cut. The operating shaft is a bar, centered at both ends and having semicircular grooves milled on opposite sides.

In use, the holder is gripped in the toolpost, with the shaft held between centers and driven by a dog. The lathe is run backward, and the stock fed by hand; at each revolution the punch cuts two disks, which are forced out of the hole, and slide down the tapered groove into a box.

A Simple Locknut

The drawing shows one of the simplest forms of locknut, that will stay in place without loosening until forcibly removed with a wrench. A $\frac{3}{16}$-in. or larger hole, the size varying with the size of the nut used, is drilled through the side of the nut. After the nut has been tightened, a nick is cut across the bolt thread, using a small chisel punch as shown. The

BURR
CHISEL PUNCH

hole serves a double purpose, as it permits insertion of the punch and forms a cavity for the upraised burr, which prevents the nut from turning. Naturally, to be the most effective, the cutting edge of the chisel should be held parallel to the axis of the bolt when raising the burrs.

Grinding Troubles

If the wheel glazes, the work is burned or the wheel cuts slowly, the remedies are, for the first, to use a coarser wheel; for the second, to use a softer wheel, and for the last, to decrease the table speed or increase the feed. If the wheel wears too fast, increase the table speed or decrease the feed; if this has no effect, try either a harder or a finer wheel. For a finish that is too rough use a finer wheel, or, in some cases, an elastic wheel; or, these remedies failing, try a little cutting oil in the grinding solution, if only soda water is being used.

Formula for Breaking Strength of Rope

For three-strand Manila rope with a regular lay, and from ½ to 4½ in. in diameter, the following computation will give the strength of the cordage: The average breaking strength in pounds equals 5,000 multiplied by the diameter of the rope in inches, and the product then multiplied by the diameter in inches increased by one. Thus, in calculating the strength of a 3-in. rope, multiply 5,000 by 3, the diameter in inches, and then multiply the product by 4, which is the diameter of the rope increased by one, the total product being 60,000 lb. This method gives the average maximum weight that the rope will hold, but the working load must, of course, be much less.

Adjustable Stock Support

For a small shop, the handy stock support illustrated will be found much more useful than the usual telescopic arrangement, since it can be used to support bars very close to the floor, as in fitting a shaft to the finished machine, or high up for pipe-threading machines and work in the vise. It is made of ¾ by 1½-in. flat stock. Two pieces of stock form the base. These should first of all be dropped at the ends enough to clear a bolt head, then bent at right angles to form feet. The lever support is twisted at right angles at one end, bent upward a little, and a "V" cut. The opposite end is drilled for the pin on which it pivots, and which, being riveted at both ends, binds the three pieces together; a similar pin, with a sleeve, is used at the other end. An ordinary square-headed ¾-in. bolt slides between the two members forming the base, the top of the square on the bolt being filed a little on the sides to allow it to enter the channel and prevent it from turning. A special clamping nut is shown, which, of course, is convenient, but an ordinary nut will serve the purpose if the cost is to be considered. Made to a length of about 3 ft., this support has a range from that height to 6 in. from the floor. The bars held in this support must be fed or pulled forward so that the pressure is kept on the bolt, that is, away from the pivot.

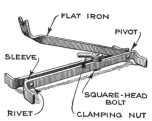

FLAT IRON
PIVOT
SLEEVE
SQUARE-HEAD BOLT
RIVET
CLAMPING NUT

Fixture for Lawn-Mower Repairs

The drawing shows a fixture that has been in use for several years in a shop making a specialty of lawn-mower repairs. It is made from short lengths of pipe and suitable fittings. The distance between the two half-tees is such that a lawn mower of any width can be placed in the fixture and held firmly. The projecting pipe ends of the fixture fit into holes drilled near the edge of the workbench, so that it can be removed when not in use. The lawn mower is supported in the fixture by the stay rod, as shown, with the handle resting on the floor. — A. W. Zimmerman, Chicago, Ill.

LAWN MOWER
TEES CUT IN HALF

Removing Tight Screws

Screws of the slotted-head variety are, at times, very difficult to loosen, especially if they have remained undisturbed for a long time in a damp place. The little tool shown in the drawing will aid in loosening such screws without destroying the slot, as any attempt to hammer them off will do, thus making the job more difficult. A short piece of ⅞-in. stock is drilled up the center with a 9/16-in. drill, knurled on the outside, and an angular slot, ⅜ in. wide, and running into the 9/16-in. hole, is cut in the side. The driver is made of 9/16-in. tool steel, drilled for a ⅜-in. pin, which is driven in when the two parts are assembled. With the pin at the bottom of the angular slot, the tool is grasped firmly in one hand and placed in the screw slot. The top is then lightly tapped with a hammer, which, while keeping the blade in the slot, at the same time continually presses it round in a left-hand direction, so as to loosen the screw. Only light taps of the hammer should be used, as heavier blows will not produce the desired effect.

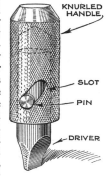

KNURLED HANDLE
SLOT
PIN
DRIVER

Unwrapping Wire in the Lathe

THERE are occasions when it is necessary to remove the insulation from magnet or annunciator wire, as when triple-covered wire is to be reduced to double, to save winding space, or when the paraffined outer layer of annunciator wire

Where No Other Method Is Available, Insulation may be Unwrapped from Cotton-Covered Wire in the Lathe, Saving Much Tedious Hand Labor

is to be removed to convert it into single cotton-covered magnet wire. This is an extremely tedious operation when done by hand, particularly when the wire is of any length.

The drawing illustrates a lathe set-up designed to unwrap the insulation mechanically. The insulated wire is carried on a reel, or spool, held on a bolt clamped to the compound rest. A metal thrust washer, a spring, and two locknuts on the end of the bolt, hold the spool by friction and prevent it from being too easily turned. The wire is carried along above the lathe bed through a sleeve held in the steady rest and through the headstock spindle to another spool, arranged with wooden bearings and a hand crank, and mounted on a bench or stand beyond the lathe. A piece of brass or iron pipe is held in the universal lathe chuck; fastened over the chuck jaws is a clamp made of bar iron having its end turned over at right angles, to form a guide for the insulation stripped from the wire, two guide rings being provided for this purpose. Next, a brass thrust washer or plate is placed on the pipe, and then a hardwood spool, upon which the insulation is wound as it is unwrapped from the wire. Another thrust washer is placed in front of the spool, then a compression spring and an adjustable collar to hold it in place.

In use, enough of the wire is stripped by hand to allow the unwrapped portion to be passed through the spindle and attached to the spool at the rear, and the cotton threads are carried through the guide arm and attached to the spool on the tube, the spring being so adjusted as to allow the spool to turn stiffly, yet without pulling the wire badly out of line or breaking the strands. It can be seen that, as the wire is drawn along, the insulation will unwind from it, pass through the guides on the rotating arm and wind itself on the spool. As the rate of winding on the spool will be much less than that at which the strand is unwound from the wire, there will be considerable slippage between the spool, thrust washers, and tube, the spool being pulled around by the insulation. The success of the operation will depend upon the spring adjustment and the rate at which the wire is drawn along. An adjustment that is too loose will prevent the winding of the insulation upon the spool, while one that is too tight will pull the wire out of alinement and possibly break the strand being unwound.

By reversing the process, it is possible to wrap bare wire, but a smooth job would hardly result. For special purposes, however, such as wrapping thermocouple resistance wires with asbestos string, the method should be successful.

For a short lead, the end of the wire could be attached to a bolt clamped to the tool block in place of the spool; then the carriage would be started moving toward the end of the bed, drawing the wire through the headstock spindle and at the same time applying the wrapping. Here a good deal would depend upon giving the carriage the proper rate of feed. Two, three, or more, layers of insulation could be wrapped or unwrapped, but only one at a time, the wire being run back and started through each time another layer was to be worked upon.

❡ To drill horizontal holes accurately with a ratchet drill, make the punch mark deep, and apply sufficient pressure to the drill to prevent its tendency to slip down.

Extension for Cold Chisel

There are times when the only method to loosen a nut with the tools at hand is to set a chisel against one of the corners and strike it with a hammer. However, sometimes nuts are so located that the chisel is not long enough to reach them. In such cases, an extension can easily be made for the chisel by driving a sleeve, of pipe or tubing, over the head of the chisel, and inserting a piece of rod, the size of the chisel shank, into the upper end of the sleeve.

Grinding Piston Rings

In the small jobbing shop there is often a call for special piston rings to fit odd-sized bores of steam and gas-engine cylinders. To get an accurate fit in the ring groove, the sides of the ring must be ground or filed off; this usually difficult job can readily be done on the shop's universal tool grinder.

An angle plate is mounted on the table of the grinder, parallel with the face of a cup wheel, as illustrated. A piece of flat steel is clamped against the angle plate and serves as a stop, against which the outer surface of the ring rotates. The

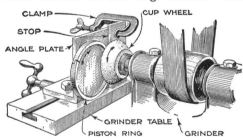

A Simple Method of Grinding Odd-Sized Piston Rings to the Proper Width on a Universal Tool Grinder Solves Another of the Problems of the Jobbing-Shop Mechanic

ring rests and revolves on the table slide. When the rings are cut off the ring "pot" on the lathe, one side is faced carefully and made straight and true. This face is then brought against the vertical face of the angle plate, with the opposite face against the grinding wheel. Rotation of the ring is effected by slowly turning by hand, the wheel producing a pulling effect on the ring in a downward direction. When one side is finished smoothly, the ring is reversed and the opposite side touched up and ground to the exact width of the groove, less about .0015 in. This trick can be applied to many other similar jobs, and, with a little care, good work is easily done.

Winding the Thresher Belt by Power

One of the hard jobs of the thresherman is the winding up of his long drive belt, and a device that reduces the manual

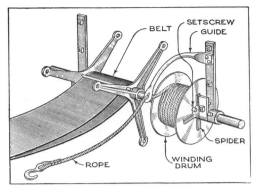

A Simple Attachment for the Grain Separator That Lightens the Labor of the Thresherman by Winding His Long Drive Belt on a Reel—the Tractor Does the Heavy Work

effort required to do this will be appreciated generally.

The arrangement shown in the drawing made it possible for one farmer to use power for the purpose of winding the belt on the reel usually provided for that purpose. A winding drum was made from a section of a maple log and fitted with two 20-in. sheet-metal flanges. This drum was fastened to the shaft on which the reel was fitted by a spider, which was originally the hub from the fan of an old separator. A 60-ft. length of ½-in. rope, with a loop at one end and a hook at the other, was then prepared. The looped end of the rope was dropped over a pin driven into the face of the drum, so that when the rope had been unwound, it would slip off. An arm, with a hole in the lower end, was attached to the frame of the separator to act as a guide for the rope when rewinding.

To operate the device, the tractor is driven to the separator as for hitching, but only the hook on the rope is attached to the drawbar. The belt is then fastened to the reel and the tractor is driven away. The pull on the rope wound around the drum serves to wind the belt in its place. When the belt is to be unwound again, the rope is attached to the drum and thus, as the belt reels off, the rope is wound up for repeated service.

❡Mercury boils at 676° F., and at that and higher temperatures it vaporizes rapidly, though mercurial vapors will rise from the metal at a lower temperature.

Rack for Steel Stock Boxes

Every factory uses standard steel stock or "tote" boxes, to carry from one operation to another materials and parts being worked upon in the shops. Usually, there are many different kinds and sizes of parts that must be accommodated, and with a variety of production, it is not advisable

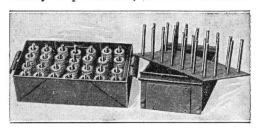

A Rack for Steel Stock Boxes That Makes Possible Rapid Counting of the Parts, and Also Prevents Them from being Damaged

to equip the stock boxes to handle only one particular piece permanently. Flexibility must be secured, and this is accomplished by a large manufacturer of lighting plants as illustrated.

A steel plate, ¼ in. thick, is cut enough smaller than the inside dimensions of the steel box so that it will drop in easily. It is drilled with a suitable number of holes, depending upon the number of spindles that is desired in the box. This number will depend on the size of the parts to be placed on the spindles and the clearance necessary between the parts. Enough space should be left between the spindles so that a variety of objects of approximately the same size can be accommodated, without danger of rubbing or damage. The spindles may be iron pipe, of any suitable size, although ⅜-in. pipe usually provides sufficient strength. They should be threaded for about ⅝ in. on one end, and the holes in the plate tapped to suit. After the spindles are screwed into the plate, a pair of thin locknuts are screwed on the projecting ends of the spindles and lightly riveted over. This provides a strong, sturdy, adaptable rack that can easily be placed in an empty box. It also allows quick counting, as anyone can tell at a glance if all the spindles are full and how many parts are missing.—Edward H. Tingley, Dayton, Ohio.

❡An arrow cut on the feed pawl of a shaper will save time and confusion, by indicating the direction in which the machine will feed for each position of the pawl.

Finishing Wooden Patterns

In making wooden patterns, the most tedious part of the work is the sandpapering between the several coats of shellac, and, also, applying the beeswax fillet. Little or no sandpapering need be done, yet a high gloss with but one coat of shellac obtained, if the pattern is first completely covered with melted beeswax. This may be applied with a hot iron held against a cake of the wax, which, as it melts can also be guided into the places to be filleted. Care must be taken not to have the iron so hot as to scorch the glue at the joints. Little wooden chisels and round-end tools are used to scrape off the surplus wax and to groove out the fillets, the wax chips being kept brushed away with a small brush. One coat of the varnish will dry with a high gloss, and the pattern will be entirely moisture-proof and ready for the foundry. This method will be found particularly useful with patterns of irregular contour.

Combination Box and End Wrench

A novel and cheaply made wrench, designed for saving time when used on a milling-machine vise, does the work of an open-end wrench and a box wrench. All operators of milling machines know that when the vise is bolted to the table, with the jaws at right angles to the travel of the table, the regular wrench can only be given half a turn at a time, when opening or closing the vise, as it strikes the table. To save a little time some use an open-end wrench to bring the jaws up to the work. If special jaws are being used on irregular work, the vise may require several turns of the screw to open or close it.

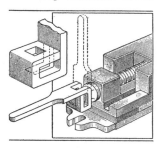

The wrench illustrated is made from ⁷⁄₁₆ by 1⅛-in. stock, forged into the shape shown. The bent-back portion has a square hole in it to fit the square of the vise screw. The front and adjacent side are also slotted to fit the square. The remainder of the stock is finished as desired, to form a handle grip.

When opening or closing the vise, the wrench is used as shown by the solid lines, but when greater pressure is required to loosen or tighten, the wrench is slipped back until the square hole is off the square on the vise handle; it is then swung around and pushed down until the end of the slot rests on the vise-handle square, and the handle of the wrench is in a perpendicular position, as indicated by the dotted lines. The wrench is then used as an open-end wrench.

Writing White on Blueprints

White ink, water color, or a strong solution of baking soda, are generally used for writing on blueprints when extra details are to be added and it is not desirable to make new prints from the corrected tracing. A fine permanent white line may be made by dissolving a small lump of unslaked lime in water and using this liquid as one would ink. The lime water does not work like whitewash, but, like baking soda, acts on the blue ground chemically.

Drill for Slate or Marble

Tile setters, plumbers, electricians, and others must frequently drill holes through hard, brittle tile, porcelain, or slate at

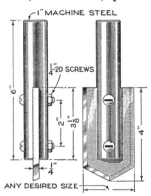

no slight expenditure of time and broken drills. The drawing illustrates a drill for such work that is particularly effective for use when large holes are to be drilled. The cutting tools, which are made of tool steel, are removable for sharpening, and can be made for holes of different diameters. The edges are milled off at an angle of about 45°, or enough for good clearance, and the lips are sharpened in about the same manner as an ordinary flat drill, the sides also being sharpened. When a hole is to be drilled with this type of tool, a guide hole is necessary to allow the dust to fall through. Very slow speeds are essential to successful drilling in slate, marble, and similar materials. The drills will not work as well at high speed as at slow speed because of the excessive friction.—Arthur F. Cox, Chicago, Ill.

Dissolving Calcium Chloride

When mixing the brine solution for refrigeration plants, calcium chloride is dissolved in water, and many hours of

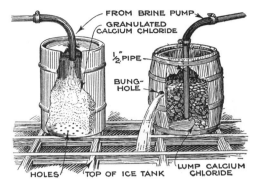

Methods of Dissolving Granular or Lump Calcium, One of the Chemicals Used in the Brine Solutions of Refrigerating Installations, without Manual Labor, the Brine-Circulating Equipment Doing the Work

back-breaking work can be saved if the machinery of the plant is made to do the work mechanically. The usual method of mixing the solution is to stir the chemical in a tub or barrel until dissolved and then dump it into the tank, and repeat.

The drawing shows two systems, depending upon whether the granular or lump chemical is used. If the calcium chloride is granular, punch a number of holes through the bottom of the drum with a chisel and cut an opening in the head large enough for the insertion of a hose. Then roll the drum over on the tank top, remove about six ice cans, and set it up over the opening. Connect with the brine-circulating pump, and run the brine or water through the granulated chemical, which will dissolve in a very short time, leaving the drum empty.

When dissolving the chemical in lump form, take a barrel, set it up over the tank in the same way as before, and connect a length of $\frac{1}{2}$-in. pipe to the brine-circulating system; dump in the lump calcium and turn on the brine. The liquid will enter at the bottom of the barrel, and on rising, will pass through the chemical and through the bunghole into the tank below. In this manner the only manual labor connected with the operation is to fill the barrel occasionally with the undissolved chemical.

❡ Engines running under widely fluctuating loads should be provided with a speed-limiting device which acts independent of the governor.

Rapid Jig Clamp

Drilling flat plates of square or rectangular shape is a common shop operation, and simple jigs are, as a rule, used to hold the work, more especially if there are any number of pieces of approximately the same size to be drilled. Such jigs generally take the form of a flat plate fitted with bushings for the necessary holes, the work itself being located against flattened pins and held by two screws at right angles to each other. For work of accurate dimensions, the double-plate clamp shown is much to be preferred to the screws, as the work is gripped or released by a single movement.

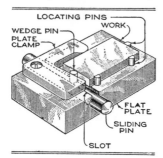

LOCATING PINS
WEDGE PIN
WORK
PLATE CLAMP
FLAT PLATE
SLIDING PIN
SLOT

The clamp is made of flat stock, which should be slightly thinner than the work, cut to the shape shown, and drilled and counterbored for a round-headed screw. Through the side of the jig body a hole is drilled for a sliding pin, which has driven in its center another pin; the latter forming a wedge that slides between the work and the taper side of the clamp. The hole for the sliding pin should be drilled as close to the top as possible and a slot cut through afterward to clear the wedge pin.

In use, the work is laid in place, and the sliding pin is tapped on the end with a light hammer. This forces the wedge pin between the end of the work and the taper of the clamp; this has the effect, as will be seen, of tightening the work from both sides at the same time. A tap on the opposite end of the sliding pin, of course, releases the work.

Laying Out Tapered Work

The work required to lay out tapered work by the methods generally used involves considerable calculation, and an easier method will be appreciated by the draftsman. For example, supposing it is desired to lay out a piece to be turned on the lathe, 7½ in.

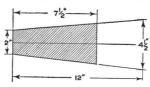

7½"
2"
4½"
12"

long, 2 in. in diameter at the small end, and with a taper of 2½ in. to the foot. Proceed as follows: Lay out the center line, and mark off, on this line, a distance of 12 in. At one end lay off two points, 1 in. on each side of the center line, and erect a perpendicular joining the two points, thus marking the 2-in. diameter. As the taper is 2½ in. per foot, add 2½ to the diameter of the small end, obtaining 4½ in.; then, at the other end of the 12-in. line, lay off 2¼ in. on each side. Join these points with the points marking the smaller diameter. From the small end, measure 7½ in. along the center line, and at this point draw a vertical line intersecting the two inclined lines. The length of this line, between the inclined lines, will be the required diameter of the large end of the piece.

Alarm Circuit for Open Fuses

On electric circuits that supply current to draft fans, electric heaters, water sterilizers, and the like, it is important that an attendant should have instant knowledge of trouble in the circuit. Frequently the attendant's station is at a distant part of the plant, and for this reason the circuit shown in the drawing was devised to give an audible alarm when a fuse blows out. Each fuse is bridged by a relay; this may be of almost any type or size, but should have a resistance of 100 ohms or more. The contacts of the two relays are bridged and connected to an ordinary doorbell and dry battery. If desired, a switch may be cut in on the bell circuit to disconnect it when necessary.

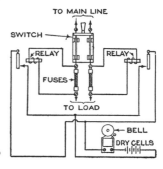

TO MAIN LINE
SWITCH
RELAY
RELAY
FUSES
TO LOAD
BELL
DRY CELLS

The operation is as follows: Current flows from the main line through the fuses to the load; the relays do not operate, because they are short-circuited by the fuses. Should a fuse go open, the circuit would still be continuous through the relay winding, causing the relay to operate and the alarm to ring. The purpose of the fuse is not defeated, because the resistance of the relay winding will not allow an excessive flow of current.—C. M. Crouch, Minneapolis, Minn.

Shop Notes

Supply of Gas Automatically Controlled

By CURTIS RALSTON

THE gas controller shown is a device which, owing to its cheapness and simplicity, may be used for many purposes where it is necessary to regulate the flow of natural or artificial gas used for heating.

The controller, or regulator, working in connection with an ordinary expansion thermostat, opens the gas valve whenever the temperature falls to a predetermined point, and when the temperature has risen to the desired maximum the valve is automatically closed, except for a sufficient flow of gas to supply a "pilot" light. Since the power for opening and closing the valve is supplied by one or two dry cells, it is of great importance to cut off the flow of electric current as soon as the work is done and thus prevent waste of power; how this is done is clearly shown.

The thermostat may be made at home, if desired, but the purchased article will generally be found more satisfactory. When the thermostat gets warm, its expanding member curves downward, closing a circuit through the electromagnetic solenoid at the right, which then pulls down into it the iron rod forming the core, thus closing the gas valve. As the valve completes its rotation, it breaks the circuit through the closing coil and closes another circuit through the opening coil at the left, thus preparing the

valve-opening coil to work as soon as its thermostatic contact closes. The whole operation takes place at a single "click" and occupies but the fraction of a second, and the amount of energy taken from the battery is so small that a single pair of cells will last for a long time. The electromagnets are of the "shell" type, each being covered by two iron pipe caps, which are connected by a nipple. The coils are wound around a hollow core of iron pipe which has a diameter sufficient to accommodate the solid movable cores. A hole is drilled through the center of the upper pipe caps to permit insertion of the cores. Bell wire is used for the coil windings, and the greater the number of turns the greater will be the "pull" exerted on the cores; also, more current will be required to operate the device. The magnetic circuit is thus mostly all iron, which produces a very powerful type of magnet. When the controller is set up, the first adjustment to make is for the flow of gas for the pilot burner, and this is done by a screw in the bottom of the valve-closing magnet. The two thin-brass contact springs, which make contact with the segments on the fiber or hard-rubber valve disk, should then be adjusted to give a positive break, late enough so that rotation of the valve is complete.

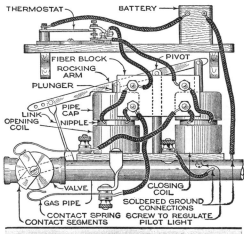

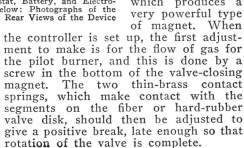

Above: Constructional Features and System of Wiring for Connecting the Thermostat, Battery, and Electromagnets to the Levers. Below: Photographs of the Regulator, Giving Front and Rear Views of the Device

Automatic Belt Shifter for Grinder

Practically every shop experiences trouble because the workmen forget to stop the grinding wheel after they have

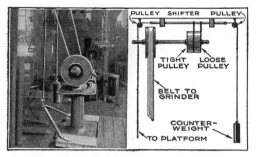

When the Workman Steps on the Platform, the Belt is Shifted from the Loose Pulley and the Grinding Wheel Started. When the Man's Weight is Removed, a Counterweight Pulls the Belt Back onto the Loose Pulley, Stopping the Machine

used it. In order to make certain that this would not occur in a small machine shop, the arrangement illustrated was installed, and worked with success.

A platform, surrounding three sides of the machine, is elevated at the end nearest the machine, and connected to one end of the shifter rod so that, as soon as the workman steps on the platform, the belt is shifted over onto the tight pulley and the wheel begins to revolve. When the weight of the man is removed from the platform, a counterweight attached to the opposite end of the shifter rod pulls the belt back over to the loose pulley, stopping the machine. This arrangement not only saves a lot of the men's time, but prevents accidents and saves power, as the grinder is running only when in use.— Ethan Viall, Barboursville, Ky.

Hacksaw as Facing for Core Boxes

The cores from a half-core box were quite satisfactory while the box was new, but as the face of the core box was unprotected, the constant rubbing of the strickle, or strike board, soon wore down the face of the box so that the two half cores, when pasted together, formed an oval, instead of a round core. The core box was repaired and faced with tin, but this was soon cut through. It was then suggested that worn-out hacksaw blades be nailed to the edges of the box. The suggestion was acted upon, and since then there has been little or no wear on the core box as the hardened saw blades provide protection for the wooden edges.—M. E. Duggan, Kenosha, Wis.

Locating Cylinder-Head Gaskets

The difficulty experienced when the cylinder-head gasket shifts while the head is being placed in position on an automobile engine, can be avoided by the use of two simple locating studs. These consist of two cylinder-head bolts with the heads sawed off and slots sawed across their upper ends to facilitate removal with a screwdriver. The studs are inserted in diagonally opposite holes in the cylinder block, the gasket is placed over them, and the head put in position; when the bolts are inserted, they will coincide with the corresponding holes in the gasket, the studs, of course, being unscrewed when the head is in place.

Knurl Holder Fits Toolholder

A quantity of small brass thumbscrews were to have their heads knurled while the stems were held in a universal chuck. It was necessary to chuck the screws with the heads close to the chuck jaws, to prevent bending, and a regular toolpost knurling tool was found to strike against the jaws, besides being too heavy for the work. A hand-rest knurling tool, on the other hand, was not altogether satisfactory, and the difficulty was finally overcome by mounting the small knurl taken from the hand-holder in a specially made bracket, fitting into the $5/16$-in. square hole in an offset toolholder. The bracket

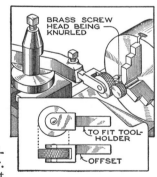

can be removed for use in a straight holder also, or in one offset in the opposite direction. While only one knurling wheel was used, the result on the small brass-screw heads was entirely satisfactory. The bracket was made of tool steel, for toughness, and the arms through which the knurl shaft passed were as thin as possible, consistent with strength, in order to allow the knurl to be used close to the chuck jaws. The square stem was offset to allow further clearance for the toolholder shank; by reversing the bracket, this offset can be made to come on the other side for use on work located close to the tailstock.

Cutting Springs after Winding

When making a heavy wire spring in the machine shop, it is generally coiled on a mandrel held between the centers of a lathe. After the spring has been wound to the desired length, it is a good plan to turn the lathe spindle backward a few turns before cutting off the wire. This relieves the strain on the spring, and makes it safe to cut the wire with a hacksaw or pliers without danger of having the end of the wire fly back.

Quickly Operated Jig Clamp

A quickly operated jig clamp is shown in the drawing. The clamp is made with four lugs, one at each corner, with the swinging leaf pivoted between two of them, the actual clamping being done by means of the cam-and-pin arrangement shown in the sectional diagram. In order to be sure of accuracy, the work is held by a floating foot, or center. A pin, driven through a hole in the top of the center shank, prevents it from falling out, and the center is ball-shaped so that it can adapt itself to the surface irregularities of the work.—J. H. Moore, Toronto, Can.

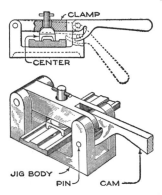

Center-Punch Attachment for Square

The attachment illustrated will be found a timesaver when laying out work. By setting the index mark on the attachment to a graduation on the square blade, any desired distance from the edge of the work can be prick-punched instantly; for greater accuracy, a pair of calipers, or an inside micrometer, can be used in setting.

The base of the device, which is made of tool steel, is machined with a shoulder that fits against one edge of the square blade; a slotted extension opposite this shoulder carries a cam or eccentric that locks the attachment in place. The slot, and the construction of the cam stud, enable the attachment to be used on blades of varying widths. The punch is carried in a sleeve, forced into a hole in the shouldered end of the base; in line with the punch point, an index mark is cut on the base, and the edge of the slotted extension is milled or ground exactly in

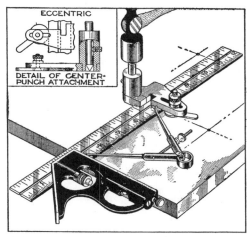

A Center-Punch Attachment for the Combination Square That will be Found Very Useful on the Laying-Out Bench

line with the punch point also. A flat, filed on one side of the punch, and a small setscrew in the sleeve, prevent the punch from dropping out.

Guard Plate for Knife Switch

An unprotected knife switch is a real menace to the lives of those who work around it, especially if the switch is carrying a heavy current. If it is not possible to use the safety switches that are now accepted as standard, the exposed knife switch can be made practically safe by applying an insulating cover that will prevent accidental contact with the switch.

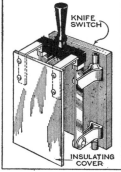

The drawing shows a method in use at one plant. Here a piece of sheet fiber, or other insulating material, is attached to the switch by metal brackets. The insulating material completely covers the switch blades so that in opening or closing the switch, the operator cannot come into contact with anything but the handle.—Clementine Paddleford, New York City.

SOME UNUSUAL JOBS
FOR THE TRACTOR

By GEO. G. McVICKER

MANY farmers seem to be laboring under the impression that a tractor is only useful for drawing plows and other implements, and, when fitted with a power pulley, for driving a thresher or a circular saw. There are many other jobs around the farm, however, for which the tractor could be used with a consequent saving in time and labor. A few such jobs are here described.

The foundations of many barns and other farm buildings extend but a few feet below the surface of the ground, and very often the foundation walls will settle away from the building, due sometimes to undermining by rats, sometimes to heaving of the ground by frost. When this happens, only a small portion of the wall supports the building. I found this to be the case with one of my barns after the frost had loosened the ground. Rather than employ a mason to relay the wall, section by section, I decided to try using the tractor to push it back into place. This was accomplished as shown in Fig. 1. A 3 by 12-in. plank, as long as the wall, was placed with its broad face against the latter. I then attached a 4 by 6-in. timber to the drawbar of the tractor by means of a chain, allowing the timber to extend forward between the wheels and protrude several feet ahead of the tractor. I toenailed this timber to the 12-in. plank, started the tractor, and, allowing the clutch to slip slightly, moved slowly forward in low gear. The foundation was thus pushed into position and held firmly until I had tamped earth solidly underneath it. I did this job alone in a little over an hour; with jacks or crowbars it would have taken several men much longer. It might be necessary, in some cases, to relieve the foundation of the weight of the building side, but this could easily be done by using levers.

A jack is a tool seldom found on the farm, and when a small building is to be lifted, either for repairs to the foundation, or for making the foundation higher, or for placing rollers and skids under it, preparatory to moving it to a new location, crowbars are the tools commonly used. This method requires two or three men,

and makes a tiresome and time-consuming job. The building can be lifted, one side at a time, by using the tractor; this demands but little preparation and no materials that cannot be found on the average farm. The first step is to spike or bolt a 2 by 6 or a 2 by 8-in. timber to one side of the building, at a suitable height above the ground. The tractor is backed to within about 6 ft. of the building, and a 4 by 6-in. timber is cut to such a length that it will reach from a point on the tractor frame just above the drive axle to the timber attached to the building wall. When this timber has been set so that it will stand a good push without slipping, the clutch of the tractor is slowly engaged, and the tractor, in reverse gear, moves back until it is against the building, as shown in Fig. 2. This action provides a powerful lifting effect, and raises the building as steadily and easily as a number of jacks. When the building is lifted, the tractor will hold it until blocking or skids can be placed in position, and then, by driving the tractor slowly forward, the building is allowed to settle on the blocks. The opposite side is lifted in the same manner, and if the building must be raised still higher, the operation is repeated, moving the timbers on the building lower, or using a longer lifting timber. This is a safe and practical method, and the work can, if necessary, be done by one man.

Removing rocks from a field to be seeded appears to be an ever-waiting job for the farmer in localities where the ground is very stony, and many are inclined to farm around the larger ones because of the work involved in moving them. With the aid of the tractor, however, rocks too large to be otherwise moved, without first breaking them, are easily loaded on a sled, hauled to the rock pile or stone fence, and unloaded, without any hand lifting at all being necessary.

The sled used is no different from any common stone sled, except that a steel pulley is attached to the front end, as shown in Fig. 3. The only other piece of equipment necessary is a length of $\frac{7}{16}$ or $\frac{1}{2}$-in. steel cable, one end of which is fas-

Fig. 1 Shows the Tractor Replacing a Foundation Wall; Fig. 2, Lifting a Building for Foundation Work, or Preparatory to Moving; Fig. 3, Loading, Hauling, and Dumping Heavy Rocks; Fig. 4, Removing a Heavy Wagon Box by the Aid of a Simple Device, and Fig. 5, Loading Felled Trees with a Minimum of Exertion

tened permanently to the front end of the sled, while the other is provided with a hook that will go into the eye of the tractor drawbar.

A hole is poked underneath the stone with a long curved bar, and the cable worked through it. The end is then passed under the pulley, and hooked to the drawbar. As the tractor is driven ahead, the cable rolls the stone up onto the sled, the backward pull on the sled holding it in place until the cable rolls the stone forward against the pulley. The sled will then start to move forward, and without having to stop, the journey can be continued to the rock pile. When this has been reached, the cable is unhooked, run over the top of the pulley, and hooked to the drawbar again. The tractor is then started, the cable rolls the rock from the sled, and then pulls the sled on over the rock, without stopping the tractor, as it is driven back.

I can, if necessary, lift a wagon box on or off the running gear by the exercise of "brute force and ignorance," but I don't like to do it, and I won't, so long as my tractor is at hand. I have a device rigged up, by the use of which so little time and manual exertion are required that it is a pleasure to watch it work.

I set one 4 by 6-in. post, 10 ft. long, 2½ ft. in the ground. At the top of this post, I pivoted a crossarm made of 2 by 8-in. timber, 9 ft. long, the pivot being a ¾-in. bolt, and the pivot hole bored 18 in. from one end. The bolt passes through the upright post on one side, the other end being held by a piece of flat iron, bent and attached to the post as shown in Fig. 4. To the short end of the 2 by 8-in. piece I bolted a 7-ft. length of 2 by 6-in. lumber, bracing the two as shown, with two pieces of flat iron. It will be seen that, when the wagon is on the gear and the crossarm is just at the top of the box, the upright arm is standing at an angle to the main post. Two loops of rope are placed around the box and over the crossarm, and the tractor is then backed against the upright lever arm. This raises the box clear of the running gear, which is then drawn from beneath, the cross supports shown in the illustration are placed in the brackets, and the box is lowered. One man does the whole job.

Loading the trees felled for the winter's fuel, or for a lumber supply, before hauling them to the saw, is easily a two-man job as ordinarily undertaken, and involves some heavy lifting. By using the method shown in Fig. 5, one man can do the

work if necessary, and all manual lifting is eliminated. The necessary implements are a rope, ⅝ or ¾ in. in diameter, 50 ft. long, a piece of the same rope about 10 ft. long, a chain long enough to reach around the largest of the logs, and a jack pole, as illustrated, 10 ft. long.

Drive alongside the log to be lifted, about 3 ft. to one side. Wrap one end of the long rope around one of the mud lugs near the top of the tractor drive-wheel, at the rear, and, at a point on the rope near the center of the log to be lifted, take a half hitch around one of the forks on the jack pole. The jack pole is set in a shallow hole, to prevent slipping, at the outside of the log, and inclined at an angle of 45°. The other end of the long rope is fastened to a stump, or a stake driven in the ground, about 6 or 8 ft. ahead of, and to the outside of, the jack pole, as shown. The log is attached to the jack pole with the short rope and chain; then, with one hand holding the end of the rope that is hitched around the mud log, slowly engage the clutch. As the tractor moves forward the rope will be wound on the drivewheel (the tractor should be steered so that it will), and the log is lifted. As soon as this happens, the jack pole begins to swing in, as the part of the rope between the pole and tractor is always taut, while that between pole and stump begins to slacken as soon as the log is lifted. As the forward movement continues, the jack pole is pulled in farther until the log is dropped in the center of the wagon.

The placing of the jack pole, wagon, and stake demands a little bit of judgment, but after a few trials, the correct relative distances can be estimated with considerable accuracy, and the work will proceed with dispatch.

Several other unusual chores for the tractor have come to my attention, such as using it as a snowplow, by attaching a V-shaped frame covered with boards to the front axle, and for heavy hoisting, by attaching the end of the falls of a block and tackle to the drawbar, then driving the tractor forward; these are but a few of the many that will occur to the wide-awake reader.

––––––

Prolonging the Life of Emery Belts

The life of emery belts can be considerably extended by treating them with paraffin wax. The wax is applied to the surface of the moving belt, or may be put on when the belt is idle. After applying the wax, it will be observed that only the cutting edges of the abrasive grains are visible, the voids between the grit particles being filled with wax. This is the secret of the extra-long wear. As any chips or metal dust cut from the work are forced into the wax, the emery is free to cut instead of clogging and breaking off. This method is especially useful in brass and aluminum work, as this material has a tendency to fill in more than harder metals. However, when the belt has finally filled up and become smooth, it may be made to look like new by using a file card to clean out the accumulated cuttings, after which another coating of wax is applied.—S. S. Sutherland, Detroit, Mich.

Increasing the Oilcan's Reach

By the simple expedient of making a small collar, having a tapered hole, to fit over the spout of an oilcan, and attaching

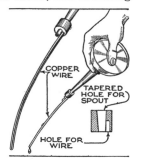

a suitable length of stiff wire to the collar, the range of the oilcan may be considerably increased. The wire, preferably of copper, is soldered into a hole in the collar. In use, the collar, with its attached wire, is slipped over the spout of the oilcan; the oil follows the wire and makes it possible to direct the lubricant into otherwise inaccessible places. The attachment can be put on or taken off the spout in a second.

Driving Screw Hooks Quickly

The manual-training class of a high school, in carrying out a project that required a gross of screw hooks to be inserted into boards, found the job very tedious, until the tool shown in the

drawing was made. It was made from a stove bolt having a shank that would fit into the chuck of a spiral screwdriver, a flat being filed on the end of the shank to correspond with that on the screwdriver bits. The slot in the bolt head fits over the screw hooks, and inserting them then became a very simple matter.—N. E. Studebaker, Houston, Tex.

A Carriage-Bolt Holder

Carriage builders, automobile - body workers, and others who have frequent occasions to remove carriage bolts, are familiar with the tendency of the bolt to turn with the nut. As the head of the bolt is round, it is not always an easy matter to get a grip on it that will hold without damage to the adjacent woodwork. The simple tool illustrated has been used for a number of years

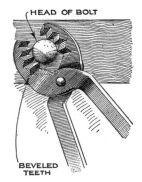

by a man of long experience in work of this character; it should be made of the best tool steel and tempered as hard as a screw-plate die. The teeth are beveled, and the bevel must be on the upper side.— C. S. Simmons, Cache, Okla.

Holding Nonmagnetic Materials on Magnetic Chuck

In surface grinding brass, or other nonmagnetic parts, considerable trouble is experienced if the grinding machine is equipped with a magnetic chuck. In order to do the work, either the vise or special planer clamps must be used, that is, if the work is flat, as in the drawing. Such flat work, however, having

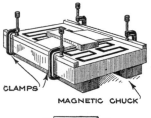

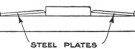

plane surfaces, can be held on the magnetic chuck by using two steel plates of the kind illustrated, one on each side of the work, with a support behind them. The plates should be of such a width that, when placed between support and work, they will lie at a small angle to the surface of the chuck. The edges of the plates are beveled, and the beveled edges are placed as shown; when the current is turned on, the plates are pulled tightly against the work, clamping it to the chuck.—John Homewood, Ontario, Calif.

Stacking Hay by Gravity

A western rancher raises alfalfa in summer on the plateau above a swiftly running river, which never freezes. His home and feed lots are located in the river valley below. It was not long until he encountered trouble in hauling the

A Western Rancher's Method of Stacking Hay by Gravity: His Crop is Raised on the High Land, Whence It is Shot down a 400-Foot Chute to His Feed Lot in the River Bottom

hay down to the river bottom, and he proceeded to eliminate the necessity of hauling, as well as much labor, by building a chute from the hayfield above to the feed lot. The chute is about 400 ft. long, about 8 ft. wide, and has a semicircular cross section. Throughout most of its length the chute rests on the earth. The lower end, being elevated so as to form a stack, is carried on a timber frame.

From 50 to 75 tons of hay are shot down the slide each season, and a load can be put down in the same time as required to put it on a stack below, as a stacker is also used at the top to move the hay from the wagon and drop it onto the chute.

Flesh or Grain Side for Belts

Many discussions have taken place in the past as to whether the grain or the flesh side of a leather belt should be run next the pulley. Definite data were entirely lacking, however, until a series of tests, covering a period of more than two months, and using five 4-in. single-ply belts, made by various makers, each belt being 30 ft. long, were made at Cornell University. All five belts were thoroughly run in before the tests, and every effort was made to reduce the possibility of error to a minimum.

The method of testing was to take horsepower readings from the belts, when running on each side, the power being increased gradually until four per cent slip was reached. The results indicate clearly that the grain side is undoubtedly the best for power transmission, the flesh side transmitting, under shop conditions, on an average only about 50 to 60 per cent as much horsepower as the grain side. Under a higher tension than is usually found in the shop, however, the flesh side shows a higher efficiency than this; under very favorable conditions, as high as the grain side. The tests show that there is a distinct advantage to be gained by running a belt with the grain side next the pulley.

Lever for Tailstock Handle

When drilling large holes in the lathe, extra leverage on the handwheel of the tailstock spindle makes the work easier for the operator. The attachment illustrated forms a handy way of getting the extra pressure against the drill point, as it is quick-acting and need not be removed from the handwheel in order to clear the lathe bed. The lever is made from two pieces of cold-rolled steel, one of

½ by 1½-in. flat stock, which is forged to form the forked section, and the handle, made of stock to suit the width of the wheel. The ends of the fork are bent over to conform to the contour of the wheel, while the handle is turned at one end to form a good grip, and drilled near the other for the stud that holds it to the fork. The end of the handle is filed to the same radius as the wheel, and a piece of soft leather is passed around this end and held in place with screws. Downward pressure on the handle causes it to grip the wheel tightly, and apply the necessary pressure. When the lathe bed is reached, a quick upward movement releases the wheel and enables the operator to take a new grip.

Raising a Water Tank 25 Feet

As a rule, when increased height is required for a water tank, the old one is scrapped and a new one erected, or if the condition of the old tank warrants, it is dismantled and then rebuilt on a new support; both of these methods involve the expenditure of considerable time and money.

The photographs illustrate a method by which a 60-ton tank was elevated a distance of 25 ft., and new sections built into the steel tank support, without disturbing the tank. A wooden support was built around the base of the tank, the corner members of which were 14 in. square and 40 ft. long, while the rest of the framework and the braces were made from 8-in. timber. Two heavy chain falls were fastened to the crosspieces, at opposite corners, and cable tackles and winches were attached to the other two corners. The cables

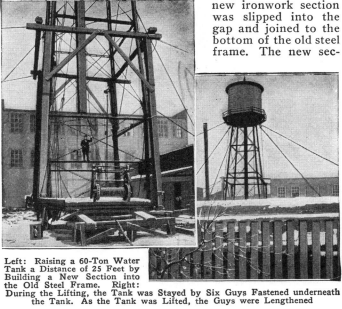

were then fastened to each corner of the tank supports. Six guy wires were attached to the bottom of the water tank

proper, to prevent it from falling or moving under the influence of the wind. Each of the guys was provided with a tackle block, and as the tank was raised, the guys were slacked away, while keeping them tight enough to hold the structure steady.

When the tank had been raised the proper distance, the new ironwork section was slipped into the gap and joined to the bottom of the old steel frame. The new sec-

Left: Raising a 60-Ton Water Tank a Distance of 25 Feet by Building a New Section into the Old Steel Frame. Right: During the Lifting, the Tank was Stayed by Six Guys Fastened underneath the Tank. As the Tank was Lifted, the Guys were Lengthened

tion measures 24 ft. square, and the tank now stands 100 ft. in the air.—W. K. Crosson, Detroit, Mich.

Testing Engines at the Muffler

Many present-day automobiles are built without muffler cut-outs, and with such effective mufflers that it is difficult to tell, from the exhaust, when the engine is missing explosions. In a noisy shop the exhaust can hardly be heard at all if the throttle is nearly closed. Under such conditions, a strip of tin can be used to determine when the engine is "hitting" on all cylinders.

This strip, which should be about 12 in. long and 4 in. wide, is held by one end in the fingers, so that the opposite end rests over the exhaust-pipe opening. The rhythmic striking of this tin strip on the pipe indicates perfect operation. A pause, or "miss," in the stroke is noticed when explosions are missed, regardless of how slowly the engine is operating. By this means, adjustments may be made on the spot without the necessity of a road trial.

Scale Used as Depth Gauge

Mechanics and others who frequently have occasion to measure the depth of small openings such as countersunk holes, short slots, and the like, will find the scale altered as illustrated very convenient, because, as a rule, the width of the ordinary machinist's scale is too great to permit the taking of such measurements. To convert the ordi-

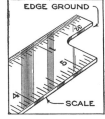

nary 6-in. pocket scale into a combination scale and depth gauge, it is only necessary to grind away one side of it for a short distance from the end, reducing the width of the scale so that it can be used in the smallest opening encountered.—P. A. Daschke, Astoria, N. Y.

Magneto and Generator-Testing Base

By J. V. ROMIG

NO electrical-appliance repair shop, or even garage, is complete in its magneto and generator department unless it

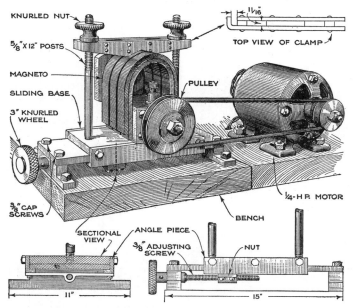

KNURLED NUT

5/8" X 12" POSTS

MAGNETO

SLIDING BASE

3" KNURLED WHEEL

3/8" CAP SCREWS

KNURLED NUT

TOP VIEW OF CLAMP

PULLEY

1/4-H.P. MOTOR

BENCH

SECTIONAL VIEW

ANGLE PIECE

3/8" ADJUSTING SCREW

NUT

11"

15"

When Testing Magneto and Generator Units, Some Sort of Test Stand is Required to Hold the Piece Securely If It is to be Tested under Service Conditions. The Device Illustrated Eliminates Vibration While under Load

has a testing stand or base on which to clamp the repaired units and test them under actual running conditions. In the device illustrated, the generators, starting motors, or magnetos are held rigidly, and a ¼-hp. electric motor is large enough to drive nearly all ordinary types of generators and magnetos. The magneto or generator is placed on the sliding base of the tester, the pulley adjusted in line with the driving pulley on the motor, and the clamp tightened. By moving the base away from the motor, which is done by turning the adjusting wheel on the front of the device, the proper belt tension is secured for driving the unit under test.

Cold-rolled steel is the best material for building the base, a piece ½ by 7 by 15 in. being used for the bed. This is bolted to two pieces of 1 by 2-in. stock, shaped as shown, to form the feet of the tester. The sliding base proper is made from a piece ¾ in. thick by 7 in. wide and 10 in. long. This piece is fitted with angle members on its sides, to make a carriage that will slide on the bed, and is also drilled and tapped for the two upright standards, which have a short thread on their lower ends. A flat piece of brass,

is shaped with a boss, and, when drilled and tapped, is used as a nut for the adjusting screw; this piece is fastened to the angle members by small ¼-in. round-head screws. The adjusting screw is made of steel, and is fitted with a knurled handwheel, 3 or 4 in. in diameter. The clamp that holds the electrical units down on the base is built up of ⅜ by 2-in. flat-bar stock, riveted together, with 11⁄16-in. spacers between the two sides. One end of the clamp slips under the tightening nut in a longitudinal direction while the other swings radially, making a handy and quick-acting clamp. By notching it out in the center, as shown, it will hold the units under test tightly and squarely, and prevent them from slipping around. Holes are drilled in the feet, and the device is bolted to the bench in line with the motor. The motor switch should be mounted underneath the bench, to prevent it from being damaged by accident.

Acetylene as a Primer for Cold Engines

There is no question but that acetylene gas is very effective when used to start cold or balky internal-combustion engines, but in the opinion of many engineers of wide experience, such use is very dangerous. The explosion of acetylene gas is so much more violent than that of gasoline or kerosene vapor, for which the engines are designed, that there is considerable likelihood of blowing off the cylinder head or breaking the piston.

Acetylene gas is more easily ignited than a mixture of gasoline vapor and air, especially at low temperatures; with some motors, if reasonable care is exercised, no accident is likely to occur, but with others, especially with those having heavy flywheels, representing considerable inertia, it is highly probable that the cylinder head or some other part of the combustion chamber will give way before the flywheel has turned sufficiently to remove the pressure, by permitting the piston to move on the downward stroke. This is also largely true of ether used as a primer without dilution.

The use of an open flame in the air intake of an internal-combustion engine, as an aid to starting in cold weather, is seldom recommended, strange to say, yet this is very effective, offers no danger to the operator and practically none to the machine.

Jack Prevents Distortion of Pistons

The illustration shows a device used to avoid the danger of springing pistons out of shape when new pin bushings are to be fitted. It consists of a round steel body, the smaller diameter being threaded, and the head having a recess cut in it to allow the bushings to project the proper amount through the boss without coming into contact with the jack. The threaded shank is fitted with a hexagon nut, the outer face of which is recessed in the same manner as the head on the opposite end.

RECESSED HEXAGON NUT

RECESSED HEAD

To use the jack, it is placed between the pin bosses, screwed tightly against them, and the bushings are inserted, after which the nut is slacked far enough to allow the device to be removed.—Edwin Kilburn, Spring Valley, Minn.

A Riveting Kink

In cases where a stud is being turned in the lathe for insertion into any part to which it is to be riveted, the work of riveting can be greatly facilitated, and a more permanent fastening obtained by means of a simple dodge. This consists in cutting a concave spot in the end, as shown in the drawing; the resulting ridge is quickly upset with the ball peen of the machinist's hammer, and considerable time is saved, as the ridge turns over quickly under the hammer blows and provides a substantial head.—G. A. Luers, Washington, D. C.

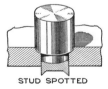

STUD SPOTTED

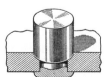

AFTER RIVETING

Scribing Long Straight Lines

When a long straight line is to be scribed on a metal surface, and no full-length straightedge is available, a close approximation can be reached, with careful work, by means of a fine steel wire,

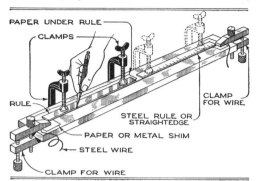

PAPER UNDER RULE
CLAMPS
CLAMP FOR WIRE
RULE
STEEL RULE OR STRAIGHTEDGE
PAPER OR METAL SHIM
STEEL WIRE
CLAMP FOR WIRE

When a Long Straight Line is to be Scribed and a Single Straightedge of Sufficient Length Is Unavailable, an Approximately Exact Line can be Drawn by Alining Two or More Straightedges

tightly stretched, and clamped to each end of the work. In the drawing, a steel bar is shown, as a simple example, which requires a line scribed down its length. The wire used is preferably steel piano wire, although iron or copper wire can be made to serve. There must be no kinks or bends in the wire, and to help remove such as are not noticeable, clamp one end of the wire in a vise and stretch it by hand as much as the material will stand without actual rupture; then do not allow it to become bent before using. Stretch the wire as tightly as possible upon the work and clamp the ends; if the scribed line is to extend to the ends of the work, carry the wire down over and clamp it at some other point. Make sure the wire does not touch the work enough to be thrown out of true, though it should lie as closely as possible to the surface. Shim up under the ends with paper or thin metal if necessary. Then procure two or more steel rules or straightedges and clamp them along so that their edges just touch but do not move the wire. Use a magnifying glass in setting them, if accuracy requires it. After the straightedges are alined and clamped, with thin paper under them as a safeguard against slippage, remove the wire and scribe a line against their edges.

¶Small protruding points in the bottom of the box that retains the oilstone, will prevent it from slipping when it is used on the bench.

Protecting Small Thread Gauges

Thread gauges of the smaller sizes used around the shop very frequently have their usefulness impaired by the numerous knocks they receive in the course of the day's work. Often, too, vibration will jar the gauge off the bench, or some heavy tool will be dropped on it by the careless or busy mechanic. Accurate thread gauges are expensive to make, and are well worth protecting; for this purpose the device shown in the drawing will be found simple and effective. A sleeve is made to fit the largest diameter of the gauge, and long enough to cover its entire length. A slot is cut in the sleeve for about half its length, and at right angles to this, near the slotted end, is a hole is drilled, and a pin driven in. The gauge shank is then drilled, close to the end, a drive fit for a ³⁄₃₂-in. wire, after which it is inserted in the sleeve, and a piece of the wire is driven in. The ends of the wire are bent over the end of the shank in the manner shown, and adjusted until the ends will just spring over the pin in the sleeve. When in use, the gauge is pushed forward by grasping the bent wire, and when not in use, it is pushed back into the sleeve until the ends of the wire snap over the pin.

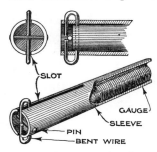

Type Cases to Hold Small Parts

Every workshop has as a part of its stock or equipment an assortment of small screws, nuts, bolts, and similar small articles, which are difficult to store and classify. To keep these things in order and within reach when wanted, requires a number of small compartments or containers.

One of the best ways of sorting and keeping in order such a stock of small articles is to use printers' type cases. The case is a drawer about 32 in. long, 16 in. wide, and 1⅜ in. deep. It is divided into small compartments by wooden partition strips. A "double" case has 49 compartments or "boxes," 2 in. square, on each side, or a total of 98 divisions. A "triple" case has three lots of boxes, 1¼ by 2 in., or a total of 147 compartments. Several other arrangements of the partitions and divisions can be obtained. The boxes or compartments give room for but a few of each of the pieces and parts, but they provide a rather complete stock in a very small space, where they are always kept in order and ready for use.

Old type cases can be obtained at bargain prices from print shops and supply houses, or new ones, together with stands for holding them, if a number are to be used, can be obtained from type founders. Such a case, mounted as a drawer, underneath a bench, will quickly prove its value.—James W. Cottrell, Hammonton, N. J.

A Simple Punch and Die

A die for experimental work, which is simple and economical of construction, is shown in the drawing. The die is made of casehardened machine steel, and is screwed and doweled to a cast-iron stripper. The shape of the die is scribed off onto the stripper, which is then machined out to fit the punch. The punch should be made a good fit in the stripper, as it serves as a guide for the former. The punch is made sufficiently long to permit a rubber washer or sleeve to be slipped over it; this sleeve rests on top of the stripper plate. A hole is drilled near the top of the punch for a pin which holds a steel washer in place against the rubber. The rubber sleeve is compressed when the blank is being punched out, and is strong enough to pull the punch from the stock. Such a die can be operated in a vise or arbor press.

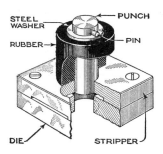

Testing Ink for Acid

A simple method of testing ink, or other fluids, for the presence of acid, consists in dropping some of the liquid under suspicion into a solution of washing, or baking, soda. If the ink is acid, the resulting reaction between the acid and the alkali will cause foam to appear. Blue litmus paper can also be used; this turns to a red or pinkish tint when brought into contact with an acid.

Tightening Nuts with Rounded Edges

When repairing the car, it often happens that nuts which are to be removed from some awkward location have been "chewed up" to such an extent that the edges have become rounded, and it is difficult to grip them properly. A socket wrench will usually slip around over such a nut without moving it, especially if the wrench itself is a little worn. One car owner, who does his own repairing, finds that by placing a piece of fairly heavy cloth over the nut, and then forcing the socket wrench over this, nuts in this condition can be loosened or tightened easily.—A. E. Swanson, Los Angeles, California.

Trimming Drawings with a Knife

When trimming drawings with a pocketknife, using the T-square as a straightedge or guide for the blade, it

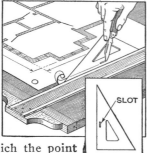

often happens that the blade of the T-square is damaged. To prevent this, yet insure that the drawing will be cut in a straight line, a narrow slot can be cut in a triangle through which the point of the knife blade is inserted. In trimming a drawing, the T-square is placed so that the slot in the triangle will fall on the trim line; it is then only necessary to insert the knife blade and draw it to the right, the triangle sliding easily along the edge of the T-square.—A. K. Harrison, Chicago, Ill.

Grinding Holes Straight

A simple visual method of testing holes for straightness, while grinding, is as follows: When the wheel is in to the full depth of the hole being ground, feed it to the opposite side until it just touches the wall. Then withdraw it from the hole and note the sparking. If the sparks are heavier near the front of the hole, the diameter is smaller at that point. When the grinding wheel is moved over to the opposite side and the sparking is the same throughout the bore as the wheel is withdrawn, the hole is straight.

Preventing Hasp from Breaking

When a padlock hasp becomes jammed between the door and its frame, it is not uncommon that the hasp is broken or pulled from its fastenings. Naturally, if the hasp could be kept out of the way, this would not happen. The arrangement illustrated not only keeps the hasp from between the door and frame but does it automatically. A hole is drilled in the hasp at the point

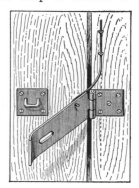

shown, and a bicycle spoke is run through it and fastened to the door frame with staples, so that it can just slide. Owing to the tendency of the springy wire to straighten itself, the hasp will be thrown back automatically as soon as the lock is removed.

Adjustable Block for Hacksaw Vise

The movable jaw of a hacksaw vise is made to swivel on a stud or screw in order to get a firm grip on rough work,

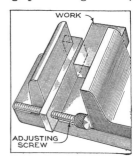

that is, in consequence, probably of unequal width. This, however, is the cause of a great loss in time when it is desired to hold short pieces of work which may be less than half the length of the vise jaws. It is impossible to hold such pieces securely without packing up the other end of the jaws to the same width as the work to be held.

The attachment shown in the drawing will be found much handier than the usual array of nuts, washers, broken saw blades, etc., generally used. The fixture is clearly illustrated, and is simply a piece of flat stock bent over at one end and tapped at the opposite end, as close to the vise as possible, for a knurled screw. The work is held between the attachment and the movable jaw, gripped tightly, and the screw tightened against the opposite end of the jaw.

Some Ingenious Uses for Dynamite

By J. L. BALL

IT requires an emergency job to sharpen the wits of the mechanic to a keen edge; this is especially true around mines, where crude methods are sometimes required to get results, and some of these

Left: A Sheave Wheel from the Headframe of a Coal Tipple, Removed without Injury to the Shaft. **Center:** The Effect of Two Charges of Explosive on the Sheave Hub. **Right:** Blasting Out a Tight Key

methods are as unusual as they are effective. It was necessary to replace some sheave wheels because the rims had become badly worn by the hoisting cable. These sheaves, or bull wheels, are in the headframe of the tipple, and should one of them fail from any cause, the damage would be considerable on account of the heavy weight of the steel cages and the loaded pit cars.

The new sheaves were exact duplicates of the old ones, and it was planned to use the old shafts, to avoid the necessity of fitting new journal boxes. After every known method had been used, without success, in the attempt to remove the old shafts, it was suggested that dynamite be used to burst or crack the hubs. The wheel was blocked up, 1-in. holes, 6 in.

deep, were drilled in the hub at two opposite points, and a V-shaped notch was chipped from the hole to the outer edge of the hub. It required a half stick of dynamite, fired separately on each side of the shaft, to crack the hub, the shaft not being injured in the least. The left and center illustrations show the sheave before and after firing the charge.

The teeth of a large solid gear wheel of a clay-grinding machine were so badly worn that it was necessary to replace it with a split gear. The position of the gear, however, was such that it required considerable work to get at the key. A very small piece of 40-per-cent dynamite was placed in the keyway of the shaft and fired, driving the key out quickly. It will be well to remember that but a small quantity of explosive is required to do this work, and experiments should be made to determine this quantity, in order to avoid injuring the shaft and bearing.

In another case two cracked spokes made it necessary to remove a 6-ft. flywheel from a high-speed steam engine. The key was quickly removed by placing a small piece of dynamite behind the head of the key, as shown in the right-hand illustration, the end of the key being supported by a stout bar, to prevent its being bent downward.

Planting Sweet Corn

That sweet corn planted in June gives the best quality of corn is the contention of many expert gardeners, who maintain that the very highest quality is not obtained by earlier planting.

Sweet corn sown in the early part of May will produce a crop for the table in the latter part of July or early August, just when the summer is usually hottest. In these sizzling days the corn ripens so rapidly that only a portion of it can be picked at top quality. However, smaller early plantings, with the heavier plantings in June, will bring out the bulk of the crop during the last of August and early in September, when the weather is not so hot, so that the corn will ripen more slowly, and its quality remain at

its best for a longer time. Corn is likely to remain longer in the "dough" stage in cooler weather, and be available for the table over a longer period. Plantings of corn 10 days apart until the end of June, provided the first was planted early in May, will give a crop succession from the last of July until well into September.

Corn planted in June gets a faster start because of the warmer weather, and grows more rapidly than that planted earlier, the young plants developing under ideal temperature conditions, which is also another reason why June corn is likely to have finer ears and be of better quality.

When the corn has reached a height of about a foot, a light sprinkling of nitrate of soda is of great benefit. Avoid getting the nitrate upon the leaves of the plants, and rake it lightly into the soil. When the corn is from 2 to 3 ft. high, some of the balanced fertilizers, or bone meal, can be sprinkled lightly and hoed in; that is usually all that is necessary to produce a good crop. These extra applications will not be necessary if the soil is good, is rich to start with, and has been manured, but if there is any doubt about it, or in the absence of common manure, they will insure a good crop.

Making a Clutch Shifter Stay "Put"

A manufacturing concern had trouble in making the clutch on the countershaft of a bolt cutter stay in the forward, reverse, or neutral positions, until the device illustrated was installed by one of the foremen. Two pieces of ⅜ by 1¼-in. steel were welded together at right angles to make a T-shaped piece, the horizontal member of which is screwed to one of the overhead timbers. The other member

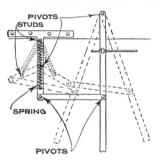

extends down, parallel to the shifter lever when the latter is in neutral. To the end of the vertical member of the T a short length of the same stock is pivoted, making a link that is free to swing to either side of its stationary support. Another link connects the shifter lever to the end of the pivoted arm in the manner shown. A coil spring is hooked over a stud riveted into the upper link near the lower pivot stud and over another located near the angle of the T. When the shifter lever is perpendicular, the link and spring are perpendicular also, and the lever has no tendency to move in either direction, but when the lever is thrown either to the right or left, the spring shortens and holds the clutch firmly. — Ralph Hanenkratt, Northville, New York.

¶The hole in which a broach is to be started should be drilled or bored. Using a broach in a cored hole soon impairs its accuracy. The face of the work that rests against the faceplate must be true with the bore, otherwise accurate work is impossible.

Novel Tap Holder for the Drilling Machine

Very often it is found necessary to retap large batches of nuts, which, for some reason, are too small. The holder shown is very convenient for securing and driving a tap quickly without any tightening device, thus enabling the operator to insert and withdraw the tap while the machine is running. The shank of the holder is turned to fit the drill chuck, while a slot, the width of the square on the tap, is cut across the front end. A collar is made, of the same diameter as the holder, and fastened to the latter by two screws.

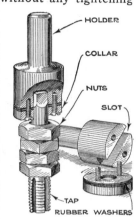

Between the collar and holder two rubber washers are placed. With the nuts held suitably on the drill-press table, the tap is pushed up in the holder. The rubber washers, being a wringing fit on the tap shank, will grip the tap sufficiently to keep it from falling, while the slot, of course, receives the square end of the tap shank and drives it. As many nuts as the tap shank will hold are tapped before the tap is pulled out and the nuts taken off.

Keeping the Drawing-Board Drawer in Place

Draftsmen and artists using drawing boards of the type with a drawer on the underside, sometimes forget the presence

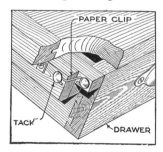

of the drawer and tilt the board, dumping pencils and other materials onto the floor because the drawer slides out. In order to overcome this objection, and keep the drawer in its proper place on the drawing board, a paper clip is bent in the manner shown, thumbtacks being used to fasten the wire to the side of the drawer and the drawer slide respectively.

Potato Planter Made from Old Corn Planter

The owner of the old corn planter shown in the photograph saved consider-

An Old Corn Planter That was Made Over into a Serviceable and Efficient Potato Planter: The Seed-Potato Cuttings are Placed in the Wooden Boxes and Dropped through a Spout into the Furrows

able money when he conceived the idea of making it over into a potato planter. The seed-corn boxes were removed, and in their place two wooden boxes of the same size were attached. A hole was made through the bottom of each box, at the inside corner, and a length of galvanized-iron spouting was run down to within 3 in. of the bottom of each shoe. In using the planter, one man sits between the boxes and another drives. A peck or more of potatoes is placed in each box, and the cut potatoes are dropped through the holes in the boxes into the furrows. The ground should be prepared for planting by using a corn lister, which ridges the ground, leaving furrows between the ridges. After the potatoes have been planted, they are covered by driving a harrow over the ground. This method is much quicker than planting by hand, and when large tracts are to be seeded, there is considerable saving.

Windlass Holds Hay on Truck

With the introduction of fast motor-truck transportation into the business of farming, there came a demand for some means of securing loose hay in a manner that would make fast delivery safe. The solution comes in the form of a windlass. With this arrangement, the ends of a rope are fastened to the forward corners of the truck body, the loop is passed over the top of the load, and down to the rear frame, where it is wound around a windlass; this draws up the rope tightly. The windlass consists of a roller, in the center of which a pin is driven to hold the loop of the rope. The roller is mounted in brackets on the rear of the truck bed, with sufficient distance between the roller and truck to clear the rope. The windlass is turned by a rod, passed through a hole in the roller, and when the load has been tightened, the

rod is allowed to bear against the frame so that it prevents the windlass from unwinding, but is still immediately ready for use. This last feature is one of considerable importance, since the hay will often settle, after a short distance over rough or bumpy roads, to such a degree that the rope will have to be drawn tight again, before further progress, without danger of spilling the load, can be made.—Roy A. Houston, S. Charleston, Ohio.

To Prevent Nails from Splitting Thin Wood

Having to nail a number of narrow strips, I found that the brads, as ordinarily used, would split them. Accordingly the points of the brads were flattened out or cut to a chisel-like point. By driving the nails with the chisel end at right angles to the grain not a strip was split. Of course, a bradawl would have answered the same purpose, but, even had there been one handy, it would have been a tedious job to punch a hole for each brad. Where the grain of the lower piece is at right angles to that of the top one, and is in danger of splitting, the nail is driven through the first piece as described, then given a quarter turn with a pair of pliers and driven home. This idea has been used on 20-penny nails with success.

Making Concrete of Maximum Strength

By A. J. R. CURTIS

ALTHOUGH concrete is already recognized as having more diversified structural uses than almost any other material, some of its important characteristics have still to be thoroughly investigated.

The principal ordinary ingredients of concrete are Portland cement, sand, pebbles (or stone), and water. Early in the history of concrete the conclusion was reached that the quality of the product could be controlled largely by constant tests, to insure the quality of the binding element—cement. Further study revealed the equal necessity of testing and rectifying the defects in the "aggregates," the latter term being used to designate the sand, pebbles, stone, or other nonmetallic minerals united by the cement. In good practice the aggregates usually compose from two-thirds to four-fifths of the concrete mass.

For many years these tests were supposed to provide about all the scientific data required with respect to the concrete mixture. The water

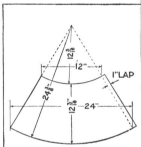

amount of cement present are vital considerations so far as the strength of the resulting concrete is concerned. The curve shown in Fig. 2 illustrates diagrammatically the manner in which similar concrete mixtures develop greater strength with the use of more water up to a certain point, beyond which an addition of water causes

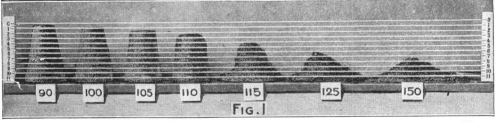

Lower Illustration: "Slump"-Test Specimens Made with Varying Amounts of Water. Notice How the Piles on the Right have "Slumped" from Their Original Height. Upper Left: Plan for Galvanized-Iron Form for Making the Slump Test. Upper Right: Removal of the Slump-Test Mold by a Steady, Vertical Pull

present was considered merely a lubricant, to be used in the mixture in almost any quantity found convenient. It is only recently that the staff of the Structural Materials Research Laboratory, Lewis Institute, Chicago, of which Prof. Duff A. Abrams is chief, discovered that the plasticity of the concrete mixture and the relation of the amount of water to the

the strength to diminish. This curve is a composite of many similar curves, plotted from results obtained by adding various amounts of water to mixtures of different proportions, using various typical concrete materials.

The amount of water required to produce a concrete mixture of greatest strength is designated in this diagram as

100 per cent. It may be noted from the curve that a 10-per-cent reduction of water from the 100-per-cent point produces at least a 25-per-cent reduction in strength; an increase of 10 per cent in

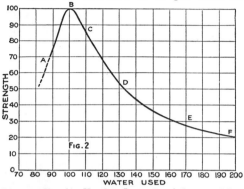

Diagram Showing Varying Strengths of Concrete Mixtures Due to Variation in the Amount of Water Used

water above the 100-per-cent point produces a 15-per-cent reduction in strength. These are, of course, average figures, but show clearly that there is one consistency for every mixture which produces greatest strength, and that deviations from it are accompanied by a sacrifice in strength.

Compare this curve with the illustration in Fig. 1. The latter shows a number of piles of concrete made of identical materials, in identical proportions, but with various amounts of water. The pile marked 100 represents the consistency designated as 100 per cent in the diagram, and the other piles represent corresponding percentages from 90 to 150. The wetter the concrete in the pile, the greater the "slump." This method of determining consistency, although but recently introduced, has come to be used commonly in scientific laboratories, and is known as the "slump test."

Slump-test cones are made 12 in. high, and the extent of the slump in inches can be measured conveniently by means of an ordinary rule equipped with a sliding crossbar. Fig. 1 shows a plan for a galvanized-iron form for producing specimen batches for the test.

The form is placed on a smooth, level floor, or substantial table, and the concrete is deposited in it in four or five small batches, each batch being tamped briskly with a ¼-in. round rod before the next batch is deposited. When the mold is filled with the mixture, the top is struck off level. The mold is then withdrawn by a steady vertical pull without vibra-

tion. After a few minutes the amount of the slump is measured, and comparison is made with the illustration in Fig. 1 or a corresponding table. The result will reveal whether the mixture is too dry or too wet for maximum strength. In some cases the probable reduction in strength on account of too much or too little water can be judged approximately. Owing to the variation in methods of handling concrete for the many uses to which it is put, the employment of the consistency that will give maximum strength is frequently impracticable, it being more economical to use a little more material than to use the ideal consistency. In all cases it is desirable to use the proportion of water that gives the greatest strength within the practical limits of the handling methods employed. It is also desirable to know the probable approximate reduction in strength caused by limitations of handling methods, so that this may be taken into proper account in the design.

Scriber for Marking Patches

For locating and scribing setscrew holes, oil holes, or slots at any point, on a patch or ring that has been shrunk over

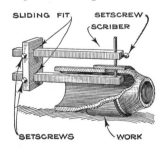

the hole or slot, the scriber shown will save considerable time. As an examination of the drawing will show, the device is extremely simple, consisting of only a square steel block and two movable arms, the latter sliding through holes in the block, and locked, when adjusted, by means of setscrews. The lower arm is fitted with a locating pin driven tightly into a hole drilled near the outer end of the arm, while the upper arm has a scribing point fitted near its end, a setscrew making the scriber adjustable for different thicknesses.

When a hole is to be located, it is only necessary to insert the arms into the work, until the locating point on the lower arm enters the opening; the scribing point is then adjusted and the device manipulated until the location of the hole has been scribed on the surface of the ring or patch.—Leon Yacobyan, New York City.

Casting without Rolling the Flask

Ordinarily, in casting a steel annealing box, having three ribs on the bottom, a wooden bottom board would be placed on the foundry floor. Then the pattern, bottom down, would be laid on this board, and sand would be filled in and rammed in the usual manner. A roll-over board would be placed on top, and flask hooks would be put around the outside to clamp the bottom board to the flask and the roll-over board, and then the whole thing would be turned over ready to receive the cope. This method would be perfectly satisfactory in casting one or two pieces, but when 25 or 30 are to be produced, not every foundry is equipped with the necessary number of boards.

By a simplified method, illustrated in the drawing, all these boards, the clamping hooks, the rolling of the flask and the extra labor are eliminated, the molds being made in a few minutes by a laborer. The first operation is the filling in of the bottom or drag flask with sand, which is rammed and then struck off; the next is the filling, ramming, and striking off of the pattern, which is then inverted and placed on the sand bed at about the cen-

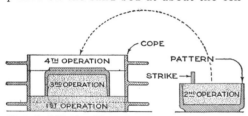

Method of Making Molds for a Number of Cast-Steel Annealing Boxes, in Which Bottom and Roll-Over Boards, Clamping Hooks, and Rolling of the Flask are Eliminated

ter of the flask; the pattern is settled down by a few strokes of a hammer on the bottom, and the cheek of the middle flask is put on the drag, filled with sand, rammed, and struck off flush with the bottom of the pattern. The cope flask is next placed on the cheek flask, and sand is filled in, rammed, and vented in the usual way. Afterward the cope is lifted, the pattern drawn out, and the cope replaced, thus finishing the mold. The molding of this pattern can be done in a two-part flask, cope, and drag by filling in about enough sand to bring the pattern flush with the top of the drag, as shown by the lower dotted line.

¶Under no conditions should acetylene be used where the pressure is greater than 15 lb. per square inch.

Perforated Business Signs of Sheet Metal

The drawing shows a neat type of small sheet-metal sign on which the letters, instead of being painted, are cut out. Sheet

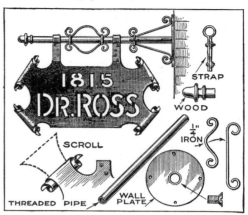

Effective by Night as Well as by Day, a Sheet-Metal Sign with Cut-Out Letters Is Attractive, Is Not Hard to Make, and is Easily Read

brass is preferable for such signs, although black iron will answer. The letters may be cut out with a chisel or with a jeweler's metal-cutting saw. The sign is supported on a horizontal bracket, made of pipe, to which it should be rigidly attached, as a swinging sign becomes very noisy. The advantage of a sign of this type is that it is effective by night as well as by day, as any light from the opposite side will cause the letters to stand out distinctly.

Planer Clamp for Awkward Pieces

In order to clamp down irregularly shaped work quickly and firmly, the fixture shown in the drawing was made, reducing materially the time formerly required to set up the pieces on the planer. Two clamps of the shape shown were made and bolted to a special hold-

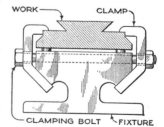

ing block. The work rested on the short pins, and the ends of the clamps were machined to fit over it. When the bolts were tightened, the work was held with an even pressure on both sides. The fixture was bolted to the bed of the planer in the usual manner.

Homemade Air Compressor

Where a small volume of air under pressure is wanted, as for operating blow-pipes or inflating tires in a bicycle shop

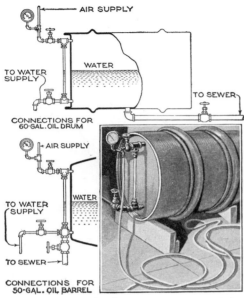

Air under Pressure for Blowpipe Work or for Other Purposes, is Furnished by a Simple Air Compressor Made from an Empty Oil Drum

or private garage, a serviceable air compressor can be made from a steel oil drum or barrel that is free from leaks. It should be placed in a horizontal position with the large 2-in. side opening, or bunghole, down, in the case of the drum. There are also two openings tapped for ¾-in. pipe in the head of a 60-gal. drum. The lower opening is connected to the water system, using a suitable valve for regulating the flow of water. The bunghole is the drain, and is connected to the sewer. To operate, the water is let into the drum, forcing the air out under the same pressure as that in the water system. When the drum is nearly filled, the water is shut off, the air valve opened, and the drum drained, ready for repeating the operation. A pressure gauge and gauge glass can be added, as illustrated, although neither is necessary.—H. C. Rowell, Hudson, N. H.

¶A broach should only be used in work for which it is designed. If the broach is to be used for work of varying length, the broach maker should be given this information. Then, if the variation is not too great, the broach may be designed to meet the conditions.

Shrinking Oversize Bushings

Frequently, in lapping hardened steel bushings, the hole is accidentally lapped too large. It may also happen, after lapping to size, that the hole has not cleaned up, and the bushing must be scrapped. However, by the method of rehardening described, the hole can often be shrunk sufficiently to make a new bushing unnecessary. Turn up a piece of machine steel in the lathe, about .004 or .005 in. under the size of the hole in the bushing. Leave a shoulder on one end of the turned piece, place the bushing over the small end and reharden, quenching the shoulder end first. The water or quenching solution cools the outside of the bushing first and shrinks the hole several thousandths, allowing more stock for relapping.

Holder Protects Cutting Tools

The practice of throwing tool bits into a pile in the most convenient place is admittedly bad, but the lack of some simple yet efficient holder is, in most cases, responsible. The type of holder adopted in many shops is an oblong or square wooden block drilled with rows of holes, in which the tools are placed. Most lathe operators grind tool bits on both ends to save time, and this custom makes it necessary to lift each tool from its hole when searching for some particular type or shape, which may be concealed on the bottom end of a bit. Another objection to a holder of this kind is that, when filled with tools, it presents a dangerous

surface, bristling as it does with sharp-pointed tool bits, which may cause severe cuts on the arms and hands of the operator when reaching across the tray.

The holder illustrated is as cheap to make as that described above, and it has the double advantage of being perfectly safe and of presenting both ends of the tools to view at the same time. A piece of hardwood is turned to a diameter of about 4½ in., one end is hollowed out, and a groove is machined near the bottom. About a dozen ½-in. holes are drilled, as shown, to accommodate the ⅜-in. square tool bits, and the holder is complete. The depth of the holder should be greater than the longest tool bit used. It will be apparent that, with the upper ends of the tools protected by the edge of the holder, injuries due to contact with the sharp edges and points are impossible, and that both ends are clearly visible as the holder is revolved.

Resetting Diamonds in Wheel Dressers

In tool and grinding rooms, where diamond-pointed emery-wheel dressers are extensively used, it is not an infrequent occurrence that a diamond becomes loose in its holder; it should be reset at once to prevent it from coming out entirely, with the possibility of its becoming lost.

One of the best methods of resetting such a diamond is illustrated by the drawing. A piece of standard-size drill rod is obtained, and a hole the size of the diamond is drilled in the end to a depth of about ⅛ in. Next, crosscuts are made with a hacksaw, as shown in the drawing, to a depth of about ⅜ inch. The diamond is then placed in the hole, and the edge of the hole is slightly riveted over, to prevent the stone from coming out. A machine-steel sleeve is made to fit tightly over the end of the drill rod; this sleeve is made long enough, so that when pressed in place it will cover up the hacksaw slots and extend beyond the end for about ½ in. The diamond is now ready for brazing in, and the sleeve is filled with borax and spelter; when heat is applied, this melts and flows down, packing solidly around the diamond. Add more spelter until the sleeve is full, and be sure to keep it at a good heat for about a minute after the sleeve has been filled. Then the sleeve and surplus spelter can be turned off in a lathe.—Chas. Homewood, Ontario, Calif.

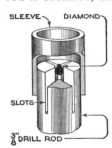

Self-Contained Hammer and Chisel

There is nothing quite so unhandy to hold and work with as a small chisel. Many and hard are the knocks the workman receives on the fingers and knuckles when chipping in confined places and difficult corners. Even on work easily reached by hand, it is a ticklish job to chip a slot or small keyway if the chisel must be held by hand. The "hand gun" illustrated was designed to overcome this, and is extensively used on fine tool and die work. With it, there is less abuse of the tools, and by using bent and shaped

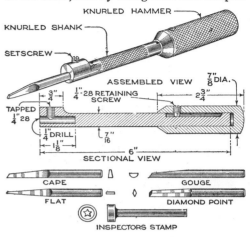

A Combination of Hammer and Chisel That Makes Chipping and Tooling in the Confined Corners of Tool and Die Work Comfortable

chisels, some work can be done that would otherwise be considered impossible.

The shank of the tool is made of drill rod, turned to the dimensions shown, the center is knurled for a good grip, and a flat is filed, or a groove cut, near the rear end. The hammer sleeve slips loosely over the end of the shank, on which it is retained by a small screw; this part is also knurled and has a polished round end.

In use, the chisel is fastened in the head, and the shank of the tool is held by the left hand. The sleeve is drawn back, and then brought sharply forward, with the desired degree of force. Any weight of blow can be obtained, though for light work it is sometimes desirable to provide a smaller and lighter hammer sleeve. The chisels are made of ¼-in. drill rod, ground or filed to shape, and of various widths and sizes to suit the work in hand. Inspectors' stamps can also be made up to fit the tool, and, so used, will save time and trouble. Commonly, either the stamp or the hammer is mislaid, and holds up the inspection; with both combined into one tool, this is not likely to occur.

¶ Scissors sharpened with too much bevel will not hold their edge, but if sharpened to an angle of 30° or 35°, the edge will hold for a long time.

An Auxiliary Caliper Leg

An extra leg on a pair of inside calipers is handy in many instances, as it enables the user to obtain two measurements with the same tool. The leg is made of flat stock, of the same thickness as the caliper legs, bent over at one end, as shown, and clamped in place with a

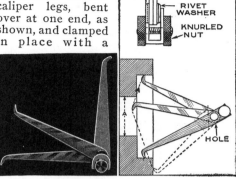

Two Measurements can be Taken at the Same Time with One Pair of Calipers by Attaching an Easily Made Auxiliary Leg

knurled screw and nuts. The leg is drilled to fit over the joint washer, upon which it swivels. In the illustration, the calipers are shown set for two inside dimensions, but they can be used also for inside and outside measurements by turning the auxiliary leg around. In use, the calipers proper are set first, and the auxiliary leg afterward. As an effective means of reducing the number of tools required on a job or as a handy method of finally testing dimensions before removing a piece of work from a machine, the auxiliary caliper leg is worth the time required to make it.

The Strength of Fiber Boxes

The direction in which the fibers run in fiber-board boxes has been found to have a considerable effect upon the life of the boxes. Fiber-board does not tear as easily across the grain as with the grain; it may have two or three times as much strength in one direction as in the other, the difference varying with manufacturing conditions. This excess strength may be used advantageously to reinforce the weakest points of the box and so produce a more perfectly balanced construction.

The weakest parts of fiber boxes are the scores, or folds, forming the edges of the box. It is impossible to have the fibers running perpendicular to every score, but usually they may be made to run perpendicular to the scores that receive the hardest usage, or that tend to break open first. The location of the scores most likely to fail, of course, varies with the shape of the box and the nature of the contents, and can be best determined by test.

In a test on fiber boxes, some were packed with 2 doz. food cans, and some with 4 doz. tall milk cans. It was found that the first break nearly always occurred in the horizontal end scores. By making up the boxes so that the fibers ran vertically instead of horizontally, on the sides and ends, the first break in the horizontal end scores did not occur until the boxes had been under test almost twice as long as before, and the horizontal side scores, which received the next hardest usage, were so strengthened that they never failed until some other part had first given way.

The gain in strength of the horizontal scores was, of course, accompanied by a weakening of the vertical scores. But since the upright scores are not ordinarily under as great strain as the horizontal scores, and in these tests were not as likely to come in contact with the sharp edges of the cans, they were able to stand a reduction in strength and yet not become the point of first failure.—U. S. Forest Products Laboratory, Madison, Wis.

Twisting Iron Bars

The occasional worker in ornamental iron often finds it difficult to twist two round bars, or a square one, so that the

resulting piece will be straight and the pitch of the twists uniform. By applying the idea illustrated, however, excellent results may be obtained. One end of the bar to be twisted is clamped in a vise and a close-fitting piece of pipe is slipped over it as shown, allowing the upper end of the rod to project beyond the pipe. This end is seized in a wrench, which is used to twist the rod.—W. Norman Fox, Atlantic City, New Jersey.

BUILDING A SIX-INCH
TURRET LATHE

By J. V. ROMIG

[Arrangements have been made to supply the necessary castings for this lathe, at a low figure, to any who are interested. This magazine has no financial or other interest in this, beyond that of service to the reader. The name and address of the maker will be furnished, upon request, by the Shop Notes Department, Popular Mechanics Magazine, 6 N. Michigan Ave., Chicago.—Editor.]

WHILE the turret lathe is essentially a tool for the production of work in large quantities, a 6-in. lathe of the type described in this article will be found exceedingly useful in the small experimental shop. With a center held in the main turret, the machine may be used as a simple engine lathe, and when a number of similar pieces are to be turned out in a hurry, the work may be performed in almost as expeditious a manner as on a commercial turret lathe.

This machine was built and used by the author in his own workshop, on fine precision work, and many accurate jobs have been done with it very quickly. Most of the work of building can be done in a workshop equipped only with a vise and bench drill, with the necessary small tools, as flat cold-rolled steel is used for the ways, carriage, and other parts of that character; it will be necessary, however, to have certain things, such as the machining of the headstock and the cutting of the feed screw, done in a machine shop, but this is a small item.

The headstock is made of gray iron, and is fitted with an overarm steadyrest, which allows the carriage to travel the full length of long work, as the work is supported from the top and rear. The spindle is carried, at the rear, by a double-row ball bearing, .75 in. wide, of the combined axial and radial-load type, and at the front by a single-row bearing, .629 in. wide. Both of these bearings have an outside diameter of 2.441 in., and an inside diameter of 1.181 in. Care must be taken to bore the bearing housings a push fit for the bearings, and to have all faces square and parallel with each other.

The spindle should be made of a good grade of steel, of about .3-per-cent carbon content, and is hollow. It is best to bore the spindle first, then re-center and finish the outside. The nose is taper-bored to take the collets, and threaded eight threads per inch, U. S. standard, to fit the faceplates and chucks. The taper seat for the collets should not be finished until the lathe has been completely assembled; it should then be machined with tools held in the toolpost of the lathe itself.

The inner races of the ball bearings should be a good fit on the flat threads on the rear of the spindle, and on the outside of the spindle at the front. Bearing-

Photograph of the Completed Lathe as Used in the Author's Workshop: It Is Capable of Performing Both Fast and Accurate Work

retaining rings are fitted at the rear, clamping the outer race of the bearing firmly, and taking up the end thrust. These are fitted with felt dust rings, bearing on the collars on the spindle; the rings at the front are also fitted with dust rings, running on the spindle, but these rings do not clamp the single-row bearing, which is permitted to float.

When the headstock is assembled, the bearing housings should be packed with a good grade of vaseline, which will last a long time; see that the vaseline supply is at all times sufficient for good lubrication. Spindles fitted in this manner are far superior to those fitted with plain bearings, as they consume less power, are free from vibration, and allow of accurate as well as heavy work. The writer has taken a $\frac{1}{8}$-in. cut on a piece of $\frac{1}{2}$-in. cold-rolled steel at a distance of 5 in. from the collet, the reduced diameter being very accurate as to size.

The drawbar for the collets is a tube, the outer diameter of which fits the bore of the spindle. It is threaded at the front to fit the collets, and is fitted with a handwheel at the rear. A tiebar at the top of the headstock keeps the two arms stiff and rigid. The cone pulley is fastened to the spindle by a setscrew, spotted into the spindle; two cone pulleys, of the same size, should be cast and machined, one being used on the countershaft. The arm for the steadyrest is a length of 1-in. cold-rolled steel; it is clamped in position by $\frac{3}{8}$-in. capscrews, which compress the slotted headstock arms. The headstock is fastened to the bed by two $\frac{1}{2}$-in. bolts, running up through pieces of pipe cast into the bed; by this means no strains are put on the cement.

The construction of the bed is somewhat of a novelty, although it has been thoroughly tried out by the writer in this and other machines, and found to be very satisfactory. This method of making the bed eliminates the hardest work of making a small lathe, as it does away with the bed casting and the necessary machining.

A piece of $\frac{1}{2}$ by 4-in. cold-rolled steel, 30 in. long, is used for the shears. This is first drilled and tapped for a number of $\frac{3}{16}$-in. stove bolts, of varying lengths, which are used to anchor the shears to the cement, also drilled and countersunk for the leg screws and for the $\frac{1}{2}$-in. headstock bolts. It is next carefully straightened and scraped to a true surface on top and sides, testing the width throughout with a micrometer, and using a knifeedge straightedge on the surfaces; these

must be as true and straight as it is possible to make them, as upon their truth depends the accuracy of the lathe. When trued, all surfaces should either be frosted or polished.

The shear anchor bolts should now be screwed home, the pipes, leg and rear leadscrew-bearing bolts placed in position, and a wooden form made to fit closely around shears and legs, in which to pour the cement. The cement used is a mixture of one part Portland cement to three parts clean, sharp sand, mixed with just enough water to enable a handful of the mixture to be picked up and squeezed and to leave the impression of the fingers in it. This cement is tamped down firmly in the form, poking it around the screws and into the corners with an ice pick, or some similar tool. When the concrete has set thoroughly, the boards are removed and the cement thoroughly wetted twice a day for about a week; this will temper the cement, and is a very important part of the work. The resulting bed is as strong as anyone could wish. Reinforcing rods may be laid down in the cement, as it is being placed, or wires twisted throughout the bolts, adding further to the strength of the bed.

The main member of the carriage is made of cold-rolled steel, $\frac{1}{2}$ by 5 by $5\frac{1}{4}$ in. in size, machined as shown in the carriage-detail drawing. A piece of $\frac{1}{4}$ by 2-in. cold-rolled steel, 7 in. long, is fastened to the top of the main member by $\frac{3}{16}$-in. screws; on this piece the cross slide runs. The cross slide is also made of steel, machined as shown, and is fitted with a turret toolpost. The cross slide is held to its ways by means of angle pieces, as shown in the front view of the carriage. The turret is made of steel, and is casehardened; four tools can be

Method of Making the Bed: The Bolts for the Rear Leadscrew Bearing are Not Shown, but should be Cast In like the Leg Bolts

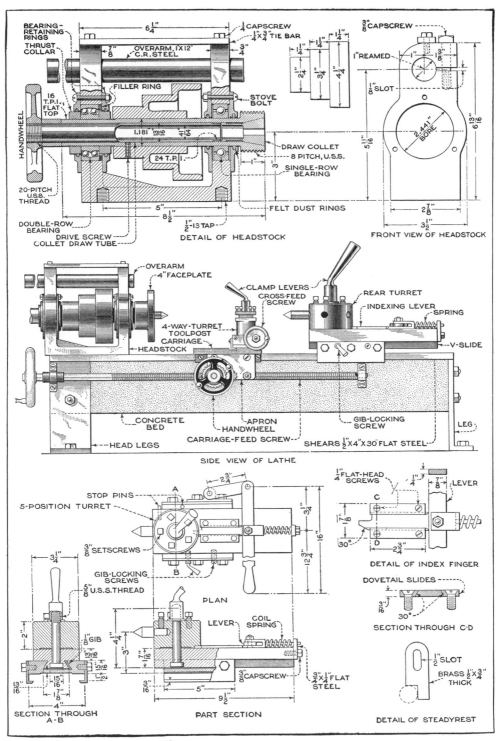

Details of the Headstock and Main Turret, and Side Elevation of Completed Lathe: When a Center is Used in the Turret, as Shown, and the Gib-Locking Screw Tightened, the Tool can be Used as an Ordinary Bench Lathe, for Turning Work between Centers. Five Tools can be Used in the Main Turret, and Four in the Toolpost Turret, Making for Speed in Production

mounted in this at once. On the boss of the cross slide is mounted a small index post, into the countersunk top of which the elevating screws fit, allowing each tool to be adjusted to its correct cutting height. A spring pushes the turret upward when the clamping handle is loosened, allowing the turret to be turned to bring another tool into cutting position. A ¼-in. square-thread screw operates the cross slide, and the tools are held in the toolpost by ¼-in. square-head setscrews.

The apron of the carriage is made of steel, 2 in. wide, and is fastened to the main carriage member by flat-head machine screws. The front angle piece of

against the edge of the shears. Brass shims, or wearing pieces, 1⁄32 in. thick, are set in the ends, to take the wear on the filler piece. The rear angle is plain, machined as shown in the drawing.

Behind the apron is fitted a bronze nut; this rotates in a bearing fastened to the apron, and is screwed into one of a pair of miter gears, which, in turn, are driven by 3-to-1 spur gears; the larger gear is pinned to the handwheel, and the smaller is pressed onto the hub of the second miter gear, which runs in the apron. The handwheel runs on a stud screwed into the apron; this stud is fitted with a knurled friction nut, so that, if

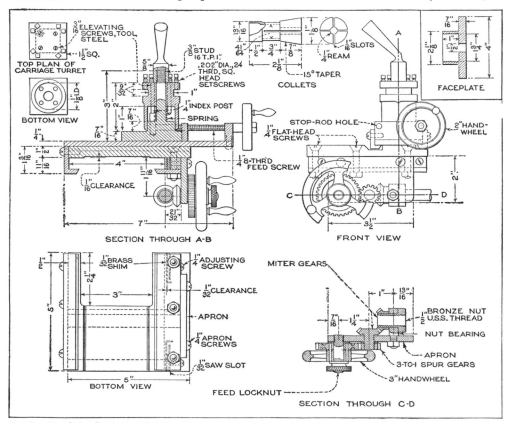

Full Details of the Carriage and Apron Mechanism: Note the Employment of the Small Index Post and Elevating Screws in the Toolpost to Secure the Correct Height for Each Tool. The Post is Set in the Inner Left-Hand Corner of the Turret Base

the carriage is built up, as shown, the filler piece being slit at each end, so that wear may be taken up as it develops, by tightening the adjusting screws. The holes for these screws do not go clear through the filler piece, but stop at the slits, so that, by screwing the screws in, the inner ends of the filler are pressed

change gears are fitted to the lathe or it is desired to feed by means of the handwheel on the end of the leadscrew, the nut can be tightened and the whole assembly of spur and miter gears and nut locked firmly.

The rear, or main-turret, base and slide are made of cast iron, a dovetailed slide being used, fitted with a ⅛-in. gib. The front gib-adjusting screw is fitted with a handle and is used to lock the turret in position for plain turning operations. The turret pivot pin, of cold-rolled steel, casehardened, is ⅝ in. in diameter, with a ⅝-in. U. S. standard thread cut on the upper end, and fitted with a clamping handle. The turret is made of steel, undercut as shown in the drawings, and has five equally spaced slots milled around the lower surface for the index finger. One side of each slot is radial, the other being tapered, and the index finger is made to correspond. By making the finger and slots of this form, the radial side does the actual locating, and the tapered side moves the turret to position; only the radial side need be of great accuracy, while the wear is chiefly on the inclined side, where it does no harm.

The holes for the tools should not be bored until the indexing mechanism has been assembled and the lathe set up; then, by boring the holes with a tool held in the chuck, and correctly supported, the greatest degree of accuracy is obtained. The details of the indexing device are so complete that little description is necessary; care should be taken, however, to see that the coil spring is heavy enough to prevent the index finger from being withdrawn from the turret until the stop pin on the back of the turret base strikes the pin on the slide; the backward movement of the lever will thus move the whole turret back until the stop pins engage; further movement disengaging the index finger, and allowing the turret to be revolved to the next position. The index finger slides between beveled strips of ³⁄₁₆-in. steel, and must be a good fit; both slides and finger should be casehardened to insure long life.

The speed of the lathe, and the arrangement of the countershaft, will be determined by the work to be undertaken and the shop conditions. A reversing countershaft should be fitted if tap and die work is to be performed on the lathe. A quadrant and stud can be fitted on the head end, and a set of change gears provided, if the lathe is to be used for screwcutting; in this event, no care should be spared to secure an accurate leadscrew.

The builder of this lathe will have a very efficient machine, one that could not be purchased for many times the cost of building.

¶A round file and a monkey wrench make an excellent pipe wrench in an emergency.

Combined Reamer and Gauge Holder

For various reasons an adjustable reamer may cut larger or smaller than the size to which it has been set. This demands careful gauging to avoid a number of spoiled pieces with a consequent loss in time. In the drawing is shown a holder that gauges the work as it is finished. The expansion - shell reamer shown is 1½ in. in diameter, and is used to ream out cast-

iron rings that vary from 2 to 5 in. in width. The reamer is held in the ordinary manner, and two sleeves, or rings, are made a running fit on the holder. One sleeve, used as the "go" gauge, is left plain, the other, or "not go," is tapped for two knurled-head screws. The go gauge is always held in a position just behind the reamer, but the not-go gauge can be set by means of the knurled screws to various positions to suit the width of the rings. When the work is reamed, the go gauge enters before the reamer passes through and shows that the hole is above the low limit, and if the not-go gauge fails to enter, the hole is right. Being loose on the holder, the gauges cannot score the work, as they revolve with it. The shank of the holder as well as the gauges should be casehardened and ground to size.

Filing the Crosscut Saw

The drawing shows a new method of filing a crosscut saw in such a manner as to make a bevel on each side of the drag tooth, similar to that of the cutting tooth. When filed in this manner, the drag quality is not impaired, while the cutting speed is considerably increased. When filing the teeth in this manner, the drag should be al-

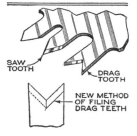

most as long as the cutting tooth, but never set as the cutting teeth are.—Elmer Hufferd, Rushville, Ind.

Oiling Loose Pulleys

Inadequate lubrication of loose pulleys causes excessive wear on countershafts and necessitates frequent rebushing of the pulleys, and to keep the ordinary loose pulley well lubricated requires con-

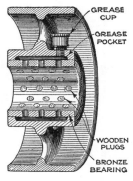

siderable more attention than can be given it in the average shop where no oiler is employed. The drawing shows a method of lubricating that has been adopted by a large shop. The pulleys are bored for an oversize bushing, and recessed to form a grease pocket around the hub. Bronze bearing metal is used for the bushings, which are pressed into the hub. Before taking the finishing cut on the bushings, ⅛-in. holes are drilled in them, as shown, and plugged by driving in hard-maple pins; the finishing cut turns these flush with the bearing surface. After placing the pulley on the shaft, the annular pocket is filled with a good grade of light grease. The pulleys are well oiled when first placed on the shafts; afterward the grease works down through the plugs and good lubrication is insured.—Lowell R. Butcher, Des Moines, Ia.

Increasing Weight of Tractor Front End

My first experience with a tractor was in the days when the designs were created more by guess than by practical experi-

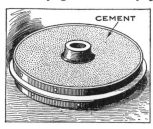

ence, and my first tractor would act more like a balky horse than most of the present-day tractors do. Not that it refused to go so often, but when it was overloaded, it tried to turn a back somersault. I decided to break it of this habit, and found that I could do so by filling the front wheels with cement. To do this, the wheels were removed and placed over a concave depression scooped out of the ground to the form desired, and a place was also provided for the hub to lie in. Then the space between the rim and hub was filled with a mixture of one part cement to four parts sand, and troweled off on top. The extra weight amounted to about 350 lb., and was sufficient to hold the front end down. Making the front wheels solid in this manner not only provided the extra weight required, but made it easier to turn in loose ground and to steer.—G. G. McVicker, North Bend, Neb.

A Novel Facing Tool

Every shop has a collection of soft arbors, usually well decorated with cuts and small burrs, all along the surface, caused by careless operators who dig into them with the tool when facing work. This uneven surface is very apt to seize the work as it is being driven off, with the result that the hole will be roughed up and probably spoiled. Hardened arbors do not suffer in the same way, but they

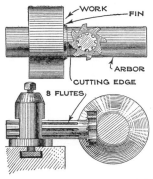

dull the tool immediately if the operator feeds it in a little too far. The facing tool illustrated can neither dig into a soft arbor nor be dulled by contact with a hard one, and once made, will last a long time, as it possesses eight cutting edges. The drawing shows clearly the shape of the tool; it is made somewhat like an ordinary milling cutter, but the front face is left perfectly flat, only the backs and faces of the teeth being backed off. Milled along the shank are eight half-round grooves, the centers of which are in line with the cutting edges. The work should be roughed down with an ordinary round-nose tool until close to the desired length; this will leave a rough fin to be removed by the facing tool. The tool is gripped lightly in the toolpost, the point of the toolpost screw entering one of the grooves in the shank, which brings one of the cutting edges in the right position. The tool is then moved in until it touches the arbor and lies flat against it, when the former is tightened up. The fin is removed in one side cut, and the tool fed outward in the final finishing cut. It will be seen that the tool cannot dig in or be dulled by contact with a hardened arbor as the wide, plain face prevents this, and since it involves only one change of tools, as with the ordinary tool, it is worth making as a saver of arbors.

Quick Nut-Locking Device

Two nuts, locked together on a threaded bar, are used on many machines as a means for holding some part at a required setting; some makers of milling machines use this method to set the travel of the table, while on many hand-screw machines, turrets and cross slides are set by the same method. The use of two wrenches is required to tighten or release two ordinary hexagon nuts, with the danger of slipping or altering the setting by unequal pressure. The device shown enables two nuts to be locked together with one wrench easily and without fear of the setting being disturbed while

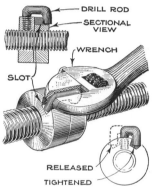

DRILL ROD
SECTIONAL VIEW
WRENCH
SLOT
RELEASED
TIGHTENED

so doing. Instead of the usual hexagon, the nuts are made circular, one being drilled and tapped on the outside, while the other has a slot cut into its circumference. A piece of drill rod is threaded to fit the tapped hole in the first nut and bent over as shown, to fit into the slot of the second. The following method will determine where the slot should be cut: Screw both nuts onto the bar on which they will be used; tighten them up, face to face, until they move freely together, and then scribe a line through the center of the tapped hole and across the other nut to mark the center of the slot. When this is cut, as shown, and the bent drill rod put in place, both will, of course, screw onto the bar in the same position; they can then be moved to any adjustment by hand and tightened with a single wrench by moving the bent rod as shown. The nuts are released by moving the U-shaped drill rod in the opposite direction.

¶When milling aluminum, use kerosene as a lubricant.

Keeping the Soldering Flux Handy

When using the blowtorch for heating the soldering iron, or for soldering electrical connections, the worker often mislays the soldering flux, so that just when it is needed, it cannot be found, and time must be spent in hunting for it at the risk of "burning" the copper bit. This can all be avoided by attaching a small container between

FLUX CONTAINER

the handle supports of the torch. The flux container can easily be made removable, but the best plan is to make it a permanent part of the torch, as it is never in the way, and is very convenient.

Taking Up Play in Solid Bushings

Frequently, when the solid bushings of machine parts become too worn, they are discarded and new ones fitted. In cases where it is found impossible to get new bushings at once, a handy way to "doctor up" the old ones is shown in the drawing. A hole is drilled and tapped in the journal box right over the point of greatest wear, where the bore will be oval, in line with the pull of the belt. Allow the drill barely to spot the brass, and use a bottom tap to finish tapping the hole. After this operation, the shaft being withdrawn, slit the bearing with a hacksaw blade, holding the

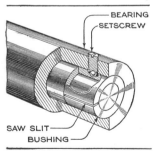

BEARING
SETSCREW
SAW SLIT
BUSHING

saw with the fingers if the frame cannot be used. Then drop a $\frac{1}{16}$ or $\frac{1}{8}$-in. steel ball into the hole, and screw in a cup-pointed setscrew. Pressure applied to the bushing by the screw will enable the worn part of the bearing to be brought into contact with the shaft and take up the play. The ball fits nicely between the bottom of the setscrew and the bottom of the hole, and keeps the bearing from turning. Where the bearing bushing is long, place two or more such screws along its length.

Double Welding-Rod Holder

Acetylene welders will find many uses for the welding-rod holder illustrated. When a single-rod holder is used, the welder must lay down the rod he is using and grope around for the other as the work pro-

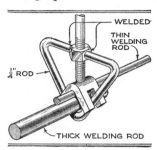

gresses. This can be avoided by holding the thick and thin welding rods in the same holder, and the one described can be made from scraps. An iron rod ¼ in. in diameter, is heated and bent to form one jaw of the clamp, the other being made from a piece of flat stock, bent and sawed out on the sides to clear the rod. An iron-pipe nut is welded between the ends of the ¼-in. rod, and a piece of pipe is used to tighten the welding rods in the holder and serve as a handle. The different sizes of rods extend in opposite directions, so that it is only necessary to turn the holder around to bring either rod into use.

Making the Plane Adjustment Easy to Reach

The drawing shows how a woodworkers' plane of a familiar type was rearranged to bring the adjusting screw

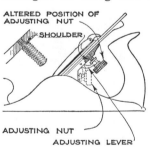

within easy reach of a short-fingered workman. The screw was removed from its original position, as shown by the dotted lines, and a shoulder was turned and threaded

on one end, as in the detail. The pin holding the lateral adjusting lever was driven out, and a hole drilled and tapped for the shouldered screw. The end of the screw should project a trifle and be riveted over. In reassembling, the adjusting lever is reversed to fit into the nut, as shown. The job is a simple one, and when completed, the adjusting nut is right at the user's finger tips, so that he need not remove his hand to set the plane.
—M. E. Duggan, Kenosha, Wis.

Siphon Pump for Heavy Liquids

A pump, suitable for oils and similar heavy liquids, that is self-operating when once started, can be made from ordinary pipe fittings.

The barrel, or other container, is elevated from the floor about 2 or 3 ft., and the cap or bung is drilled to take a ¾-in. pipe; this vertical length of pipe should extend almost to the bottom of the container and project about 4 in. from the top. An elbow and a horizontal length of pipe with another elbow is fitted to the first pipe, then a second vertical pipe, the

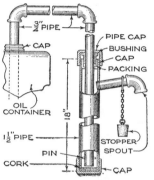

end of which must come level with the bottom of the container, is screwed into the outer elbow. This last pipe is rubbed off with emery paper to make it smooth and round. A small hole is drilled through the

lower end and a metal pin driven into it that will project about ¼ in. on each side.

The vacuum chamber, which starts the siphon, is made from an 18-in. length of 1½-in. pipe. Cap one end, which is the bottom, first lining the inside of the cap with a piece of cork. The top end contains the gland. This, as shown in the drawing, is made by first forcing a pipe cap down inside the end of the pipe and brazing the edges together. Drill a hole to fit the ¾-in. pipe in the center of the cap. Next, grind off the outside threads of a ¾ by 1-in. bushing, so it can be easily forced inside the cap. The outside flange of the bushing should not project over the outside edges of the pipe. Finally, drill a hole to fit the ¾-in. pipe in the center of a 1½-in. pipe cap, and screw that down over the pipe. With packing under the bottom of the bushing, the screwing down of the outside cap will force it outward and around the ¾-in. pipe, so that some effort will be required to move this vacuum chamber up and down on the pipe. The smoother the pipe and the better the packing is adjusted, the easier the chamber can be operated to produce the vacuum necessary to start a flow of liquid.

A spout, consisting of a short length of ¾-in. pipe, and an elbow, is screwed into the side of the chamber, about a fourth of the distance from the top; this is given a slight upward angle to prevent dripping. Keep a cork stopper near by, to hold the vacuum in the chamber by closing the spout when not in use. Make all joints in the piping air-tight, and steady the line from swaying and undue vibration.

With the bottom of the vacuum chamber against the bottom of the pipe and the spout closed, pull the chamber down slowly until the fluid in the container is sucked into it. If the first stroke does not suffice to start a flow of the liquid, open the spout, push the chamber back up, close the spout and repeat until the liquid begins to flow. With the flow once started, the spout can be left open as long as desired, and the flow will continue until the container is exhausted. To stop the flow, it is only necessary to push up the chamber until the bottom of the pipe touches the cork. Only the liquid remaining above the spout will then flow out.—L. B. Robbins, Harwich, Mass.

A Self-Gripping Arbor

A simple self-gripping arbor that is especially useful in facing up the bosses of brackets, links, or any work of a similar character, is shown in the drawing.

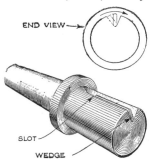

One end is turned to fit into the lathe spindle, while the opposite end is turned to the diameter of the hole in the work. Next, the slot is cut with a V-cutter and a wedge made to fit into it; the wedge is shaped as indicated, and should be of such width that, when the work is placed on the arbor, the wedge can just be felt when in the position shown in the lower view.

When the lathe is started, the work and wedge will move in the direction of the arrow, and the more pressure exerted against the work, the tighter the grip. To loosen the work, pull forward in the direction opposite the arrow.

¶In milling steel, use oil liberally; the cutter will do better work and remain sharp longer.

Tools from Umbrella Ribs

The ribs of an umbrella frame are generally made of a good grade of steel, to give them elasticity and the ability to keep the covering tightly stretched, even in a wind. Excellent small tools for special purposes can be made from pieces of the ribs, and, as they can be

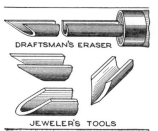

hardened and tempered, may be made into small tools for the jeweler and engraver. A very good eraser for the draftsman can also be made from one of the ribs.

A Handy Drill Plate

Many times work is drilled on a heavy drill press because there is no sensitive drill available, or because the work requires clamping to the table. In such cases, and a variety of others, the drill plate illustrated can be placed on the table of the heavy drill press, clamping the work, and saving the table from becoming pitted when the drill breaks through the work. The plate is made of cast iron, and the shank is turned to fit the hole in the table, the outside diameter being tapered slightly, to facilitate the removal of the plate. Two pins are driven into the plate, engaging the T-slots of the table to prevent the plate from turning, and a 1/2-in.

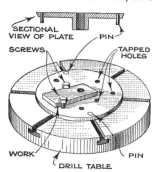

hole is drilled through the shank. As the plate is cheaply made, holes can be tapped in any position desired, and when its surface becomes too deeply pitted, the plate can be scrapped and a new one substituted. Hexagon screws with larger heads than standard are handy as clamps, as they not only prevent flat pieces from flying around when the drill breaks through, but also stop the work from climbing up the drill, as it very often will if only a pin or stud, set into the drill-press table, is used as a stop.

Drawing a True Waterline

After the height of the waterline has been determined at bow and stern, plumb

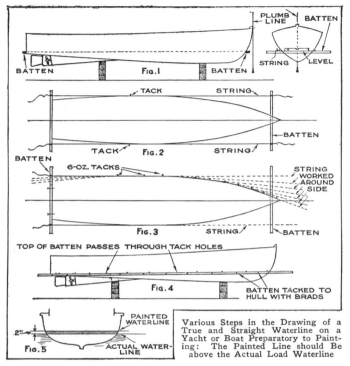

Various Steps in the Drawing of a True and Straight Waterline on a Yacht or Boat Preparatory to Painting: The Painted Line should Be above the Actual Load Waterline

the boat by hanging a plumb line directly in front of the stem, and aline the stem with this. Place a batten at right angles to the bow and stern at the proper height, level these with a spirit level, as indicated in Fig. 1, and fasten them securely. Tie the end of a chalk line to one end of the after batten, so that, when the line is carried forward, it will just touch the widest part of the hull, as in Fig. 2. At the point where the string strikes the planking, stick a small tack into the hull, directly under the line, and with one man carefully moving the forward part of the line inboard, or toward the hull as in Fig. 3, continue to insert tacks into the hull as the string strikes it, at intervals of about a foot. The string must not be moved too fast, as it will tend to follow the form of the hull, and crowd under. Continue in this manner until the stem is reached, and then work from amidships aft, repeating the operation on the opposite side.

The line of small holes made by the tacks should be plain enough to serve as a guide for the fastening of light battens

on each side of the hull, as shown in Fig. 4. This batten should be in one piece, the whole length of the boat if small, about ¼ or ⅜ in. thick by ¾ in. wide, and planed so as to have at least one true edge and face. By tacking this batten with the true edge just "splitting" the tack holes, a straight waterline can be drawn. A hard pencil is good for marking the waterline along the top edge of the batten. The writer has used this method many times and has found it to be both simple and accurate.

It has been my experience that, on small boats, from 25 to 50 ft. in length, it is always best to plan the painted waterline from 1 to 3 in. above the actual waterline, as this will keep the paint on the sides above the line from becoming fouled with dirt or growths of any kind. With this in view, the small-boat builder, if painting, say, 2 in. above the actual load waterline, as in Fig. 5, has a margin of about 40 per cent of the displacement of his boat to come and go on. With fair judgment, there is very little danger of getting this line too high.—J. Arthur Stevens, East Boothbay, Me.

Danger in Directing Hose Stream onto Charged Wires

Recognizing the danger present when a stream of water is directed onto a heavily charged electric wire, a power plant in Washington, D. C., has marked the location of all high-potential wires and conductors with green lights. These burn continuously as a warning to firemen, in case a fire should break out, that the hose should not be used without observing the precaution of wearing heavy rubber boots and gloves. The significance of the green lights has been explained to the fire department and the information has been distributed to the several fire stations. This is an idea well worth copying in any plant where the same danger is present. The water serves as a path for the current to the ground.

How to Make an Electric Soldering Iron

By CURTIS RALSTON

MAKING an electric soldering iron, using a coil of resistance wire as a heating element, is, for several reasons, not a simple matter, yet if the right methods and materials are used, it is entirely possible to make a tool that will give very satisfactory service.

The drawing shows a sectional view of the iron. The dimensions given are not to be adhered to with any great accuracy, as the materials used will depend largely upon what is available. The heating element is intended to be wound with wire known to the trade as "No. 193 alloy," which can be bought from or through any electrical-supply house. The figures given for the resistance wire are based on the use of a coil about ¾ in. in diameter by about 3 in. long, so that if the

quicker. An excellent heating element can be made by winding the resistance on a piece of quartz tubing. A piece of old clay pyrometer tubing is also good material, and even a piece of hard-glass tubing, such as is used for water-gauge glasses, will serve the purpose.

About 85 turns of No. 28 bare wire of the kind mentioned will be required, spaced about 28 to the inch, so that some kind of automatic feed will be found advisable for spacing the turns uniformly. This winding is designed to consume about 150 watts at 110 volts, which means a current of 1.36 amperes. Electric heating devices operate equally well on direct or alternating current.

In connecting the heating element to the lead wires, the suggestions given in

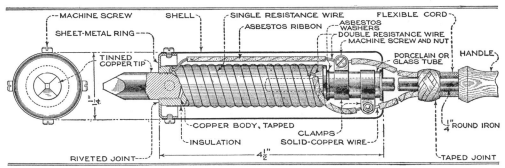

An Electrically Heated Soldering Iron That is Provided with Means for Using Interchangeable Copper Tips for Different Kinds of Work: Such a Tool can be Used on Any 110-Volt Alternating or Direct-Current Circuit with Very Satisfactory Results

copper body varies from the dimensions given, the amount of wire used will have to be changed accordingly.

The main heat reservoir formed by the copper body is tapped out at one end so that copper tips can be screwed into it, making it possible to use a variety of tips.

Insulating the hot wire from the copper body is one of the biggest problems, since the insulation must be proof against the 110-volt electrical pressure, even at very high temperatures, and must also conduct heat easily from the wire to the copper body. The best insulator for the purpose is ½-in. asbestos ribbon, which can be bought from electrical-supply houses. Wind the copper body tightly with one or two layers of the ribbon, and then the resistance wire directly on it. A much better job will result if a little water glass (sodium silicate) is used as a cement on the asbestos. Besides providing mechanical firmness, the cement will greatly improve the heat conductivity of the asbestos, making the tip heat up

the drawing should be closely studied. The ends of the resistance wire are brought out to two screws on insulated clamps; these are shown fastened around a piece of porcelain or glass tubing, but if plenty of asbestos tape is at hand, it will be just as well to wind some of it around the iron-rod stem of the tool directly and fasten the clamps on it. If the piece of tubing is used, some asbestos washers should be made and inserted between it and the copper body and steel shell, to prevent rattling.

It is important that the resistance wire should be brought out double to the clamp screws; otherwise it will get very hot at the ends as well as in the portion wrapped around the body. Doubling the wire provides a path of twice the conductance and reduces the energy loss in the leads. These doubled portions of resistance wire, as well as the copper leads brought in, should be wound with asbestos tape. Do not use rubber-insulated lamp cord for the leads into the shell, as the rubber will burn off. Use No. 16 or 18 solid-copper wire, and solder it to the flexible cord at a point well back from the hot shell. This point must be far enough back so that the shell can be slid off without striking the taped joint, when the four small screws fastening it to the ring are removed.

It should be noted that the winding data given are not to be considered final; they are suggested only as a starting point in making the first heating element. So many factors enter into this question that it is impossible to say, without repeated trials, just how many watts can be safely drawn by a soldering iron. If it is found that the iron does not get hot enough to melt solder in less than 10 minutes, fewer turns of the wire should be used or some of the windings short-circuited. If the tip gets hot enough to melt solder in less than three minutes, or the element burns out, or if the water glass seems to be acting chemically on the resistance wire, then too much energy passes through it, and more turns or smaller wire must be used.

In using any electrical heating device, care must be taken not to leave the current turned on when not in use, and some kind of stand or rack should be provided on which to set the iron down when hot.

Micrometer Attachment for Measuring Tapers

Measuring tapers with a micrometer is always an awkward job, owing to the unsatisfactory surface presented to the flat faces of the measuring tool. To take a measurement, and then advance the piece a definite distance to test the amount of taper in that distance, is still more awkward, unless some more or less

Measuring Tapered Work with a Micrometer is Greatly Simplified by the Method Shown, Which Requires Nothing but a Few Tools Always Included in the Machinist's Equipment

expensive device is used. The illustration shows a method that gives very accurate results without requiring any addition to the machinist's tool equipment. To obtain correct alinement, a rule is clamped to the top of the micrometer anvil in the following manner: The micrometer spindle is first brought down until the scale is held between spindle and anvil, exactly as though the scale were being measured. A small clamp is then pressed close to the side of the micrometer and tightened on the scale, a second clamp being used to hold the first to the micrometer. In this way the scale is held flat on the face of the anvil and at right angles to the spindle.

To measure the work for the amount of taper per inch, either end is placed upon some even inch of the scale and a reading taken, after which the piece is moved to the next inch graduation and measured again, the difference between the two readings being, of course, the amount of taper per inch. By this arrangement both hands are left free, as the clamps may be arranged to support the micrometer in a vertical position.

Grinding Miller Index Centers

Difficulty in getting the head center of an index head to run true is overcome by using the following method of grinding in a surface grinder. Bolt the head to the auxiliary plate, which comes with the grinder. Place on the table of the grinder, swing to 30° and bolt it down. Turn the index crank and move the table in and out until the desired amount of metal is removed from the center. A center ground in this manner will be perfectly true with the spindle, something that is nearly impossible if the center is removed for grinding.—Louis M. Steffen, Dayton, Ohio.

A Useful Pencil Marker

Draftsmen and others using several grades of pencils will appreciate the

merits of the pencil marker illustrated, which, besides indicating the hardness of the lead at a glance also prevents the pencil from rolling. These markers are easily made in a few minutes by whittling down an ordinary thread spool, the hole in which is usually the right size to fit the pencil.

Reproducing Building Dimensions without Plans

On many occasions it is desired to duplicate a home, store, warehouse, or other building, the plans of which are not available. If the original building is of brick, a competent brick mason can very accurately determine the dimensions from photographs showing all four sides. These photographs should have sufficient detail to permit counting the number of courses of brick, which will enable the mason to obtain the approximately correct proportions, and place doors and other openings in their correct positions. This procedure holds good for either standard-size brick, concrete blocks, or special-sized brick, but if either of the last two is used, the dimensions of the face of one of these are necessary to obtain the corresponding over-all dimensions.

A Safe Ladder Extension

When painting or working on the side of a building, if the only ladder available

is too short, an extension that will provide a solid base can be easily and quickly made from heavy lumber, as shown in the drawing. The upper end of the extension rests against the side of the building and the ladder rests on substantial flat-iron hooks fastened to one of the crosspieces of the frame.

An Accurate Box Toolholder

The box form of toolholder has one great disadvantage when used for finishing work smoothly and accurately. The work being so well piloted in the bore of the holder, it is prevented from springing away from the tool when the latter is withdrawn after a cut, and a slight spiral groove is left in the work if the holder is withdrawn quickly; if withdrawn slowly, the tool removes a shaving of metal and reduces the diameter. For this reason, on accurate work, a slight allowance is made to be filed off later.

The box toolholder illustrated over-

comes this objectionable feature by releasing the tension between tool and work when the latter has finished the cut. It is, of course, used as a finishing tool only, the work having previously been roughed down to within $\frac{1}{64}$ in. of its fin-

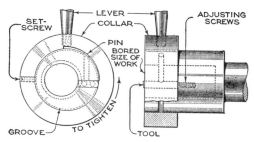

Box Toolholder for Finishing Work That does Not Cut When Withdrawn Because the Cutter is Released from Contact with the Work

ished size. The body of the holder is turned on the shank to fit the turret hole and bored at the front to the size of the finished work. The hole is bored eccentric, to permit the use of lighter stock. Next a collar is made to fit the front part of the body, drilled and tapped in one place for a lever, and at an angle of about 90° to this, for a headless setscrew. This screw bears in a groove cut in the body and serves to hold the parts together. A slot is cut in the front of the body, on the heavy side, to take the tool, and two holes are drilled and tapped in the back of the slot for adjusting screws. A hole is then drilled in the body at right angles to the slot, to take a loose tightening pin, which is filed on the top to conform to the radius of the cam surface filed inside the collar. When using the holder, push over the lever until the collar reaches the position shown in the drawing. It will be seen that the end of the tool is now backed up by the collar, while, at the same time, it is held down on the face by the pin. Before withdrawing the holder, pull the lever down until the end of the cam portion strikes the pin, which forms a convenient stop. The act of pulling back the lever relieves the pressure on the tool and also, as the tool is slightly tapered on the top so that the pin forces it back against the collar, allows it to slip back a little against the cut-away cam surface. The tool is ground on the front only, the adjusting screws at the back of the slot being used to keep it always slightly ahead of the holder.

¶When preheating a large casting for welding, always use a soaking heat.

Automatic Shut-Off for Thresher Grain Spout

When operating a thresher, it is much more convenient to have a team hitched

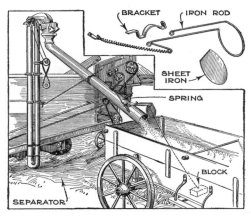

An Automatic Shut-Off for the Spout of a Grain Separator, That Acts as Soon as the Team Begins to Pull the Wagon Away

to each of the grain wagons than to unhitch the horses from the wagon being filled, but there are times when the horses will pull the wagon from under the grain spout before the attendant can reach them. To prevent the waste of grain that results from this, an automatic cut-off for the grain spout, that operates as soon as the wagon begins to move, can easily be made. A flat iron bracket is riveted to the spout; this has upturned ears, to which the iron-rod support for the shut-off is pivoted with bolts. The shut-off consists of a piece of sheet metal that closes down over the spout opening. A spring, fastened to a hook riveted on the spout, holds the shutter up until a cord, attached to the shutter, which is tied to a 3-in. square block of wood placed in the bottom of the wagon, starts the shutter to close; the spring then quickly closes it over the end of the spout. The block on the end of the spring is allowed to remain in the wagon box, and the grain covering it causes a pull when the team starts.

A Handy Mixture for the Garage

I have found that a mixture composed of equal parts of benzol and *denatured* alcohol is very handy in the garage or repair shop; it is kept in a bottle and called "remover." This mixture removes spots from fabric without injury or stain. It will also remove paint; simply apply a little of it to the painted surface, and in

a few minutes the paint will soften up so that it can be scraped off easily. It is good to remove carbon; in this case an ounce of the fluid is poured into each cylinder and allowed to stand for from 2 to 12 hours, loosening the carbon so that it will be blown out through the exhaust when the engine is started. Finally, the mixture is excellent for cleaning the hands of grease and grime.— Ralph Hanenkratt, Northville, N. Y.

Timing Test for Blueprints

Anyone who has made blueprints knows that the print must be given just the right exposure in order to get the best results, and that the length of the exposure will vary greatly, according to the quality of the sensitized surface, and of the tracing cloth, and the intensity and actinic value of the light used. When printing by natural light, the time necessarily varies according to the hour of the day and atmospheric conditions. Therefore, when starting to make prints, it is always best to make a test to determine the proper exposure, for each condition of light, etc.

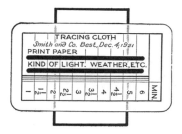

The easiest and most thorough method of doing this is to use a special tracing for the purpose, marked and lettered somewhat after the manner of the one shown in the drawing.

The test print is made from the special tracing in this way: Mount it in the frame as usual, and cover with a heavy card held in the hand. At a given time by the watch, say, 9:54 a. m., for instance, expose the 6-minute strip to the light. At 9:55, move the card down to expose the next strip; in another half minute uncover the 4½-minute strip and so on. At one minute before the hour, remove the card entirely and at 10:00 o'clock take the print out and wash as usual. The resulting print will form a graphic record showing exactly what exposure will produce best results. Data can be written, if desired, on the white spaces provided for the purpose.

¶Send your radio inquiries to our Bureau of Information.

Two Practical Garage Conveniences

By J. S. HAGANS

EITHER or both of the devices illustrated will be found as serviceable in any garage and repair shop as they are in the large establishment in which they were photographed.

One of them is used for lifting engines from their chassis. It consists of nothing more than a length of steel rod and two old spark-plug shells. The cores are removed from the spark plugs, leaving only the metal shells, which are slipped over the ends of the rods so that their threaded ends will be on the outside.

tween two of the spark-plug holes in the cylinder-head casting of the engine to be removed. In use, two of the spark plugs are removed from adjoining cylinders of the engine, and the loose shells on the lifting device are screwed into the holes. The engine can then be lifted out in the manner shown.

A portable hoist or dolly, built of wood throughout and mounted on ball-bearing casters, such as the one shown, will find a variety of uses around any garage or shop where repair work is

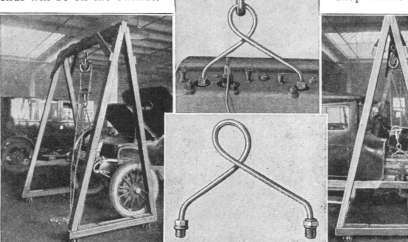

Left: A Portable Hoist, Built from Timbers and Mounted on Ball-Bearing Casters, Center: An Engine Puller Made from Two Spark-Plug Shells and a Piece of Steel Rod. Right: Both Devices Shown in Use for Lifting an Engine from Its Position on the Chassis

After the shells are in place on the rod, the ends of the latter are riveted over to prevent the loosely fitting metal parts from slipping off. Either before or after the attachment of the spark-plug shells, the rod is bent to the form shown, to make an eye into which the hook of the chain block is inserted. The distance between the ends of the device should correspond as closely as possible to that be-

done, as it is cheap to build, and can be easily moved from one part of the shop to another. Four-by-fours are used for making the triangular end supports, while a piece of 4 by 6-in. stuff should be used for the horizontal crosspiece. All parts are rigidly bolted together, and the legs are fastened to the bottom crosspieces with angle plates. The whole dolly is built wide and high enough to clear the sides and top of a car. An eyebolt is provided in the center of the top crosspiece for the attachment of the usual chain blocks. The value of such a device in the shop is not fully appreciated until it becomes necessary to lift an engine, or elevate the front or rear of the chassis for the removal or insertion of springs, shackle bolts, and other parts. With the dolly, work of this kind can be done by a workman single-handed, so that time and money are saved for the busy repair shop, and the work is delivered to the customer quicker.

Stretching Tracing Cloth Properly

Many draftsmen, amateur or otherwise, seem unable to acquire the ability of stretching tracing cloth properly on their

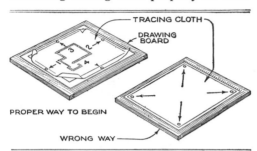

PROPER WAY TO BEGIN

WRONG WAY

Inserting the Thumbtacks as Illustrated, Instead of at the Corners, the Draftsman can Smooth Out a Piece of Tracing Cloth So That It will Lie Perfectly Flat and Smooth

drawing boards. In the first position illustrated the thumbtacks are placed at the center of the edges and not at the corners. By inserting the thumbtacks in this manner, the cloth is left free at the corners so that it is a very simple matter afterward to stretch the cloth toward each corner and fasten it in a manner that will make it lie perfectly flat and smooth.

A Piloted Taper Reamer

Having to ream out a number of taper holes accurately, the taper reamer shown in the drawing was devised and used with satisfactory results, by grinding the pilot on the same centers as the flutes. The work was prepared by first drilling the hole and hand-reaming with a straight reamer. Then the pilot was lapped down to a close sliding fit in the hole, after which the taper-reaming operation was performed. The result was a job having the taper hole absolutely square and without chatter marks. Also, the time of production was reduced by about one-third.—W. Burr Bennett, Honesdale, Pa.

Dissolving Slide for Stereopticon

A simple but effective dissolving shutter, that can be used by moving-picture and stereopticon operators for changing from one slide to another, is shown in the drawing. Two sheet-metal blades, having V-shaped notches cut out of their inner edges, slide in grooves in a wooden frame. Each slide is connected to a pivoted lever by a short connecting arm so that movement of the lever is communicated to the blades, opening or closing them. Such a shutter can also be used on an enlarging lantern. If it is desired to obtain a true dissolving effect on a double stereopticon, two shutters can be used, one in front of each lens or at each projection port, but some connection must be made between the shutters so that both can be operated at the same time from a single lever. One of the shutters, in this case, should open while the other is closing.—H. Hughes, Henrietta, Tex.

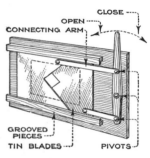

A Simple Boring Gauge

The drawing shows a gauge that is very useful on boring work, as it is cheaply made, accurate, and worn parts are easily renewed. A piece of tubing is cut a little shorter than the diameter of the hole to be bored, and both ends of it are turned over to retain the balls with which it is filled. One end of the tubing is slotted so that the balls can be sprung in or out. As steel balls are made to limits of .0001 in., the possible error will be very small.

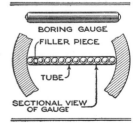

If the gauge is a long one, greater accuracy can be obtained by carefully selecting the balls, calipering each before using. Of course, such a gauge will ordinarily measure in dimensions that are multiples of the diameter of one ball, but, by using a filler piece in the manner shown, other sizes can be measured as well.

Spring Dog for Small Lathe

Two things are done by the type of lathe dog illustrated. The work is held in close contact with the live center, and it is revolved by the faceplate. The dog spring is made of stiff sheet metal, and is permanently bent so as to bring the ends closer to the faceplate than the center, although they must be drawn toward the faceplate by the machine screws; for this reason the ends of the spring are slotted. The work is held in a collar which is fastened to the center of the spring with two screws. The hole in the collar is machined with a "V," to provide a three-point bearing for the work when the setscrew is tightened.

In using this dog, the clamp or collar is so adjusted that, when the work is on the live center, the slotted ends of the spring

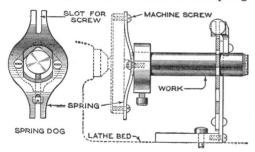

A Spring Lathe Dog for Light Work That Holds Work Close to the Live Center: It Is Convenient for Work One End of Which is Held in the Steady Rest

will be a sufficient distance from the faceplate to provide the necessary pressure against the center when the screws are tightened, drawing the ends into contact with the faceplate. A dog of this type is particularly useful when working on a job one end of which is held on the live center and the other in a steady rest, for centering or other operations.—H. E. Balfour, Ottawa, Can.

❡In starting a trial cut on a milling machine, feed the work toward the cutter slowly; this will prevent the tool from digging into the work, which might loosen the setting, break teeth from the cutter, or spring the arbor.

A Double-Point Soldering Bit

The tinsmith and electrician will appreciate the advantages of the double-point bit illustrated, especially when working on

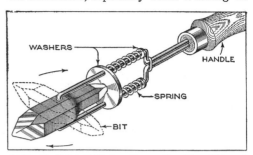

A Double-Point Soldering Copper for Tinsmiths and Electricians: This Saves Carrying Two Bits, and One Bit is Kept Warm While the Other Is in Use

jobs that require continual changing from a light to a heavy bit. A large copper bit is removed from its shank, heated, a small bit point forged on the shank end as shown, and a hole drilled through the body to take the ends of a new shank. This shank is made of ¼-in. rod, bent as indicated, and fitted with springs on each arm, small washers being placed behind the springs, on the handle end of the arms. A large washer, drilled to fit the arms, and with a hole in its center in which the bit points will fit, is then slipped on, and the ends of the arms bent and sprung into the hole in the copper body. The springs and washer hold the bit firmly in position, and when it is desired to change from one point to another, it is only necessary to push the washer back. This allows the bit to be revolved; the washer is then released, locking the bit again.

Removing Outer Ball Race

The outer ball race, or cup, in the front wheel of the light automobile is easily forced from its seat with a length of an old rear-axle spindle from the same make of car. The axle is just the right size to bear against the inner edge of the cup, which is forced out

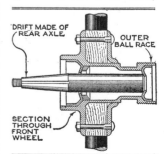

by striking the outer end of the shaft with a hammer.

Catcher for Japan Clover Seed

While intended primarily for catching the seeds of Lespedeza or Japan clover, the device illustrated can be used with similar results in the harvesting of common clover. The attachment is very simple, and consists of a sheet-metal pan,

An Attachment for the Mowing Machine for Catching the Seeds of Plants That are Harvested at Maturity or That Scatter Easily

the sides of which are tapered; the pan is covered with a screen with mesh large enough to allow the seed to fall through it. The catcher is mounted on the mowing machine, just behind the mower bar. An extra man is required to keep the plants raked off the catcher, but the expense of this item is overcome by the value of the seed obtained.—Bessie Staller, Memphis, Tenn.

Setting a Countersinking Tool

When numbers of different-sized screw holes are to be countersunk, the device illustrated is a real timesaver as well as a means of preventing unsightly holes. Whether a countersink has an adjusting sleeve, or whether it is set by the machine stop, it is necessary to use the cut-and-try method for the first hole or two, and naturally it is not uncommon to see work with a poor appearance, caused by one or two deep countersinks. To make the gauge illustrated, obtain a long piece of ⅛-in. flat steel, and fasten it to a short piece of

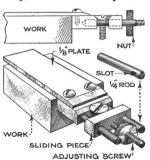

WORK
⅛ PLATE
NUT
SLOT
¼ ROD
WORK
SLIDING PIECE
ADJUSTING SCREW

⅜-in. stock with two screws; then bevel off one corner at the same angle as the screw heads. Two ¼-in. pins are driven into one end of the ⅜-in. piece, and sliding on these is another piece of ⅜-in. stock, beveled on the upper and inner edge to correspond with the angle on the head of the screw. The center of the sliding piece is tapped for a ¼-in. stud that carries a knurled nut, the outer diameter of which fits easily in two shallow slots filed or milled near the ends of the pins. When in use, the device is laid on the work and held down by one hand, and the screw to be used is dropped between the beveled edges. The nut is then turned until the screw lies flush with the surface of the ⅜-in. pieces; it is then removed, the countersinking tool is brought down, and the stop set. It will be apparent that in this manner the tool will be set to its correct depth at once without any preliminary cuts.

Auxiliary Bushings for Toolmaker's Buttons

When boring jigs, buttons are used to locate the holes; if they are very close together, trouble is encountered when indicating them to ascertain whether they run true, or, in the case of a milling machine, to find whether the spindle is in perfect alinement with the bushing. To overcome this difficulty, an auxiliary bushing should be made, with one side

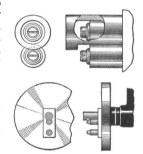

ground away in the manner shown. It is absolutely necessary that this bushing should be a wringing fit on the button, so that it will run true, and that there may be no danger of shifting until the work has been trued up.

Winch Improvised from Lathe

Our shop was a new one and was built with a runway for a traveling crane, but no appropriation had been made for a crane, so one was designed and built in the shop. It was not an elaborate affair, but certainly substantial, so much so that when the time came to set it on its runway, there was no machinery in the plant capable of lifting it in place. We had already installed a 30-in. heavy-duty lathe, which was bolted to a concrete base. I was finishing, on this lathe, a casting that resembled the "niggerhead" or capstan of a hoisting crab. This suggested an idea, which was acted upon at once. A snatch block was fastened opposite the lathe, the tail rope of the hoisting tackle passed through the block and around the casting, which was held by the chuck and a bell tailstock center. One man took care of the tail rope, another guided the crane into place with a hand line, and a third operated the lathe. This improvised winch landed the crane in place in a few minutes without a jar.—Thos. B. Norris, Birmingham, Ala.

Drill for Use in Small Space

On a repair job, several holes were to be drilled in a space so small that it was impossible to use either a portable electric drill, or any ratchet drill that was available. As immediate action was imperative, the drill shown in the drawing was used. A short drill of the proper size— in this case $2\%_4$ in.— was obtained, a portion cut off the shank, and the shank squared to fit a small ratchet-wrench socket. A hole was drilled and tapped in the end of the shank for a $\frac{1}{4}$-in. setscrew, the head of which was 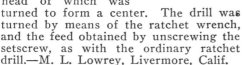 turned to form a center. The drill was turned by means of the ratchet wrench, and the feed obtained by unscrewing the setscrew, as with the ordinary ratchet drill.—M. L. Lowrey, Livermore, Calif.

Grain Soaker for Swine

A considerable economy is effected by soaking grain fed to swine so that it is softened, because, otherwise, a considerable part of the ration of hard grain passes through the animal without having been digested.

The illustration shows a device built by a farmer from two discarded steel wheels from a hayrake. The hydrant was run up to the proper height for the purpose. Then, one of the wheels was laid flat on the ground and the space between the rim and hub filled with cement. After the cement had hardened, a larger pipe

was slipped over the hydrant pipe to serve as a support for the cement-filled wheel; then this was placed over the water pipe also. The space between the rim and hub of the second wheel was filled with wood,

A Device for Soaking Grain Used as Swine Feed: It is Attached to the Yard Pump

and it was placed on the water pipe so that it would just clear the grain-filled containers placed on the circular cement table underneath; this arrangement prevents poultry from scattering the grain and keeps the sun from causing rapid fermentation. One section of the covering on the upper wheel is hinged to make a door, as shown, which forms a convenient opening for filling the baskets of grain with water from the hydrant.

Extension "Hand" for Stores

For removing articles from the display window or high shelves of a store without considerable inconvenience, some device to increase the salesman's reach is necessary, and this is provided in the "hand" illustrated. At the extreme end of the square wooden handle, two pieces of thin oak are fastened, to form jaws; these are connected to a lever, pivoted in a slot cut in the handle, by means of a cord. To grip an article, the jaws are placed around it and 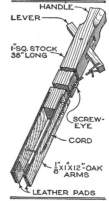 the lever is pulled to tighten them.— Howard Fowler, Rogers, Ark.

¶Double riveting is from 16 to 20 per cent stronger than single riveting.

Electric Sand and Soil Sifter

Two pecks of soil a minute is the record of the homemade electric sifter used in the greenhouse of an agricultural col-

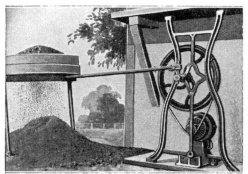

Soil and Sand are Sifted at the Rate of Half a Bushel per Minute in the Greenhouse of an Agricultural College with This Machine

lege. The device was made by one of the students from an electric motor and part of an old sewing-machine stand, together with a few miscellaneous parts, as shown. In making the machine, the ordinary soil sifter is bolted in an iron hoop that is supported on two legs, fastened to pivots bolted to the floor in such a manner that a back-and-forth movement of the sieve is permitted. The motor is bolted directly beneath the crank wheel, and drives it by an ordinary round belt. The shaking motion is transmitted to the sieve by a connecting rod made of pipe, one end of which is fastened to the crankpin and the other to the sieve.—Clementine Paddleford, New York City.

Holding Round Work in a Vise

A handy kink that will be found useful in many cases, when cylindrical work must be clamped in an ordinary bench vise, is to use a monkey wrench in the manner illustrated. Adjust the wrench jaws until the work will rest only on the edges of the jaws; clamp the wrench and work in the vise in the

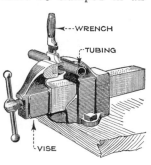

position shown, and the stock will be held as securely as in a pipe vise.—Floyd D. Elmore, Bethesda, Md.

Marking Celluloid with Type Slug

Draftsmen, particularly those who work in large drawing rooms, find it very convenient, if not necessary, to mark their celluloid instruments with their name or other identifying mark. This is commonly done with the point of a knife blade or other pointed instrument. A better method, which gives excellent results, is to use a linotype slug set with one's name, which can be obtained from almost any print shop at little or no cost. A good size of type for the purpose is known as 14-point. Cut the slug with a hacksaw along the dotted line so that it will be easier to

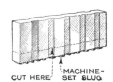

manipulate it in the process. Lay the celluloid article to be marked on a flat surface, and place the slug on it. Now press a hot iron on the upper edge of the slug, watching carefully and removing the iron when the type face begins to sink into the celluloid. The result is a very attractive and finished mark. The impressed characters can be filled with some dark pigment, such as jewelers' wax or enamel.

Adjustable Centers for Laying Out

Previous to turning or drilling cored castings, the circles and divisions are usually laid out from a center block—

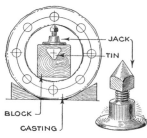

generally a block of wood cut to the length of the cored space and driven into the hole —a small piece of copper or tin being tacked to the wood to carry the center mark. As a means of saving time in layout work, this individual fitting of wooden blocks should be avoided, and the method shown in the drawing used instead. A block of wood that will enter the hole of the casting loosely is seated solidly against the side, a small jack screw on the opposite side of the block serving to hold the block firmly against the work. The same blocks can be used repeatedly, and the time necessary to wedge them in place and remove them is much less than that required for the older method.

SMALL SINGLE-PHASE TRANSFORMERS

By H. H. PARKER

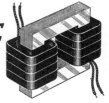

A HOMEMADE transformer, operating from the alternating-current house or shop-lighting circuit, can be put to a large variety of uses, such as Christmas-tree lighting, lighting low-voltage lamps for decorative effects or night lights, operating toy motors or electric railroads, ringing doorbells in place of dry cells, heating soldering or lead-burning apparatus, and so forth. These devices require a low or stepped-down voltage; transformers are also made to step up the voltage; these are suitable for radio or high-frequency work, but are not considered in this article. A small step-down transformer is not hard to build, once the principles of operation are understood, and few tools are needed, but the amateur electrician's main difficulty consists in obtaining data to start the design; he wants to know the size of core to use, the size and quantity of wire for the windings, and especially the number of turns to wind on the primary and secondary coils. Just how to obtain the desired secondary voltage is another stumbling block.

The method of working out the design as described here is mainly a cut-and-try, with little mathematics, but the amateur, with the aid of the accompanying tables, ought to be able to work out a satisfactory and fairly efficient transformer. At the start, however, he should understand that a transformer will work only on

alternating current; if attached to a direct-current circuit not only would there be no secondary current produced, but the primary winding would probably burn out. Though most house circuits are 110-volt 60-cycle, data are also furnished for a frequency of 25 cycles. To wind a primary for 220 volts, double the number of turns listed for 110 volts are used, but a wire having half the area, or half the number of circular mils, as shown by one of the tables, must be selected.

To illustrate the simplest type of transformer, imagine a closed iron ring, or core, with two separate coils of insulated wire wound around the ring; they can be either superimposed, one upon the other, or placed on opposite halves of the ring, but in both cases must be insulated electrically. One of the coils is connected to a source of alternating current, thus causing a succession of impulses to be sent through the coil, first in one direction and then in the other. One impulse tends to magnetize the core; the succeeding one magnetizes it again, but with opposite polarity; thus the magnetism in the core is being continually built up, broken down, and built up in the opposite direction. This means that the number of lines of force through the iron continually changes, building up to their maximum number, dying down to nothing, and then building up again with opposite polarity. A well-known fact is that

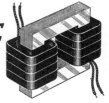

Fig. 1 Shows How Core Shape Influences Length of Wire Necessary; Fig. 2, Poor Core Designs; Fig. 3, How Coils are Connected in Series and in Parallel

a change in the number of lines of force in a magnetic circuit will induce an electric current in any coil of wire surrounding the magnet; hence currents will be set up or induced in the second coil, and as the core changes its polarity at every alternation of the energizing current, the induced, or secondary, current will be alternating like that in the primary, though the two coils are insulated from each other and have no connection electrically.

The amount of electrical energy obtained from the secondary coil, however, can never quite equal that sent into the primary. What causes this loss? In the first place, it takes work to magnetize, demagnetize, and reverse the magnetism in the iron core many times a second, and, especially if the core is of solid iron, much energy is lost through heating the core. Never attempt to construct a transformer core of solid iron; all cores used in alternating-current work must be built up of thin iron or steel sheets, or "laminated"; this is to break up the mass of the core and prevent the formation of stray or eddy currents within the core, which cause a big rise in temperature. In fact, a solid-iron core would cause the windings quickly to burn out. Even with the best laminated core, there will still be a certain core or iron loss, and a copper loss due to the heating of the windings and the self-inductive effect of the alternating current. We will assume these losses to total from 5 to 10 per cent for a small transformer.

The coil connected to the alternating-current supply is always called the primary, and the one furnishing the induced current the secondary, no matter what the voltage ratio is. Assuming the primary circuit to be closed, but the secondary disconnected, or on open circuit, only a very small current will flow through the primary coil, the few watts that are consumed being used up in magnetizing the core. This can be observed experimentally by putting a low-voltage lamp in series with the primary of a small transformer, and leaving the secondary circuit open. Now suppose that a light load is put on the secondary, such as a couple of low-voltage lamps or a high-resistance coil. This load will draw a small secondary current, with a slight increase of the current through the primary. Then, as the secondary load is increased, as by putting more lamps in the circuit, the primary current will increase with the secondary, until, assuming that the secondary terminals are directly connected

so as to form a "dead short," an enormous amperage might be drawn from the secondary and a corresponding current through the primary, resulting in the blowing of fuses, or the burning out of the transformer. Thus we see that there is automatic regulation between the amperes flowing through the two windings, and that they increase and decrease in proportion, which should dispose of the question often asked: "How many amperes can be obtained from the secondary winding?" This depends altogether upon the character of the load connected to the secondary. There is a type of commercial transformer known as the constant-current transformer, in which the amperage is kept practically constant at varying loads, but this kind is not considered here.

The voltage of the secondary, on the other hand, can be assumed to remain practically constant as long as the primary voltage does not change. This brings up another of the common inquiries: "How much wire is required to give a certain secondary voltage?" The secondary voltage depends absolutely upon the ratio between the *number of turns* in the primary and secondary coils, and is proportional to the number of turns. If a transformer has 1,000 turns in the primary and the primary voltage is 100, then with a secondary of 1,000 turns the voltage will be 100 also; with 500 turns, one-half of 100, or 50 volts; with 250 turns, one-quarter, or 25 volts, and so on. The formula is:

No. turns primary : No. turns secondary =
Primary voltage : Sec. voltage.

To change to a different secondary voltage, it is only necessary to alter the number of turns of wire in the secondary coil according to the above proportion; no change is made in primary winding or core.

Assuming that it is desired to design a small single-phase transformer to operate on an alternating-current circuit of known voltage and frequency, there is a fundamental formula that will enable one to start the work:

$$N = (E \times 100,000,000) \div (4.44 \times F \times B \times A),$$

in which

N = Number of turns of wire in primary coil, (unknown).
E = Primary voltage, (known).
F = Frequency of current, (known).
B = Number of magnetic lines of force (flux) through the laminated core of transformer, (assumed).
A = Cross-sectional area of transformer core, (unknown).

B varies with the different core material used; with ordinary sheet iron or "stove" iron, often used by amateurs, 40,000 lines per square inch may be assumed; with transformer iron or silicon steel, if a definite figure cannot be obtained from the makers of the steel, 60,000 may be assumed. We are now left with two unknown quantities, N and A, and the usual method is to assume a value for A and then calculate N. The larger the core cross section A, the fewer the number of primary turns required, but the larger and heavier the core; reducing A means a lighter core but more wire, so the thing to do is to strike a happy medium; if a quantity of suitable wire is at hand, but the core iron has to be bought, the amateur can well afford to reduce the size of the core for the sake of economy, and vice versa. For instance, the core of a 500-watt transformer, 1½ in. square, will contain 13 lb. of iron, which may cost $4.10, assuming a certain market value; 770 ft. of No. 14 copper wire would be needed for the primary winding, costing $7.40, making a total cost of iron and copper of $11.50. If the core is made 2 in. square, 20 lb. of iron, costing $5.50, will be used; but 440 ft. of No. 14 wire will now be required, at $4.12, the total cost thus being $9.62. The smaller core, however, is lighter and better proportioned, so the prospective builder will have to figure out the most suitable combination for his purpose. As a guide, the core proportions given in the accompanying tables can be followed, being modified where necessary. A core need not be square, but this shape requires a minimum length of wire for the same number of turns (see Fig. 1, B); a wide narrow core, while of the same cross-sectional area, as in Fig. 1, A, will take more wire for each turn, resulting in a considerable increase in weight, length, resistance, and cost of the wire. A core should not be too heavy and stocky nor too long and thin, as in Fig. 2, unless some special purpose, as in the magnetic-leakage type of core, requires a sacrifice of efficiency. For the same number of primary turns, a lower frequency means a larger core, as can be seen by comparing the dimensions of the 60 and 25-cycle cores in the table. Having set a value for A, leaving but one unknown quantity N in the fundamental formula, the number of primary turns N can now be found by substituting the known values.

To simplify matters, the actual laying out of a 500-watt transformer, adapted to amateur design and construction, will be described; one of any other capacity may be worked out by substituting values and referring to the tables. Suppose the volt-age E of the supply mains is 110, and the frequency F 60. Allowing a 10-per-cent core and copper loss for an amateur-built transformer, the total primary wattage would have to be 500 plus 10 per cent, or 550. To find the actual primary current

COPPER-WIRE TABLE

GAUGE B.&S.	DIA. BARE IN.	DIA. S.C.C. IN.	DIA. D.C.C. IN.	FT. PER LB. S.C.C.	FT. PER LB. D.C.C.	AREA, CIR. MILS
10	0.1019	0.108	0.112	30.8	30.5	10,380
11	0.0907	0.097	0.101			8,234
12	0.0808	0.087	0.091	50	48	6,530
13	0.0719	0.078	0.082			5,178
14	0.0641	0.070	0.074	84	77	4,107
15	0.0570	0.063	0.067			3,257
16	0.0508	0.056	0.059	125	125	2,583
17	0.0452	0.050	0.053			2,048
18	0.0403	0.045	0.048	200	200	1,624
19	0.0359	0.040	0.044			1,288
20	0.0319	0.036	0.040	311	461	1,022
21	0.0284	0.032	0.036			810
22	0.0253	0.029	0.033	491	745	642

ENAMELED WIRE

GAUGE, B.&S.	FT. PER LB.	TURNS PER INCH		
		ENAMEL	S.C.E.	D.C.E.
12	50		12	11
14	79		15	13
16	126		18	17
18	200		22	21
20	319	29	25	25
22	507	36	31	30

S.C.E.=SINGLE COTT. AND ENAMEL.
D.C.E.=DOUBLE " " "

This Table will Be of Assistance in Selecting the Proper Size of Wire to Use in the Transformer

in a circuit of this kind, we cannot use Ohm's law, but must consider the power factor; this can be assumed at about 85 per cent for a small-transformer primary. First find the current as though the circuit were direct current, dividing the watts by the volts, or 550 divided by 110, or 5 amp. But the actual current will be more than this; divide the 5 by .85, the power factor, the result being 5.88, or nearly 6 amp., which will be the full-load primary current. Use will be made of this a little later.

A well-proportioned core, if made of stove iron—usually easiest obtained by the home worker—would have a cross section of 1½ by 1½ in., or 2¼ sq. in.; this will be A in the formula, while B is assumed as 40,000 lines per square inch. The number of primary turns N can now be calculated by substituting in the fundamental formula:

$$N = (110 \times 100,000,000) \div (4.44 \times 60 \times 40,000 \times 2.25) = 460 \text{ turns}$$

If silicon steel or transformer iron is available, a smaller and lighter core can be made, using 460 primary turns as above. This can be seen by calculating A from the fundamental formula, using 460 for N, and 60,000 instead of 40,000 for B; A is then found to be about 1½ sq. in

SINGLE-PHASE TRANSFORMER DATA, 50 10 1000 VOLT-AMPERE CAPACITY

60-CYCLE CORE — Core Data & Primary Winding

VOLT-AMPERE CAPACITY	STOVE IRON CROSS SECT., SQ.IN.	LEG SHEETS IN.	YOKE SHEETS IN.	THICKNESS IN., COMPRESSED	WEIGHT IN LB. APPROX	SILICON STEEL LEG SHEETS IN.	YOKE SHEETS IN.	THICKNESS IN., COMPRESSED	CROSS SECT. SQ.IN.	WEIGHT IN LB. APPROX
50	1	1X3¾	1X2½	1 *	2.9	¾X2¾	¾X2	¾	.75	1.8
100	1	1X3½	1X2¾	1	3.1	¾X3	¾X2¾	1	.75	2.2
200	1.12	½X3½	½X3¾	1⅛	3.8	¾X3	¾X2¾	¾	.75	2.4
300	2	1½X5¼	¼X4	1⅝	9.4	1X4¾	1X3½	1⅜	1.37	5.6
500	2.25	1½X5¼	1½X4	1½	10.7	1½X5	¼X3½	1¼	1.54	6.6
800	2.6	½X5¾	1½X4	1¾	13.3	½X5¾	1½X4	1½	1.72	8.0
1000	4.0	2X6½	2X5	2	23.0	2X6½	2X4½	1¾	2.62	13.7
BELL RINGER	.37	¾X2½	¾X1¾	½	.8	SAME	SAME			.8

PRIMARY WINDING (110 VOLTS, 60 OR 25-CYCLE and 220 VOLTS)

VOLT-AMPERE CAPACITY	TOTAL TURNS, HALF IN EACH LEG	110V SIZE WIRE B.&S.	TOTAL WT., LB., APPROX	LENGTH FT. APPROX	TURNS PER LAYER	LAYERS PER LEG	220V TOTAL TURNS	220V SIZE WIRE B.&S.
50	1000	22	1¼	580	50	10	2000	25
100	1000	20	2	580	50	10	2000	23
200	920	18	3	580	46	10	1840	21
300	500	14	3¾	292	50	5	1000	17
500	460	14	4	325	46	5	920	17
800	**400	**14	8	640	50	8	***800	14
1000	††270	††14	6	450	54	5	***540	14
BELL RINGER	2200	34	⅓		100	22	4400	38

25-CYCLE CORE — Core Data

VOLT-AMPERE CAPACITY	STOVE IRON CROSS SECT., SQ.IN.	LEG SHEETS IN.	YOKE SHEETS IN.	THICKNESS IN., COMPRESSED	WEIGHT IN LB. APPROX	SILICON STEEL LEG SHEETS IN.	YOKE SHEETS IN.	THICKNESS IN., COMPRESSED	CROSS SECT. SQ.IN.	WEIGHT IN LB. APPROX
50	2.5	1X4¼	1½X3½	1⅝	9.7	1½X4¼	1¼X3¾	1⅜	1.75	5.9
100	2.5	1½X4½	1½X3¾	1⅝	10.3	1¼X4	1½X3¾	1⅜	1.75	6.3
200	2.5	1½X4½	1½X4¼	1⅝	10.9	1¼X4	1¼X3¾	1⅜	1.75	6.9
300	4.5	2X6¾	2X5½	2¼	27.6	1⅜X5¾	1⅜X4½	2	3.3	16.9
500	5.3	2X7	2X5½	2⅝	33.1	1⅜X6	1⅜X4½	2⅛	3.6	18.9
800	6.2	2½X7¼	2½X6	2½	42.0	2X6¼	2X5	2⅛	4.1	23.1
1000	9.2	2½X8	2½X6½	3⅜	66.7	2½X7	2½X5½	2¾	6.1	38.1
BELL RINGER	.75	¾X2½	¾X1¾	1	.8	¾X2½	¾X1½	⅞	.6	1.1

SECONDARY WINDING, 60 OR 25 CYCLE, 110 OR 220 VOLTS

NUMBER OF TURNS

VOLTS 2	4	6	8	10	15	20	32	50	60
18	36	54	73	91	136	180			273
18	36	54	73	91	136	180	290		250
17	33	50	67	83	125	167	259	417	218
18		27	37	45	68	91	145	230	218
17		25	33	42	64	84	113	210	115
	22		29	31	55	73	116	182	
				25	36	49	79	112	

*** NO.25 B.&S., TAP AT 100,200,500 TURNS; APPROX.3,5,&7 VOLTS

$$N = \frac{E \times 100,000,000}{4.44 \times F \times B \times A}$$

WHERE N = NO. OF PRIMARY TURNS

E = PRIMARY VOLTAGE

F = FREQUENCY

B = LINES OF FORCE PER SQ. IN. THROUGH CORE
= 40,000 FOR STOVE IRON,
= 60,000 " SILICON STEEL

A = CROSS-SECTIONAL AREA OF CORE IN SQ. IN.

$$\frac{\text{PRIMARY VOLTAGE}}{\text{SECONDARY VOLTAGE}} = \frac{\text{PRIMARY TURNS}}{\text{SECONDARY TURNS}}$$

SUGGESTIONS FOR WINDING

FOR 6 V., USE #14 D.C.C., 2 LAYERS, 27 TURNS PER LAYER

6 - 20 V., 2 #14 WIRES IN PARALLEL
50 - 60 V., 1 #14 WIRE

6 - 20 V., 2 #14 WIRES IN PARALLEL
50 - 60 V., 1 #14 WIRE

15 V., 8 #14 WIRES IN PARALLEL, 8 SECTIONS OF 6 TURNS PER LAYER, 5 LAYERS EACH LEG

15 V., 18 #14 WIRES IN PARALLEL, 18 SECTIONS OF 6 TURNS PER LAYER, 6 LAYERS

BOTH WINDINGS ON SAME LEG

TO OBTAIN TWICE THE VOLT-AMPERE CAPACITY & TWICE PRIMARY VOLTAGE; DOUBLE THE CROSS-SECTIONAL AREA OF CORE, KEEPING SAME NO. PRIMARY TURNS, AND SAME WIRE SIZE.
TO " " " " " " " BUT SAME PRIMARY VOLTAGE, DOUBLE THE CROSS-SECTIONAL AREA OF CORE, & USE WIRE OF TWICE THE AREA, BUT SAME NO. OF TURNS
SIZE OF SECONDARY WIRE DEPENDS UPON MAXIMUM CURRENT TO BE CARRIED AT LOWEST VOLTAGE TAP, AND MUST BE CHOSEN FOR EACH INDIVIDUAL CASE
SEVERAL SMALLER WIRES IN PARALLEL ARE PREFERABLE TO ONE HEAVY WIRE OF THE SAME TOTAL AREA, WHICH WOULD BE STIFF AND DIFFICULT TO WIND

* - STOVE-IRON CORE (.025') REQUIRES ABOUT 35 SHEETS TO INCH WHEN COMPRESSED   ** - 400 TURNS ON EACH LEG AND LEGS IN PARALLEL, 2 NO.14 WIRES IN PARALLEL
† - SILICON STEEL " (.014) " " 65 " " " "   †† 270 "
** - CONNECT PRIMARY COILS IN SERIES FOR 220 VOLTS

Winding Data, Formulæ, and Winding Suggestions for the Design of Small Transformers for Use on Both 25 and 60-Cycle Alternating Current; It should be Borne in Mind That the Table is Intended to Serve Only as a Guide, and Some Experimental Calculation Is Necessary before Deciding Definitely on Any Size of Core or Winding

instead of 2¼ sq. in., and a core 1 in. wide and 1½ in. thick, or 1¼ in. square, would suffice. Or, if the core is kept the same size as when stove iron was used, or 2¼ sq. in., a smaller number of turns, 306, can be put on, as found by substituting 60,000 for 40,000.

Before going farther, the proper size of the primary wire must be determined. The actual full-load current was found to be 5.88 or practically 6 amp., and a wire must be chosen of such diameter or cross-sectional area that this current can be carried without overheating. A home-made transformer is generally operated intermittently and not for long periods, so that a smaller wire can be safely used than if an all-day full-load current is carried. The builder must decide upon the operating conditions and choose his wire accordingly. Copper-wire areas are expressed in circular mils, and it is customary to allow 1,000 circular mils per ampere for continual full-load running. Six amperes will, therefore, call for a wire having an area of 6,000 circular mils; referring to the table, No. 12 wire is seen to be suitable, as it has an area of 6,530 mils, but for intermittent service, No. 14, 4,107 mils, can safely be used.

Next draw out a full-size outline of the proposed core. One 7 in. high and 6 in. wide, with sheets 1½ in. wide, may be tried; this will give a "window," or inner winding space, 4 in. long, and the actual coils should be about ¼ in. shorter than this. The window will be 3 in. wide, but the core may be made narrower if the calculated thicknesses of the coils will allow it. Assume that each layer will have 50 turns of No. 14 d. c. c. copper magnet wire; the table gives the diameter of this wire as .074 in. This multiplied by 50 gives 3.7 in., which will be the length of the coil, and be within the limits of the winding space. Now to find the number of layers. Half the primary turns, or 230, will be wound on each leg, and 230 divided by 50 gives 4.6 layers. This means that the layers will not come out even, and while this would not be a great objection, there is a possibility that, with a little juggling of turns and layers, a better combination may be found.

Trying 46 turns to the layer, the length of the coil will be 46 multiplied by .074, or 3.4 in.; this will leave a ¼-in. space on each side of the coil, and the core might be shortened ¼ in. to suit. Dividing 230 by 46 gives an even 5, so that 5 layers, of 46 turns to the layer, will be decided upon. Five layers of No. 14 wire will be at least 5 × .074, or 3.7 in. thick,

and, allowing for insulation, and the springing of the wire while being wound, ½ in. is none too great for the space occupied by the coil in the inner winding space of the core.

As for the secondary winding, suppose a stepped-down voltage of 12 is desired, with a primary voltage of 110 and 460 primary turns. *The number of secondary turns* is found from the proportional formula:

460 : Sec. turns = 110 : 12, or 50 secondary turns.

The secondary output at full load being 500 watts at 12 volts, the secondary full-load current will be about 500 divided by 12, or 42 amperes, requiring a wire having a cross section of about 42,000 circular mils. This would mean a very heavy wire, even for intermittent service, impossible to wind satisfactorily in a small space, so we will use the same size wire as used in the primary, or No. 14 d. c. c., but wound in several sections which will all be connected in parallel, as indicated in Fig. 3, giving the same result as though the large wire had been used. Eight No. 14 wires in parallel will have a total area of 32,856 mils, sufficient for intermittent operation. This would correspond to a single No. 5 wire, .182 in., or nearly .2 in., in diameter. There will be four sections, each of 50 turns, on each leg; if made with 10 turns per layer, four sections would occupy 3 in. of winding space; five layers will be wound on each section. If each section is wound separately, the four will occupy about the same length of winding space as the primary coil. The total thickness of each primary coil, with the superimposed secondary sections, will be 10 × .074 in. or .74 in. for the wire alone, there being five layers in both primary and secondary. Allowing for insulation of core and windings and the springing of the wire turns, at least 1 in. should be allowed for the total thickness of the coils on each leg; or to be on the safe side, make the window in the core 2½ in. wide. The core sheets being 1½ in. wide, this would make the yoke sheets 1½ in. wide and 4 in. long, and since ¼ in. was taken from the original leg-sheet length, these will now be 1½ in. wide and 5¼ in. long; and the outer dimensions of the core, as built, will therefore be 6¾ in. high, 5½ in. wide, and 1½ in. thick.

If several taps are taken from the secondary winding, to furnish different voltages, it will be seen that the heaviest full-load current will be taken from the winding furnishing the lowest voltage, and the size wire suitable for such current may be chosen for this section and used throughout, or the remaining sections can be wound with small wire, as determined by the full-load current to be drawn from each tap. A wire sufficient to carry 10 amp. at 50 volts, for instance, would be too small for the 50 amp. that could be drawn, at full load, from a 10-volt winding tapped from the secondary coil; a 20-volt tap could carry 25 amp. The 10-volt section could be wound with eight No. 14 wires in parallel; part of this coil would, of course, carry the current going through the 20-volt tap, but the remainder could be wound with four No. 14 wires in parallel, while the number of turns necessary to make up the 50-volt winding could be made up of two No. 14 wires in parallel. The use of No. 14 wire is, of course, not essential, as long as the total area is correct, but this size is easy to obtain, and fairly easy to wind on a small core.

As actual constructional details of small-transformer building are not to be taken up in this article, practically all the fundamental points of design have been described, and, with the assistance of the tables for guidance—there is nothing hard and fast about the data given—the amateur should be able, with a little good judgment and common sense, to build a small transformer suited to any of his needs.

Saving Seed from Barn Chaff

Thousands of dollars' worth of clover and timothy seed are lost every year in handling it as food for stock. When the

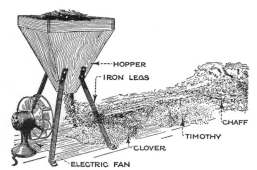

Saving the Timothy and Clover Seed from the Waste of the Hay Loft: This Is Only One of the Uses to Which the Fan can be Put on the Farm

hay is taken from the loft, quantities of chaff or sweepings are left; this is used for bedding, destroyed, or thrown away, and the seed contained in the refuse is wasted. Much of this could be saved with a fanning mill, but in the absence of such equipment, an electric fan, driven by the farm electric plant, will answer.

A small wooden hopper, set on iron legs, is made as shown. After a quantity of sweepings have accumulated, a space in the driveway is swept clean, and the apparatus set up as illustrated. When the fan is turned on, the chaff is fed into the hopper, and it sifts down into the air blast, which separates the refuse in the manner shown, according to the weight of chaff and seeds.

¶When broaching cast iron, use soda and water as a lubricant.

Template for Laying Out Keyways

In machining a number of small rocker arms, it was required that the keyway be placed exactly on the center line of the two holes. As there was no great quantity of these to run, an expensive jig for laying out the keyways was out of the question, so the template illustrated was used for accurately locating the grooves. A piece of $\frac{1}{8}$-in. flat steel was used to make the template. The center distances were accurately laid out on this, and the position of the pins located. The pins were $\frac{1}{8}$ in. in diameter, and when pressed in, projected $\frac{1}{8}$ in. on each side of the plate. These pins were placed so that the edge of the plate was parallel to the center line of the rocker arm, at a distance of half the width of the keyway from it. By placing the template over the rocker arm and rocking it until the lowest position is found, one side of the keyseat may be scribed, then by turning the plate over and repeating the operation on the opposite side of the holes, the other side of the groove is marked.

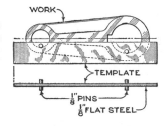

Salvaging Interior Woodwork

In the wrecking, remodeling, and altering of buildings, it is sometimes imperative or expedient to save the inside finish, such as casings, baseboards, molding, or other trim, for use again. Efforts to draw the nails generally result in marred surfaces, as the puttied nail heads cause the surrounding wood to splinter, leaving an ugly wound that is difficult for the painter to conceal entirely. To overcome this, I have found that, by placing the piece to be salvaged with the nail head resting on a block of soft wood and striking the point of the nail a sharp blow with the hammer, the nail will, in most cases, be driven through the piece without marring it. The block of wood underneath the nail heads acts as a die, allowing the nail to punch out the putty neatly. The same hole can be used when nailing the piece up again and can be finished by the painter to look like new work.—Francis Wilkin, Pittsburgh, Pa.

Repairing Spokes in Tractor Wheels

While attempting to back my tractor into position for belting to a corn sheller, the clutch refused to disengage, and before the machine could be stopped, it had backed into a near-by stump, with the

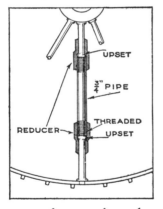

result that three spokes in one of the drivewheels were broken. The wheels were of the type using round steel spokes cast into the hub, so that it was impracticable to replace them. In order to repair the broken spokes, an 8-in. section was cut from each, and a ¾ to ½-in. pipe reducer was slipped over each of the broken ends of the spoke, after reaming the threads from the smaller ends of the reducers. The ends of the spokes were then heated with a blowtorch and upset so as to form a head for holding the reducers. After the ends of each spoke had been thus prepared, a piece of ¾-in. pipe was cut an inch longer than the distance between the reducers when they were pulled up snugly against the upset heads. The pipe section was then inserted between the reducers and each of them was screwed onto the threaded ends of the pipe by hand, after which two pipe wrenches were used to draw the reducers up until the proper tension had been obtained in the spoke. —G. G. McVicker, North Bend, Neb.

Shims Cut from Old Gaskets

When replacing some connecting-rod caps, a shortage of shims started a search for suitable material from which to cut

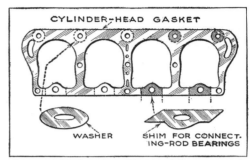

Shims and Washers for a Variety of Purposes can be Cut from Around the Stud Holes of a Discarded Copper-and-Asbestos Cylinder-Head Gasket

them. An old copper-and-asbestos cylinder-head gasket, which had been replaced by a new one, was the only available material. Pieces cut from around the bolt holes of the gasket provided satisfactory shims and washers, as the punched holes were suitable for the cap bolts and the edges matched up well with the connecting-rod caps. A pair of tin snips was found to be the best tool to use in cutting.—G. A. Luers, Washington, D. C.

A Novel Planer Clamp

The drawing shows a very useful form of planer clamp. The 60° "tooth" of the

clamping member is on a higher plane than the axis of the bolt, and this member is made of tool steel, while the body part is made of gray iron. When the elevator screw is raised, a downward and inward pressure is exerted on the work. When used on work having finished surfaces, a block of soft metal is placed between the tooth and the work. Clamps of this sort should be used in pairs, so that a clamp on one side of the work will be directly opposite the one on the other side, and the slot in the base should be long enough to allow the clamp to be bolted to the planer table in almost any position.—Ralph Hanenkratt, Northville, N. Y.

Wrench Made from a Coil Spring

A special coil spring, together with a screwdriver, form a wrench that is very handy for driving thin tubes, polished

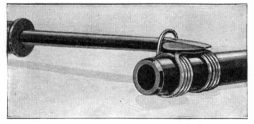

For Screwing Up Thin Tubing, the Application of a Coil Spring and Screwdriver in Place of a Pipe Wrench will be Found an Ideal Method

studs, or other work of a similar character, into place. It is not, of course, in cases of this kind desirable to use a pipe wrench, which would mar or dent the surface, and for this reason the coil-spring wrench is ideal because it grips evenly all around. The shape of the spring is clearly shown; three or four coils formed on either side of a loop, the screwdriver being inserted in the latter and pressing on the ends of the spring. The spring is made a good fit for the work, so that when the screwdriver is inserted in the loop and pressure applied, the spring coils will contract and grip the work tightly. The same idea can be used when space is so limited that a complete revolution of the wrench cannot be made, as the spring slips easily in the reverse direction and tightens immediately on the forward thrust.

On Cleaning Tracings with Gasoline

Gasoline is generally used for the cleaning of tracing-cloth drawings, and some trouble is occasionally encountered in getting good blueprints from tracings so cleaned. By experiment it has been found that, where powdered soapstone or talc has been used to rub off the surface of the tracing cloth before inking in the lines, the ink seems to be held in suspension, so that when the work is cleaned as described, the lines become quite faint. A large number of draftsmen refuse to use prepared powders for this purpose on account of their gritty and unpleasant feeling. Common chalk, however, has been found to overcome both of these objections, and allows the ink to make a permanent line that is unaffected by cleaning with gasoline.

Protecting Wood-Plane Cutters

A few short lengths of a discarded inner tube are valuable articles in a kit of woodworking tools. By snapping one over each plane, so that the edge of the iron is entirely covered, there is slight possibility of a damaged cutting edge resulting from contact with other tools.

Lathe Spindle Made from Pin Vise

A small attachment that can be applied to a sewing machine for work on small pins and similar operations is made from an ordinary pin vise, supported on bearings and driven by a small pulley. A simple casting is required to furnish a bearing for the handle of the vise, and the pulley,

placed between the bearings, prevents the tool from coming loose. A setscrew is used for fastening the pulley to the handle of the vise. In use, the chuck can be turned so that the work can be done from either side.

A Soft-Metal Anvil

The mechanic frequently needs a soft yet firm surface against which to hold polished or plated work without danger

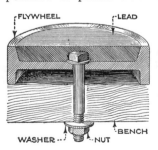

of marring it. A convenient bench anvil of this sort may be made from an old automobile flywheel. The flywheel is fastened to the bench by a bolt passing through the bench top, the head of the bolt being on top, so that the fixture can be removed from the bench when necessary. The anvil is completed by filling the hollow upper surface of the wheel with melted lead, flush with the rim. When the surface of the anvil becomes too much battered, the lead can be removed, remelted, and poured back again.

Using Old Water Colors

Those who have occasion to use water colors will have observed how hard and dry they become if stored in a dry place, making it very difficult to dissolve them. This condition can be remedied by making a small humidor from a can with a tightly fitting cover, placing a piece of damp blotting paper in the bottom, and the pans of color on top of this. Close the cover, and in 24 hours the colors will have regained their original moist condition, and will dissolve readily.

Magnifying Runner for Slide Rules

Practically every engineer saves time by using a slide rule to aid him in his calculating, but when very accurate work is required the ordinary slide rule often is useless, as, for example, when four places of decimals are required, and the rule gives only a three-place result. However, by fitting a magnifier to the rule in the manner shown in the drawing, a fourth place can easily be obtained. A suitable magnifying lens having been obtained from an optician, an aluminum or sheet-brass frame is made to hold it, as shown. The lens opening in the top of the frame is made about ⅜ in. less in diameter than the lens, which is supported by clips riveted to the frame. After the correct focal distance from the magnifier to the scale has been determined, the ends of the support are bent to fit over the ordinary runner. Two rectangular openings must be cut in the sides of the support to admit light and make the reading easier. The great advantage of such a magnifier is that the original runner of the rule need not be altered, but can be used, either without the magnifier, for rough work, or with it, for more accurate calculations, the magnifier being slipped on without disturbing the adjustment of the slide or runner.—C. A. Oldroyd, Barrow-in-Furness, Eng.

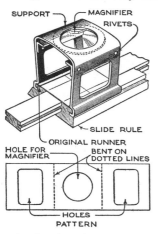

SUPPORT — MAGNIFIER
RIVETS
SLIDE RULE
ORIGINAL RUNNER
HOLE FOR MAGNIFIER
BENT ON DOTTED LINES
HOLES
PATTERN

Tumbler Made from Keg

A small manufacturing plant uses the homemade tumbler shown in the illustration for all the work that a small

A Simple and Cheap Tumbling Barrel, Made from a Wine Keg: The Barrel is Supported on Small Shaft Hangers, Bolted to a Bench

machine of this type can handle. Simplicity and economy as well as small size being essential, a small wine keg is used. The driving and bearing shafts are attached to flanges bolted to the heads of the keg. The bearings are small shaft hangers. A door is cut in the bilge for filling and discharging.

A Rapid Screw-Slotting Fixture

The drawing illustrates a simple but effective fixture for use when cutting the slots in screwheads. This clamp will hold 12 screws while a saw cuts the slots. The V-blocks will accommodate several different sizes, and blocks of various sizes can be made to fit the same fixture, as the bolt shown at the left can be loosened, the V-blocks slid off the guides, and others substituted. The V-blocks and guides are, of course, hardened to withstand wear. The clamping screw can be varied in size and enlarged to meet conditions. To insure that the screws are properly held between the V-blocks, the holes through which the guides pass must be a loose fit; this allows the blocks to adjust themselves to the inequalities of the individual screws and to hold them steady without crushing the threads.

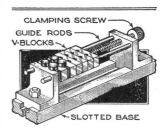

CLAMPING SCREW
GUIDE RODS
V-BLOCKS
SLOTTED BASE

A Homemade Piston Vise

When work is to be done on automobile pistons, some method of holding them firmly without danger of injury must be

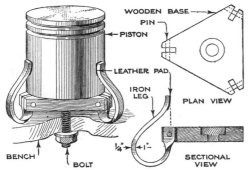

A Simple Clamp for Holding Pistons Securely, and without Danger of Distorting or Scratching Them

used. The drawing shows a piston vise that can be easily assembled by the average worker. The device consists of a wooden base having three pivoted clamps made of ¼-in. machine steel, bent to the form shown and pinned in slots cut in the corners of the triangular base, so as to allow free movement. The upper end of each leg has a piece of leather riveted to it, to prevent scratching of the pistons. A hole is drilled and counterbored in the center of the base to take a bolt that passes through the workbench.

In use, the nut carried on the bolt on the underside of the bench is drawn up, which causes a downward pull on the wooden base. The clamps are so formed that this pressure will cause the lower ends to spread apart, and make the upper ends close in against the piston. The shape of the legs also gives them a certain amount of spring, which prevents injury to the piston due to excessive pressure.—R. H. Kasper, Philadelphia, Pa.

Fire Extinguisher Carried by Watchman

A watchman is employed mainly to guard against thieves and fire, and, while he is usually provided with a gun or other weapon of defense against the former, if he discovers a fire, valuable time is generally lost while he runs for help, or a fire extinguisher. Were he prepared to deal with it at once, the fire might easily be extinguished. For this purpose it is well that the watchman should be supplied with a suitable holster in which he can carry one of the small handpump type of fire extinguishers. It is simple to

use, and in this manner a small blaze, that may grow into a fire of dangerous proportions while the watchman runs to summon help and give an alarm, can be put out at once. The holster can be made of leather, in the form of a cylinder, with one or two metal rings fastened to the edge, so that a shoulder strap can be attached with snap hooks. If desired, the holster can be made close-fitting, so that by making an opening in the bottom for the nozzle, it can be operated without removing it from the holster.

Starting Small Brads

Difficulty is usually experienced in starting small brads into hardwood. To overcome this trouble and prevent the slender

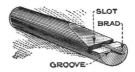

nails from bending, a tool similar to the one shown can be used to advantage. Take a 3-in. length of ⅜-in. steel rod, drill a hole in one end, ¾₁₆ in. less than the length of the brad, and a little larger in diameter. Cut a slot, the thickness of the nail head, at right angles to the hole, then shape the end as indicated. To start the brad into the wood the nail is inserted in the position shown and held with one finger, the hammer being used on the other end of the holder.—C. R. Jones, Chicago, Ill.

Cleaning Threads with Beveled Bolt

Every mechanic will appreciate the advantage of a beveled bolt of the type shown for removing dirt from the threads of a stud hole or nut, when a tap of the proper size is not handy. The motor mechanic, who, after replacing a cylinder head, finds the bolt hole obstructed by a burr, the gasket, or dirt, can use the beveled bolt to clear away the obstruction, so as to get the regular bolt started without loosening all the other bolts again. In cases where the threads have been more or less mutilated, it will help considerably if the tool is casehardened.—G. A. Luers, Washington, District of Columbia.

A Homemade Bench Punch

By CLIFFORD A. BUTTERWORTH

MADE chiefly of wood, the bench punch described in this article is a useful piece of equipment for the small shop. The cost of the materials is small, even though it is necessary to have the few metal parts needed made by a blacksmith or machinist. The compound-leverage principle used in the construction produces a total leverage of 20 to 1, so that metal up to No. 16 gauge can be handled.

The levers and their supports are best made of ash, although any other hardwood can be used. The base is 1½ in. thick, and two blocks are formed as shown and fastened to it from the underside, with screws. The long woden piece that forms the punch guide is then bolted down bushings. The outer support of the hand-lever fulcrum bolt is bolted to a block fastened to the base, another block, 1⅜ in. thick, being placed between the lever and guide. The punch holder is made from a piece of ¾-in. cold-rolled steel rod and is 6 in. long; a ⅜-in. hole, 1½ in. deep, is drilled in the lower end to take the punch, and the holder is fitted with a setscrew. It is connected to the lever by two small links, of ⅛ by ¾-in. iron, slotted at the upper end. The hole in which the punch works may be lined with babbitt, fitted with a brass bushing, or left plain. A piece of metal is fastened to the underside of the lever to prevent wear. The punches are made of ⅜-in.

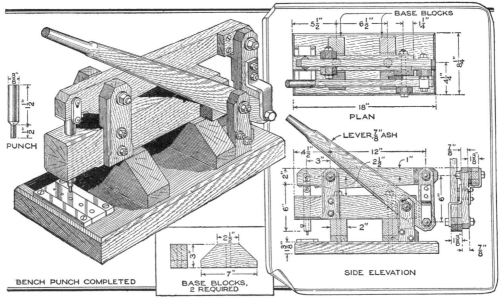

An Easily Made Bench Punch That will Prove of Much Use in the Small Shop: All Heavy Parts are Made of Hardwood, Little Metal Work Being Necessary

with ½-in. bolts, the nuts fitting into recesses in the base. The two lever supports near the front are set in so as to be 1⅛ in. apart. The supports are made of ⅞-in. stock. The length of the hand lever from end to fulcrum is 19 in., and from fulcrum to link bolt, 3½ in. Both levers are 3 in. wide at the fulcrum; they work on ½-in. bolts, and are fitted with short lengths of brass tubing for bushings. At the back end they are fitted with blocks, ½ in. thick, to bring them into alinement with the connecting link. The link is made of ash, 2 in. wide, and the two iron brackets of ¼ by 1¼-in. stock. The bolts fit in the levers tightly, and the link is fitted with

tool steel and hardened. The die is a piece of ⅜ by 1½-in. tool steel, 5 in. long, with five holes ranging from ⅛ to ⅜ in. in diameter drilled along the center line, ¾ in. apart; it fits between two pieces of ⅜ by ¾-in. iron screwed to the base.

Thread-Cutting Compound

A compound for lubricating thread-cutting dies and chasers, that works equally well on all kinds of steel, is made by adding four tablespoonfuls of gum camphor and one tablespoonful of sulphur to each half pint of a half-and-half mixture of lard oil and turpentine.

Hanging Hinged Window Frame from Inside

When a window is to be hung so that it will swing outward, the hinges being

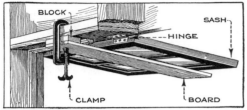

The Difficult Job of Hanging Windows to Swing Outward can be Easily Accomplished Single-Handed by Using the Method Illustrated

on the upper edge of the frame, and the work cannot be reached from the outside by ladder or otherwise, it is a difficult matter to attach the hinges properly. A method of doing this consists in first screwing the hinges to the window sash, after which the position of the holes is carefully transferred onto the upper part of the frame, and holes drilled for the screws. Then take a 1 by 6-in. plank, a little longer than the sash, and clamp this to the upper part of the window opening so that the board projects outward with a slight downward angle. This form of window is often hung in rough construction, or buildings that have not been finished inside, in which case it is an easy matter to get the clamp over the framing. If the inside is finished, the plank can be temporarily nailed in place. Next lift the window sash onto the plank and balance it there, and ease off on the clamp or lower the plank if necessary, until the hinges will lift into place and register with the drilled holes. One man can hang windows of this kind by this method.

Preventing Steel Straightedge from Slipping

A surveyor in the field found that he had been provided with a large drawing board, straightedges, and triangle, but that none of the boards was smooth enough to use a T-square with, even had there been one at hand. It was therefore necessary to use a steel straightedge, but it was found that strips of adhesive tape, applied to the underside, would not provide sufficient friction to prevent the instrument from sliding down the inclined drawing board. It was also discovered, however, that the adhesive tape was the only thing that would stick to the steel, and, in order to obtain

the necessary friction, strips of ordinary table oilcloth were glued to the adhesive tape with liquid glue. Under ordinary conditions glue will not adhere to steel for any length of time, so that it is necessary, in cases of this kind, to apply the adhesive strips first and then glue the oilcloth, with the coated, or smooth, side out, to the tape.—H. E. Balfour, Ottawa, Canada.

Surveyor's Tape Made of Rope

In surveying a piece of land where extreme accuracy is not a requisite, one man can do the job when the tape shown in the drawing is used.

Take a 100-ft. length of window-sash cord, and serve the ends of it around a couple of pins so that the bodies of the pins will be exactly 100 ft. apart. Measure off 10 ft. from one pin and wrap with colored thread, red preferably, as being easiest to see on the ground; continue this for the length of the cord so that it is divided into ten 10-ft. sections. Divide the 10-ft. sections at each end into ten equal sections of 1 ft. each.

To measure distances of less than 100 ft. it is necessary to set the tape on the nearest 10-ft. mark, and measure in feet at the end of the cord, guessing the inches, just as with the steel tape, except

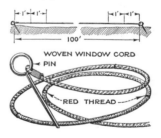

that one sets on a 10-ft. section instead of a 1-ft. division. It is impractical to mark the inches on the cord with anything except ink, which does not show well when the tape is wet. In starting the measurement, push the pin into the ground, inclining it a little in the same direction as the measure is to be taken, and carry the other end out 100 ft.; stick in the second pin, inclining it in the same direction as the other and pull the first one loose. If the line to be run is a long one, it is well to set up the range pole at 100 ft. from the instrument, so as to have something to aline with. Reverse the end of the tape and continue until the desired distance is reached, measuring the final distance in the manner described above.

To get exactly on the line, pull the tape across it as nearly at right angles to the traverse as possible, and at sufficient height to see it with the instrument, placing the middle of one of the 10-ft. sections at one end across where the line should run, as nearly as can be judged with the eye; then go back to the instrument and read the position on the tape at which the stake should be placed.— B. F. Leeper, Chickasaw, Ala.

Level for Tapered Masonry

Anyone acquainted with the operation of laying brick masonry is more or less familiar with the makeshifts used by the masons in fixing up their levels for tapered walls or chimneys. Usually a

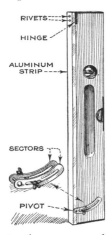

strip of wood that will give the proper taper for the work at hand is nailed to the edge of the level, and often there are no facilities in the field for cutting such a strip with any degree of accuracy. The drawing shows a very simple and practical attachment which forms a permanent part of the level, and can be fitted with very little trouble to any standard instrument. A strip of aluminum, or other light metal, is hinged to the upper end of the level, and at the other end is pivoted to a pair of slotted sectors, clamped against the side of the instrument with a thumbscrew. It will be seen at once how easy it is to set the attachment for any taper. There are many reasons why this attachment is a decided improvement, the chief among them being that time is saved; economy is another consideration, as a good level is soon ruined by constant nailing.

A Kink for Draftsmen

Those who have had little experience in detailing machine parts where very irregular curves are a part of their make-up, will find the following hint helpful. Place the article to be drawn on a sheet of paper on a flat surface with a light suspended directly above the center line of the object. A shadow will be cast by the light which can be pointed off easily with a pencil at intervals of about $\frac{1}{4}$ in. This idea is particularly effective when rapid work is required.

A Quick-Acting Jack

The jack shown in the drawing is particularly useful in a garage or service station because of the time saved in jacking

A Jack for Service Station or Garage, Which Makes the Raising of the Front or Rear of a Car a Matter of Seconds

up the front or rear of a car. The details of construction will be apparent at a glance. The long wooden lever is adjustable to different heights by altering the position of its pivot in the notches. A chain and hook are provided for holding the load when raised from the floor.— Theodore E. Landry, Baton Rouge, La.

Fastening Drawplates on Patterns

When locating and fastening drawplates on deep-lift patterns, the usual practice is to allow them to extend beyond the flat, or cope, face of the pattern. When rammed up on a bottom board, these extending drawplates prevent the molder from laying the pattern

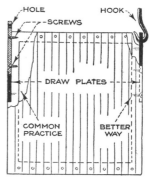

flat on the mold or bottom board; this trouble is often overcome by cutting holes in the bottom board to take the projections, or by removing the plates. A better way of attaching drawplates to the patterns is shown in the drawing, this arrangement making it unnecessary to remove the plates or cut holes in the bottom boards. The end of the plate is brought flush with the cope face, and a recess is gouged out of the pattern just back of the eye, to allow the hooks to be placed in the holes.—M. E. Duggan, Kenosha, Wis.

Preventing Leakage through Pump Lubricators

Sometimes a mysterious leak in an automobile, marine, or stationary engine,

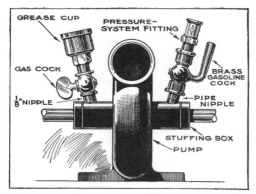

A Simple Remedy for Preventing Loss of the Cooling Water from the Radiator of an Automobile through the Grease Cups on the Pump Bearings

or any machine equipped with a rotary or centrifugal pump, may finally be traced to the grease cups, or other lubricators, supplying the pump shaft. Water will even force its way through the outer threads of a screw cup holding heavy grease, as has often been noticed in the case of small marine engines. Recently an automobile, of popular make, lost considerable water from its radiator, and this was finally traced to the grease nipples on the pump-shaft bearings, the stuffing box and connections being tight.

One sure way to overcome a leak of this character is to place a small cock or valve between the bearing and lubricator, when the lubrication is intermittent, as is usually the case with grease, so that the water cannot back through. A brass gasoline cock, preferably having female ends, may be used, and an old key cock from a discarded gas fixture will also answer. When the grease cup is to be screwed down, or the grease gun applied, the cock is opened, and closed when the greasing is completed. A pressure-system fitting may be fitted, as shown, on the right-hand side of the pump.

A Handy Tool for Farmers

It is quite impossible for the average farmer to have all the tools he could use at hand at all times. The repairman at his shop has this advantage, and when work is taken to him or he is called on some job, he has just the tools needed to make a good repair quickly.

A pair of bolt clippers, although not a common tool in the farmer's kit, is one of the best timesavers when repairs are to be made. One does not hesitate to use a new bolt or new nuts when time is the main thing to save, but usually the time required to remove the old bolt is many times greater than that required to replace it with a new one. In such cases, the bolt clippers will cut the old bolt or the nut, if not too large, in a second. They will also hold the round head of a carriage bolt while the nut is being removed, when a wrench or pliers will not even grip it. There are several sizes of bolt clippers made, but the No. 2 is recommended as the best for all-around work. The larger ones are too heavy to carry and too unhandy to get into small places.

In emergency cases, when a horse gets tangled in a barbed-wire fence, or when a rod or bar has to be cut to release a person or beast after some accident, the clippers are the surest and most rapid tool to have at hand. The clippers can be used in places where a cold chisel or hacksaw could not, and, where light castings are in danger of being broken by pounding, they are safer.

Movable Bench for Repair Pit

A desirable feature for the repair pits of automobile garages, and other shops where such pits are commonly used, as

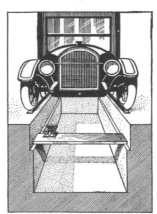

in car barns, is a strong plank that can be used either as a workbench or seat for the workman. As such pits are uniformly made in concrete forms, it is a very simple matter to provide the necessary projections, as shown. Apart from affording a comfortable working position, there will be no necessity to climb out of the pit to reach a vise.

¶To catch the sparks and emery dust when grinding in the lathe, place a small pan of water under the wheel.

Refacing Old Pulleys and Flywheels

By J. S. HAGANS

WOODEN pulleys sometimes warp so that they do not run true, which causes the belts to flap, and causes a great deal of strain and vibration on the shaft. Aside from the mechanical disadvantages, such a pulley is unsightly. This condition, in the case of wooden pulleys, is usually caused by dampness and heat. Occasionally, also, a slipping pulley that has been tightened up a number of times will not run true. Pulleys in this condition can be trued without removing them from the shaft, by using the device illustrated in Figs. 1 and 2 of the drawing. The toolrest part of the fixture is made from a piece of flat iron, bent into the form of a "U," and drilled with a number of holes for attaching the supporting legs. In use, the device is clamped to the sides of a ladder, with the legs or brackets resting on one of the rounds. After the ladder has been placed in position firmly, the fixture is adjusted so that the front edge is close to the rim of the pulley and serves as a rest for the wood chisel, or turning tool, used to true up the wheel.

A similar dodge is used by shopmen engaged in the rebuilding and overhauling of old machinery, for refinishing the faces of flywheels and steel pulleys, to remove nicks and make them like new. Even were it possible to remove the wheels and do the work on a boring or turning mill, this would increase the labor cost, which, on this class of work, must be kept at the lowest possible figure. If the work is done in a small shop where power is available, set up the engine near a lineshaft. Place a suitable pulley on the shaft to revolve the flywheel at a rate of about 30 ft. per minute; this will turn the wheel quite slowly, but the slow speed is desirable. A

Fig. 1 Illustrates the Fixture Used to Turn Down Wooden Pulleys That have Warped. Fig. 3 Shows How the Faces of Steel Flywheels and Pulleys are Finished to Look like New

box is nailed to the floor near the rim of the wheel, and well braced, as in Fig. 3; this arrangement provides a rest for the tool. A narrow belt is then run on one side of the pulley, and wood strips are used to hold the belt near the edge.

Old files make good facing tools for

such work, and are ground as in the drawing, with a square end. By using such a file as a cutting tool and holding it so as to produce a minimum of clearance underneath, like a scraper, a cut can be taken across the face of the wheel that will remove all the surface nicks, paint, and rust, and give a bright new surface. When one side of the wheel has been finished, the

positions of the belt and box are reversed, and the operation repeated on the other half.

For finishing, the workman can use a regular mill file, or if an extremely high finish is desired, it can be obtained by using emery cloth tacked to a block of wood and pressed against the revolving wheel; a little oil should be used with the emery.

Hay Hook Used to Pull Staples

A rancher, finding it necessary to remove about four miles of old fence, tried several methods of pulling the old staples

Using a Hay Hook to Pull the Staples from Wire Fence Greatly Reduced the Labor Involved

without breaking the wire. It was found that a hammer or fencing pliers would not take hold of the staples, as they were deeply imbedded in the wood. As the wire had to be used again in a new fence, it was desirable that there be as few splices as possible. After trying several schemes, the idea of using an ordinary hay hook was hit upon. It was found that the point of the hook could be driven into the wood under the staple, the curve of the tool providing just the proper leverage. Using this tool as illustrated, no time was lost, no more wires were broken, and it was found that the staples could be pulled almost as fast as they could be driven.—W. W. Parker, Firestone, Colo.

Cleaning Platinum Filings

To remove dirt from platinum filings, spread them thinly in an iron pan, and heat to burn out the dust and other inflammable matter that may be present. After cooling, pass a magnet through the filings a number of times to gather up any fragments of steel and iron that are mixed with them. At this stage the filings can be washed before melting them into a button. As some of the metal may be lost in the melting process, it is suggested that the particles be reduced to a button of pure metal with an oxyhydrogen blowpipe.

A Rest for the Soldering Iron

Soldering irons, which are necessarily heavy, have a tiring effect on the user's arm when the job takes any great length of time; especially is this so when the work requires frequent turning, so that the tool must be lifted away from the seam repeatedly. The soldering-iron attachment shown in the illustration has a double use, as it forms a convenient means of holding the iron while it is being heated in the flame of a blowtorch, as well as a rest when in use. The device can be made in a few minutes by bending a piece of flat steel, about ¾ in. wide, into a semicircle and sawing out a slot in each end to clear the shank of the

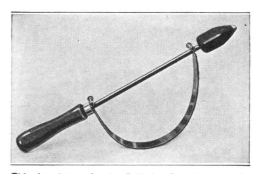

This Attachment for the Soldering Iron Removes the Weight of the Tool from the User's Wrist and Serves to Support the Iron in the Flame

tool. The sides or ends of the slots are doubled over to take pins or screws, which hold the attachment to the iron, leaving the latter free to turn if desired. With this attachment, the full weight of the tool is removed from the arm of the user, the iron being raised or applied to the work by rocking the rest as required. As the rest is intended for repetition work only, it can be slipped on or off in a few seconds. Blocks of wood are used to raise the iron to a height most convenient for the work in hand.—Harry Moore, Montreal, Can.

Guard for Lathe Grinder

The illustration shows a simple sheet-metal guard, applied to a grinder used on the lathe. This is an attachment that is usually overlooked when grinding in the lathe, but it is a very necessary one, as it not only prevents injury to the operator's eyes, but keeps particles of the abrasive from lodging in the ways of the lathe. The grinder is simply a small bench

A Simple Sheet-Metal Guard Used When Grinding in the Lathe: A Clamp Holds It in Place, Making It Instantly Detachable

grinder, bolted to the cross slide, and the guard is attached to the cross slide by a clamp.

Steel Truck for Enameled Flywheels

The problem of handling 80-lb. cast-iron flywheels, after they have been enameled, and placing them in a drying oven, without touching the enameled surface, was solved by a large manufacturer by using the steel truck shown in the illustration. The flywheels are given a coat of black enamel, which is sprayed on in a spray booth, and must be carried from it to a baking oven, where they are baked for two hours at a temperature of about 250° F. The special truck designed to handle these flywheels is made from steel angles and will hold 30 wheels at one time, making a total load of about 2,400 lb.

Owing to the weight of each flywheel, it is necessary to handle them one at a time from the spraying booth, so uprights

A Steel Truck Used in a Large Manufacturing Plant to Carry Enameled Flywheels from Paint-Spraying Booths to the Baking Oven

are placed in the framework of the trucks at the proper distance apart, and lugs riveted on to hold six rows of flywheels. Short lengths of 1-in. iron pipe are put through the shaft holes of the wheels before spraying, and the wheels are placed on the truck with the ends of the pipes resting on the lugs attached to the uprights. When the truck is full, it is pushed on its own casters to the baking oven. The casters have wheels about 6 in. in diameter.—Ed. H. Tingley, Dayton, Ohio.

Gauge for Marking Tubes

To facilitate the drilling of a circle of holes in tubing or cylindrical work, the marking gauge shown in the illustration will be found useful. Generally, if a shaft has to be drilled with any number of holes around the circumference, it is first "nicked" with a tool while it is running

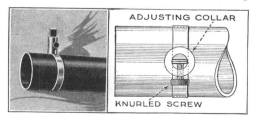

ADJUSTING COLLAR

KNURLED SCREW

A Simple Gauge for Scribing a Line around Tubing or Other Cylindrical Work: The Device Consists of a Strip of Spring Steel and a Clamping Collar

between centers, but this method is not always possible in the case of tubing, as it may not run true enough.

To make this gauge, a piece of flat, flexible steel, long enough to fit around the various sizes of tube, is required. A long collar, of small diameter, is tapped in the side for a knurled tightening screw, and drilled in the center to take the double thickness of spring steel snugly.

In using the gauge, it is slipped over the work, the two ends of the steel band are pulled through the collar and the screw tightened. A scriber is then run around the work, the point bearing against the edge of the gauge, and if the gauge is properly made, this line will be exactly true and at right angles to the bore. It is apparent that the same gauge can be used for shafts as well as tubes, as, in many cases, the appearance of the former is spoiled by a mark such as made by a lathe tool.

Boring Out Pipe-Center Base in Lead Chuck

A pipe center that required boring out to take a new thrust bearing offered a rather difficult problem, as its shape made it hard to hold it true for machining in the lathe. To accomplish this, a lead chuck was made, the center clamped in it, and the whole bolted to the faceplate. A roughly octagonal mold was built of wood, a little larger inside than the outer diameter of the center. This was placed on a flat, level board, the center placed within it, base down, and two bolts were driven into holes bored in the board to receive them. The top of the mold was finished level, so that when filled with lead both faces of the chuck would be approximately parallel and square with the center. A smooth board, with a hole for pouring and a small vent hole, was clamped over the top of the mold, with the point of the pipe center and the two bolts projecting, and the mold poured full of lead.

When cool, the mold was removed, the pipe center driven out, and the chuck bolted to the faceplate and trued up as nearly as possible. Then a light cut was taken along the side of the cavity, using the compound rest, at the same angle as the face of the pipe center, until the center, when placed therein, was found to run true. It was then clamped in place by a couple of short straps, and the boring continued, taking light cuts so as not to throw the chuck out of true. The point of the center projected through the chuck and into the center hole of the faceplate.

Driving Nails to Prevent Splitting

French cabinetmakers have a simple method of preventing large or small nails, when driven close to the edge, from splitting the wood. The nails have their points blunted by tapping the ends lightly with a hammer while resting the heads on a piece of iron. Treated in this manner, the nail, when driven, pushes the wood fiber before it, preventing splitting, whereas the sharp-pointed nail pushes the fibers of the wood to the sides, causing a tendency to split.—Edson E. Shatto, Serena, Ill.

A Precision Testing Block

Many shops often feel the need of having something absolutely square for testing purposes, yet very few have facilities for machining a piece so accurately. The drawing shows a testing block that is made up of several parts, and is so constructed that it can be made in any shop, however meager the equipment. The round body is made of machine steel, a hole being drilled or bored through the center for convenience in handling, and a groove cut around the circumference to take the four adjustable blades. The latter, which should be made of tool steel, need not be accurate except on the outside edge, which should be perfectly flat. They are attached to the body, at right angles to each other, by snug-fitting pins through their centers, which allow them to rock against the bottom of the groove.

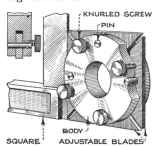

Each blade is tightened separately by a knurled screw, threaded into the body a little to one side of the pins. To set the block square, place the tool on the surface plate and bring an adjustable-blade square, bevel gauge, or similar device that is capable of being adjusted out of square, against one blade. With both pieces set approximately square, set the four blades alternately, adjusting them and the square or bevel until the block can be turned to all four positions, and the contact between blades and square is light-tight; then tighten all the screws. It will be seen that both the block and the other testing piece must be absolutely square when this result is reached, and that the fixture can be used to prove the squareness of any work, with confidence as to accuracy.

Cutting Oil Grooves in Pulleys

The drilling of an oil groove in the bearing of a loose pulley, or similar part, is a simple operation when a loose-fitted drill guide, of the type illustrated, is used.

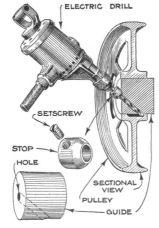

The guide consists of a piece of round bar stock, of approximately the same diameter as the hole in the pulley, with a diagonal hole extending from the center through the side. A stop, to be clamped to the drill, has one edge beveled off to correspond with the angle of the hole in the guide, against which it bears. As the drill is fed forward, the bearing metal is cut away to form a V-bottomed groove. As the guide is free to move in any but a perpendicular direction, variations of the operation described make it possible to cut grooves in a variety of patterns.

❧To clean scale from gray-iron castings, pickle by immersing in water containing not more than one per cent of sulphuric acid and let stand for two or three hours; rinse in cold water, and scour with sharp sand and a fiber brush.

Supplying Lubricant to Drilling Head

To supply lubricating and cooling compound to the eight spindles of a drill head, the arrangement illustrated was successfully used.

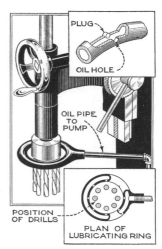

A hollow casting served as the lubricating ring. The holes through which the lubricant flowed were drilled entirely through the walls of the casting, the superfluous orifices in the outside diameter being closed with plugs. The completed lubricating ring was placed around the drilling head, and connected to the oil pump on the machine with pipe. In use, the lubricant is pumped through the holes and runs down the drills.

Roller Truck for Farm or Factory Yard

A truck, built after the style of a baggage truck, but with a long roller instead of wheels, is handy about the farm or factory yard for transporting tools, sacks of grain, and other heavy and bulky loads, the roller permitting use of the device on soft ground. The construction is simple

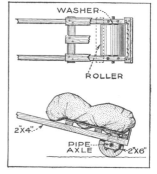

and may be modified to suit the particular use to which the truck is applied. The roller can be made from a piece of large-diameter pipe, provided with wooden ends, which are drilled to accommodate the pipe axle. For a more elaborate truck, a cold-rolled steel axle, running in cast-iron bearings, can be used to make the truck run easier. Washers should be placed on the shaft between the ends of the roller and the bearing blocks.

Cooling System for Hopper-Type Pumping Engine

A 1½-hp. gasoline engine with a hopper-cooled cylinder was used to operate a well pump that elevated water to a tank.

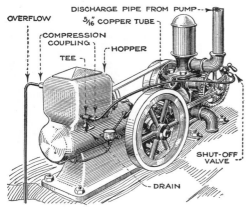

By Connecting a Hopper-Cooled Gasoline Engine to the Discharge Pipe of the Pump, It Operates by a Small Pipe Line. It Is Almost Impossible for the Hopper to Boil Dry

The hopper required periodical filling, and it was feared that this might sometimes be overlooked, so that dangerous overheating might develop. Accordingly, a continuous-flow system was installed by bringing a ⁵⁄₁₆-in. copper pipe from the discharge pipe of the pump to the lower end of the water hopper. A shut-off valve was provided in the line, to cut off the supply of water or regulate its flow. A drain cock was also fitted, close to the hopper. Near the top of the hopper, a hole was drilled and tapped; a compression coupling was screwed into this hole, and another copper tube carried off the overflow. Of course, any other size of pipe and type of couplings can be used, but ⁵⁄₁₆-in. pipe and fittings will generally suffice, as only enough make-up water is required to keep the hopper filled, the temperature of the water usually being kept close to the boiling point.

Annunciators for Group Machine Operators

Where a single operator is responsible for the output of a group of machines, such as screw machines, gear cutters, millers, and the like, an ordinary electric-annunciator and bell system can be used to call to the immediate notice of the workman the machine that requires attention, as when it runs out of stock.

Electrical contacts are arranged on the machines thus equipped, in such a manner that, on the completion of a particular operation, the needle on the annunciator will point to the number of the machine to which it is wired. The contacts, in most cases, can be attached to the bed and table, to automatic stops, or to other parts of the machine. One of the contacts must be insulated from the machine by mounting it on a fiber block.

Micrometer Height Gauge

The height gauge, although a very useful tool, is beyond the reach of many mechanics by reason of its cost. However, a very serviceable instrument can be easily made from the tools found in most kits—a micrometer, square, and depth-gauge scale, held together by the attachment shown in the drawing. The clamping device for holding the micrometer to the perpendicular scale is made from a piece of ½-in. flat steel, slotted at the top for the micrometer frame, and at the rear for the square blade and scale. The slot at the rear is the same width throughout, as the blade of the square and scale will be alike, or nearly so, in thickness. Before this slot is cut, however, the attachment is tapped for the screw which holds the square and scale parts together. The micrometer is held to the attachment by a clamping screw which binds the instrument tightly. When the micrometer has been lined up squarely, a small hole is drilled and a pin inserted; thus, when the tool is to be assembled, it is only necessary to slide the micrometer

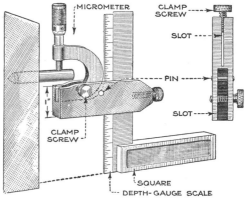

A Substitute for the High-Priced Micrometer Depth Gauge: The Mechanic can Make It Himself from the Tools That Already Form a Part of His Kit

along the slot until the frame touches the pin, when the screw is tightened.

The distance from the top of the micrometer anvil to the bottom of the clamp should be exactly 1 in. Then, when measuring the height of a plug 4.560 in. from the surface plate, the attachment would be set so that the bottom was exactly on the 3-in. line of the scale; this, plus the 1-in. thickness of the attachment, gives 4 in., the height of the anvil face. The micrometer spindle is now raised .560 in., which is the correct height of the plug. If care is taken in reading the scale, accurate results will be had. However, if 1-in. measuring blocks are at hand, the insertion of three of these would give the highest accuracy much more easily.

An Improvised Pipe Vise

When pipe is to be threaded or cut, and there is no pipe vise handy, a pair of pipe wrenches can be rigged up to serve the purpose. The wrenches are applied to the work so that they face in opposite directions, which prevents the pipe from turning either way; both the wrenches and the work are clamped to the bench with blocks.

Pipe to be cut or threaded can be held as securely by this method as in a regu-

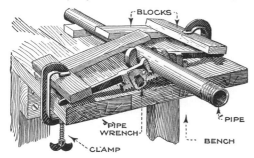

Threading and Cutting Pipe in an Improvised Substitute for a Pipe Vise: Two Pipe Wrenches are Used to Hold the Work, the Whole being Clamped to the Top of the Bench

lar pipe vise, if the wrenches are properly secured and adjusted, although, of course, more time is required to clamp and release the work.

Hand Tapping on a Sensitive Drill

The drawing shows an arrangement for tapping by hand, with the tap held in the chuck of a sensitive drill, the spindle being turned by a handle attachment clamped to the upper end. This method insures a true start of the tap into the hole, especially if the hole is drilled and tapped at a single setting of the work; there is also less chance of tap breakage. If much repetition work is to be done, it would be well to cross either the main

drive belt or the speed-changing belt on the drill press so that the tap can be backed out by power.

The handle attachment may be either a

Holes can be Drilled and Accurately Tapped at a Single Setting of the Work in a Sensitive Drill. A Handle Attachment Clamped to the Spindle Makes the Tap Enter Accurately

casting or forging, or it may be turned from rectangular stock. A key is provided, which fits into the spindle keyway, and the slot in the handle into which this key fits also serves to secure it tightly to the spindle. In starting the tap into the work, pressure is applied to the feed lever with one hand, while the other hand is used to turn the handle. After the tap is started, the feed handle is allowed to work freely, and both hands are used.

A Combined Hammer and Drift

For the particular use of drill-press operators, the combination lead hammer and drift not only saves the operator's time, but he always has at hand the means of driving a drill firmly into its socket without damage. The taper key or drift is made from flat-steel stock and somewhat longer than the usual key, because it must serve for the handle of the hammer, as well. The lead or brass hammer head is cast around the large end of the key, which protrudes about 1/16 in., to form a convenient projection to strike when the key is used for driving out the drill.—M. E. Duggan, Kenosha, Wis.

A CHEAP CONCRETE MIXER

By W. S. BETTS

THE farmer would use much more concrete construction than he does, were it not for the difficulty of mixing any large quantity by hand. A very satisfactory mixer, which should not cost more than $15, may be made by following these plans; it will mix about two wheelbarrow loads at a batch.

The mixer proper is a lime-sulphur barrel, tar barrel, or any other heavy-stave barrel with one good head, that is, a head that is perfectly flat and is firmly attached to the barrel. This barrel rotates around its long axis in a frame that is arranged to tilt within another frame, thus dumping the batch.

The gears, sprockets and chain, shafts, bearings, etc., can be salvaged from a garage junk pile, or purchased from one of the junkmen who make a specialty of wrecking cars. There should be no difficulty in finding the materials, as they are all common automobile parts.

Obtain a bevel gear, about 12 in. in diameter, and its pinion; the pair should have a ratio of about 4 or 5 to 1. This gear will be in the form of a ring bolted to a flange. Remove the flange, and bolt the ring gear to the best head of the barrel, first knocking out the other head. Be very careful to center this gear exactly on the barrel head. From the plumber, get a 3-in. boiler flange union, a 3 to 1-in. bushing to fit the union, and a 1-in. long nipple. The flange union is in two identical members, fastened together by bolts. One member should be centered on the head of the barrel and bolted to the other member on the inside of the head, sandwiching the head between the two members, as in Fig. 4. The bushing and nipple may now be screwed in. It is well to smooth the surface of the nipple with a file, or to skim it in a lathe, if one is available, as it is to turn in a bearing.

Three 14-ft. and one 10-ft. 2 by 6-in. timbers will suffice for the entire frame. It is better to get these dressed on all four sides. The dimensions of the main-frame pieces are shown in Fig. 1, and the manner of framing in Fig. 2. The half-lap joints should be carefully cut, and the inside of each joint should be painted before bolting together. The crosspieces

E, F, and G, may be fastened by means of heavy lag screws if desired, although the method shown is the better. It will be necessary to strengthen the frame in front by two angle irons, shown in Fig. 2. The inside frame, which tilts within the main frame, is shown in Fig. 3. This is pivoted in the main frame, on the right side, by means of a heavy bolt turning in a piece of pipe, as shown in Fig. 7, but the left side is somewhat different. The pivot shaft must extend beyond the main frame, and be held fast, so that the pulley, shown in Fig. 5, may turn upon it. This is best accomplished by means of a flange through which the shaft passes, and by which it is rigidly held, the flange being securely bolted to the outside of the main frame. The hub of a discarded automobile wheel will furnish the flange, and an automobile axle the 1¼-in. shaft. As the inside frame turns upon this shaft, it is well to use a piece of 1¼-in. pipe for a bearing. The inside frame may now be put in place, when it will be found that the projecting end of the board M, Fig. 3, will strike on the back left-hand corner of the outside frame. Cut this corner off so that the inside frame will be nicely seated.

The pulley that takes the belt from the engine should be of such size that the mixer will rotate 40 or 50 times per minute. This is a simple calculation, as the gear ratio at the barrel head is known, and also the speed of the engine, and the size of its pulley. Simply multiply the speed of the engine by the size of the driving pulley, and by the number of teeth in the pinion. Divide this result by the product of the number of teeth in the bevel gear and the number of revolutions the barrel is to make.

For example, supposing that the engine makes 300 r.p.m., the engine pulley is 8 in. in diameter, the bevel gear has 40 teeth, and the pinion 10, and that the speed of the barrel is to be 40 r.p.m.: The speed of the engine, 300, is multiplied by the size of the pulley, 8, and by the number of teeth in the pinion, 10. The result is then divided by the product of the number of teeth in the bevel gear, 40, and the r.p.m. of the barrel, 40; the result is 15. This is

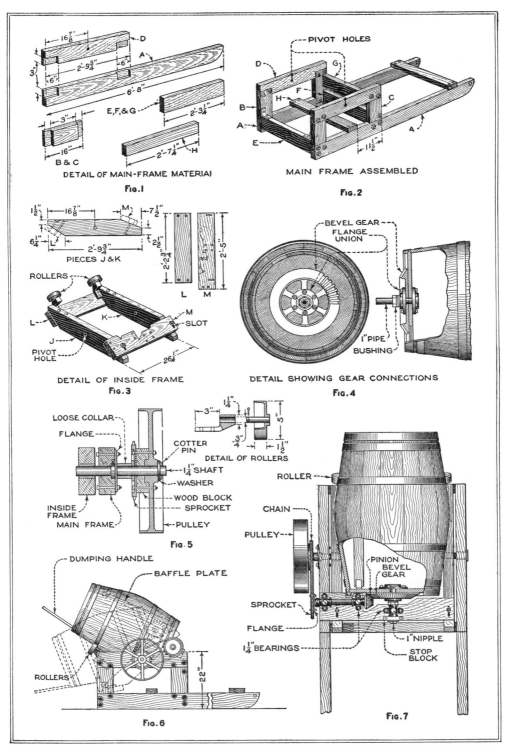

16⅞"
D
A
2'-9¾"
6"
3"
6"
6'-8"
E, F, & G
2'-3½"
3"
16"
B & C
2'-7¼"   H

DETAIL OF MAIN-FRAME MATERIAL
Fɪɢ.1

PIVOT HOLES
D
G
F
H
B
C
A
A
E
11½"

MAIN FRAME ASSEMBLED
Fɪɢ.2

1½"   16⅞"   M   7½"
6¼"   L
2'-9¾"   2½"   2'-5"
PIECES J & K   2'-3¼"
L   M

ROLLERS
L   M
K   SLOT
J
PIVOT
HOLE   26¼"

DETAIL OF INSIDE FRAME
Fɪɢ.3

BEVEL GEAR
FLANGE
UNION

1" PIPE
BUSHING

DETAIL SHOWING GEAR CONNECTIONS
Fɪɢ.4

LOOSE COLLAR
FLANGE
3"   1¼"
5"
COTTER
PIN   ¾"   1½"
DETAIL OF ROLLERS
1¼" SHAFT
WASHER
WOOD BLOCK
SPROCKET
PULLEY
INSIDE
FRAME
MAIN FRAME

Fɪɢ.5

DUMPING HANDLE
BAFFLE PLATE

ROLLER
CHAIN
PULLEY
PINION
BEVEL
GEAR
SPROCKET
FLANGE
1" NIPPLE
1¼" BEARINGS
STOP
BLOCK

ROLLERS   22"

Fɪɢ.6

Fɪɢ.7

Complete Details for the Building of a Cheap but Strong and Durable Concrete Mixer for the Farm: All
the Mechanical Parts may be Obtained from the Automobile Junk Dealer, and the
Necessary Lumber will Usually be Found around the Farm

the size of the necessary pulley, in inches. There is no reduction of motion in the sprockets, as they are of equal size. The pulley should be bored to take the 1¼-in. shaft.

From the junkman obtain two sprockets, such as are used for chain-drive trucks, and about 5 ft. of sprocket chain. These sprockets are in the form of rings bolted to flanges. Remove the flange and bolt the ring to the belt pulley, as in Fig. 5. It will be necessary to block the sprocket out from the pulley, so that the chain may clear, and this is best done with a wood block. Bolt the sprocket through the wood to the spokes of the pulley. The pulley and sprocket may now be slipped onto the shaft, where they should turn easily, first inserting a collar of 1¼-in. pipe and a washer for the pulley to bear against. Fig. 5 shows the complete details.

The builder is now ready to transfer the motion from the pulley and sprocket to the barrel. The motion is received from the pulley by the second sprocket, which is fastened to a 1¼-in. shaft, at the other end of which is keyed the bevel pinion. This pinion engages the bevel gear on the head of the barrel. The details are given in Fig. 7. The shaft turns in two 1¼-in. bearings, such as are used for automobiles. It will be seen that the board M, Fig. 7, is cut away to clear the barrel chine, gears, etc. No dimensions can be given for this, as the amount cut will probably differ in every case. The best way to do this is to put the barrel in place with the nipple resting on board M. Block up the front of the barrel 2½ in. from the board L, Fig. 3. Line the shafts up carefully, and cut away board M, so that the bevel gear may engage with its pinion. Bolt the shaft bearings into place, also the bearing for the nipple. A hardwood stop block, bored to accommodate the nipple, should now be bolted to board M, and a washer and pin inserted. This is to prevent the barrel from sliding forward when tipped.

The front end of the barrel is supported and rotates on two rollers, or casters, shown in Fig. 6. If two heavy discarded ball bearings can be obtained with the other parts, they will make splendid rollers, if protected from the cement and dirt; it will probably be necessary, however, to have these rollers cast in the nearest foundry. The cost should not be over $3 each. The measurements are shown in Fig. 5. These rollers should be bolted to board L, so that the barrel will rotate between them, and so that they will keep the nipple at the head of the barrel central in its bearing.

A dumping handle bolted to the inside frame, and a baffle plate fitted inside the barrel, as indicated in Fig. 6, complete the machine. If the work has been carefully done, the machine should give as good service as commercial types costing five times as much.

Clamp for Squaring Ends of Belts

The successful use of any of the various devices intended for joining the ends of belts requires that the ends be perfectly

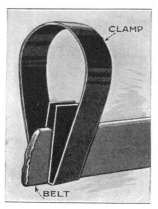

square. If a belt is repaired with its ends uneven, the strain will naturally be unequal, which tends to pull the belt more or less out of line and shorten its life. Many belt repairers use an ordinary square to mark off the broken ends and afterward cut down to the line, but it is a difficult job to cut straight across a belt, the knife always showing a decided tendency to run off.

For such work, the spring clip illustrated is well worth making. The material used is heavy, flat spring steel, annealed and formed as shown, after which it is tempered lightly. It is apparent that no matter what thickness of belt is used the inner ends of the clip always lie flat against the sides. When in use, the belt is laid on one edge and the clip sprung over until the ends rest on the bench; the end of the belt is then sliced off, with the knife held against the side of the clip. Little time and no fuss are required to trim the ends of a belt in this way, as the clip can be sprung on or removed almost instantly.

¶Milling cutters with helical teeth are better for use on wide surfaces than straight-toothed cutters, as the former shave off the metal at an angle and less power is required; they also leave a more finished surface.

A Simple Method Used by a Swimming Instructor to Keep the Surface of an Open-Air Swimming Pool Free from Dust, Sticks, Paper, and Other Débris Blown into the Tank: Left, the Device in Use; Right, the Débris is Collected at a Corner of the Tank and Removed with a Fine-Meshed Wire Scoop

Skimming Flotsam from Surface of a Swimming Pool

At a California amusement park, the Hawaiian instructor at the big outdoor swimming tank has a clever system of keeping the surface of the water free of flotsam, such as dust, twigs, paper, and the like, blown into the pool by the wind. He does the work of cleaning the pool in a few minutes from the edge of the pool without the aid of a boat, and leaves the pond as clean as a sheet of polished glass.

He ties a long rope to the ends of a long stick or scantling, so that when he grasps the middle of the rope a triangle is formed. This allows him to keep the wooden base of the triangle constantly on the surface of the water as he draws it along by the apex, the flexibility of the rope allowing the user to keep ahead of the "drag" and remain on the edge of the pool. The stick always floats with most of its surface well above water, and if dragged at an angle to the sides of the tank, with its inside end in contact with the wall, and not too fast, a perfectly clean area is left behind. In this fashion the device is pulled to a corner of the pool, where the débris is easily and completely gathered up with a fine-mesh wire scoop, as shown in the right-hand photograph.—L. R. Perry, Berkeley, Calif.

Shelter for Small Engine

Many farmers, or dairymen, have a pump and small engine at some distance from the house, the engine being protected, if at all, only by a tarpaulin, or similar covering, to avoid the expense of a pump or engine house. In such cases, a shelter of the type illustrated can be built at a trifling cost for time and materials, and will afford complete protection. The engine is bolted to a concrete-block base, and the box shelter is fastened to one side of the foundation with hinges,

The Life and Usefulness of a Small Farm Gas Engine can be Greatly Increased by Providing Adequate Protection from the Elements

which are held by bolts set in the block. Thus, it is a very simple matter to cover or uncover the engine.—H. J. Engel, New Braunfels, Tex.

Small High-Pressure Pumps

The handicap of being unable to obtain small high-pressure liquid pumps often holds up the work of the experimenter;

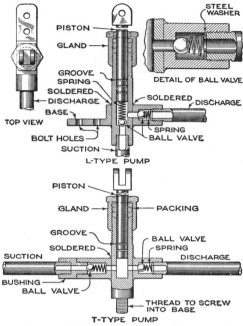

Two Forms of High-Pressure Pumps That will Meet the Requirements of the Experimental Mechanic: Of the Two Types, the L-Type Is the Simpler to Make

pumps of the styles shown, however, can be made at small expense. In these pumps, steel balls taken from ball bearings are used for the valves; where water is to be the element pumped, the use of brass throughout is recommended. The L-type pump is the simpler to make, as it requires a minimum of time and material. The pump cylinder is made of brass, with a carefully reamed hole for the bore. At the bottom of the bore is the suction-valve seat, on which the ball is held by a spring attached to the bottom of the piston. The discharge is through the side opening, which is fitted with a ball valve working outward. The cylinder and piece carrying the discharge valve are made separate, then assembled and soldered or brazed together, making a strong, tight joint; the discharge-valve piece is extended, as shown, to form a base for the attachment of the pump to the rest of the machine. The piston should make a snug fit in the cylinder, and should have two or three grooves cut in its lower end; these grooves hold the liquid and help to

seal the piston. A stuffing box at the upper end carries the packing, which can be adjusted to the proper tightness by screwing down the gland nut.

In the T-type pump, the suction is opposite the discharge, instead of at right angles to it as in the L-type, and in order to make the machining of the suction-valve seat an easy matter, it is cut in a bushing screwed into the valve body. The springs should be well fitted, with the end placed against the ball small enough to prevent it from slipping over the ball, and with the base large enough to center it in the cavity. To make a neat job of these spring seats, small steel washers, with holes in their centers, can be used to hold the springs in place. The pistons or plungers may be operated by eccentrics, cams, or small crankshafts.

Clamp Aids in Fitting Bearings

In all the larger repair or service shops for the most popular make of light automobiles, the bearings of the engine are "burnt in," or fitted with a machine. As these burning machines are quite expensive, the small shop must still use the time-honored method of hand scraping. After the babbitt in the cylinder block and in the bearing cap has been scraped to an approximate fit, the cap is bolted down and the crankshaft revolved. Often the cap bolts must be loosened and tightened several times before a correct fit is

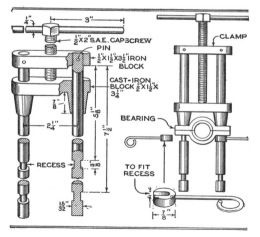

A Fixture for the Automobile-Repair Shop That Cuts Down the Time of Fitting the Main Engine Bearings of Light Automobiles

obtained or the proper number of shims inserted.

By using the tool shown in the drawing, about two-thirds of the time used in fitting the shims can be saved. The two pieces of steel rod, each 9 in. long, are turned and assembled with the other parts, the form and dimensions of which are shown. Two washers are made from tool steel, slotted to fit neatly into the recesses on the rods, a handle is screwed into each, and the washers are then hardened.

To use, place the bearing cap in position, with the estimated correct number of shims under it, place the cast-iron block upon the cap so that the holes coincide, and slip the rods through the holes. If in the first, or center, bearing, the recess near the upper end will extend beyond the upper end of the hole about ⅛ in. If in the rear bearing, the recess near the middle of the rods will be the one to use. Slip the slotted washers into the recesses in the rods, tighten the capscrew, and try the shaft. If it needs more or less shims, loosen the setscrew, pull out the slotted washers and lift off the cap. Repeat the operation until the shaft is just right, then insert the proper bolts, tighten the nuts and insert cotter pins.—Vernon Orr, Pomona, Calif.

Auxiliary Tip for Micrometer

The drawing shows an attachment for micrometer calipers that will be found

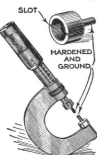

very useful when calipering narrow slots, or places that are not easily measured without their use. Either or both anvil and rod can be fitted with these caps, which are turned, hardened, and ground to the form shown. The inside diameter is a trifle smaller than the diameter of the parts they fit over, but by slotting them as shown, they make a close fit.

Attachment Increases Usefulness of Test Indicator

The drawing shows a fast and accurate way to gauge the height of projecting parts with a familiar type of test indicator to which a simple little attachment is applied. The attachment is turned from machine steel, and taper-bored to fit over the stem of the indicator. If the device is to be used for gauging a large number

of parts, it would be advisable to caseharden the points of contact. The indicator is particularly useful for grinding

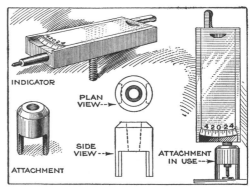

A Simple Attachment, That Slips over the Stem of a Test Indicator of a Familiar Type, Makes the Latter a Direct-Reading Height Gauge

operations. The great advantage gained by using this type of gauge is that the indicator shows how much more metal is to be removed.—T. Rod, Montreal, Can.

Drawbar for a 24-Foot Harrow

As generally equipped, the drawbars of tractor-drawn harrows have a tendency to pull the forward end of the implement either up or down. If the drawbar is made from a single heavy timber, the harrow can be made to run evenly. It is placed on steel-shod runners, which may be made of wood and shod with pieces of tire iron. The width and depth of the

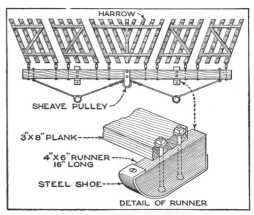

Preventing a Large Power-Drawn Harrow from Pulling Up or Down at the Forward End by Attaching the Harrow to a Single Heavy Timber Mounted on Iron-Shod Runners

runners will vary according to the character of the soil on which the outfit is used and the length of the drawbar. A little experimenting may be necessary to get the right height, but after this is obtained, no further trouble will be experienced. The harrow is attached to the tractor drawbar by means of the equalizing arrangement shown attached to the forward edge of the beam.—L. A. Krider, Hatton, Wash.

Removing Cylinder-Head Plugs

Many types of automobile engines have plugs inserted into the cylinder head so that they can be unscrewed for inspecting, grinding, or removing the valves. Such plugs are usually made to be un-

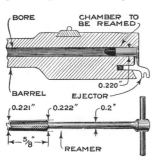

screwed with a hexagonal key or wrench, and this is sometimes lost, broken, or otherwise unavailable when most needed. In such an emergency the plug can be removed or screwed down by a simple method. A hexagonal nut, of a size that will fit into the wrench seat of the plug, is selected and put in place so that about half its thickness projects above the surface, providing a grip for a wrench.— Stephen Gladis, Forestville, Conn.

Rechambering a .22-Caliber Rifle

Those who have done considerable target shooting with a .22-caliber rifle have probably been annoyed at some time or

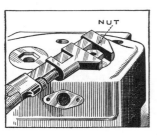

other by the frequent sticking of the shell after it has been discharged. This occurs only in rifles that have been in long and continued use, and the sticking is due to the wearing of the cartridge chamber from the lapping action of the copper on the steel barrel. This wears the forward end of the chamber a trifle larger, and as the fired shells expand to a tight fit, they will not eject on account of the taper in the chamber.

The reamer shown in the drawing was made for rechambering a rifle in which the trouble described had developed. Drill rod was used for the reamer, four flutes were milled out, and the shank turned to the dimensions given in the illustration. The original diameter at the rear of the chamber was .22 in. and the reamer was made .002 in. oversize at the back and .001 in. larger at the front. As the chamber was only ⅝ in. long, the reamer was limited to the same size. In using such a reamer, apply a little lard oil as a lubricant, and turn the tool slowly. The same idea can be applied to rifles of larger caliber when similarly worn.

The ejector is usually blamed when a shell sticks, yet, as often as not, in an old rifle, it is blameless, and the sticking can be traced to the cause assigned.—J. V. Romig, Allentown, Pa.

Vise for the Blacksmith's Anvil

Fitting into the hardy hole of the anvil, a vise such as the one illustrated makes it possible for the smith to do single-handed a variety of work that ordinarily requires the assistance of a helper. The body of the vise is provided with a series of notches along its horizontal extension,

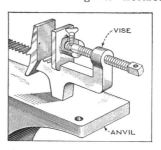

into which the tooth on the back of the rear jaw fits, making the tool quickly adjustable for work of different sizes. The vise screw is grooved on its inner end and is held to the front jaw by means of a screw, the end of which fits in the groove.

A Lathe-Center Driver

The drawing shows an easily made convenience for tapping into place the live and dead centers of a large lathe. A hardwood block is commonly used for the purpose, but this soon splits up.

A heavy body is made up from either machine or tool steel, knurled if desired, and with one end drilled a drive fit for a brass plug, which is drilled and reamed out to fit the 60°

lathe centers. A large, combined center drill and reamer should be used for the purpose; in any event a hole must be drilled beyond the conical bore in order not to injure the point of the lathe center while driving it into the spindle. If the brass plug is set in slightly, as shown, it will help protect the center hole from accidental damage.—H. H. Parker, Oakland, Calif.

Chipping Tough Steel

Every mechanic knows the difficulty of cutting or squaring off the ends of keyways in a tough steel shaft. Also, he knows from long experience that the ordinary cape chisel does not hold out long. The idea illustrated by the drawing shows how a short piece of high-speed steel may be used in a holder to make a thoroughly worthwhile chipping chisel.

The holder is made from a piece of cold-rolled rod, with a square opening broached in the end, into which the high-speed tool bit is inserted and held by means of a setscrew on the side.—John Aures, Buffalo, New York.

A Special Threading Arbor

Cutting an outside thread on work that is already provided with a thread inside, usually results in marring the outer

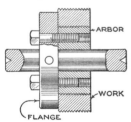

threads when attempting to remove the work from the arbor. With the arbor illustrated, when the capscrews are released, the work may be unscrewed with the fingers.

It consists of a flange, pinned to an arbor, and drilled for two or more capscrews. These capscrews hold to the flange a piece threaded to fit the internal screw on the work, bored an easy push fit on the arbor, and drilled and tapped for the screws.

The work is screwed on when the screws are tight; when the thread has been cut, the screws are loosened, and the work, being no longer screwed up tight against the flange, may be easily removed.—Harry Moore, Rosemount, Que.

Pencil Holder Made from Paper

Draftsmen, shopmen, and others who have occasion to use pencils for any length of time will appreciate the idea shown in the engraving, which allows short pencil stubs being used, to give the utmost in service. The chief objection to the use of pencil stubs is the tight and tiring grip that must be used to hold them

in the fingers. This objection is overcome by rolling a cylinder of stiff paper around the short pencils, one in each end, and binding securely with cotton thread, tape, or an adhesive strip. If the paper is glued along the unbound edge of the cylinder, it will outlast a good many stubs before it must be thrown away.

Babbitt Ladle Made from Wagon Skein

As the illustration shows, an excellent babbitt ladle for use around the farm or lumber camp can be made from an old wagon skein and a piece of iron rod, to serve as a handle. The larger end of the skein is cut square across, heated, and a lip or spout formed on the edge for convenience in pouring the metal. The lag-screw hole at the small end is filled up with a short bolt, with the head

inside and the outside end riveted. One end of the rod used for the handle is flattened, bent around the skein, and welded to the opposite side, making a continuous eye, and a small eye is turned in the other end by which the ladle is hung up when not in use.

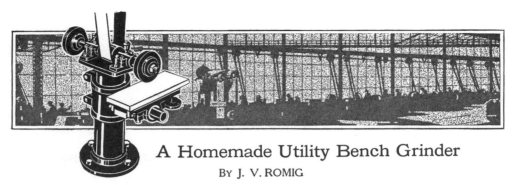

A Homemade Utility Bench Grinder

By J. V. ROMIG

THE grinder illustrated and described in this article is an ideal type of machine for use in the experimental shop, small assembly department, or even the home workshop. The construction is simple, as the parts are easily obtained, and a minimum of machine work is required. Users of a grinder of this type have the benefit of two machines combined in a compact unit without sacrifice of strength.

The head of the machine requires two 1-in. pillow blocks as bearings for the grinding-wheel arbor; these bearings can be bought for a small sum from any machinery-supply house. The spindle, or arbor, is made of good tough steel, and grooves are turned in the bearing surfaces, as shown in Fig. 3. These grooves take the thrust, and prevent the shaft from moving endwise in its bearings. This feature of construction will, of course, make it necessary to rebabbitt the boxes, to make the simplest and strongest bearing. The ends of the spindle are threaded with right and left-hand threads, as shown, for the wheel flanges that hold the grinding wheel to the shaft. The driving pulley is fastened to the spindle between the bearings, and oil cups of adequate capacity are fitted to the bearings to insure proper lubrication.

Four-inch pipe is used to make the pedestal of the machine; this pipe is turned down to an outside diameter of $3^{15}/_{16}$ in. and threaded at each end for screwing into the flanges. The flange at the bottom end of the pipe should be of the largest diameter obtainable, to make a solid base for the machine. The upper flange is shaped into rectangular form, as a base to which the two pillow blocks are bolted, and it may be necessary to have this cast.

In order to use the machine as a surface grinder, a special tee, fitted with an arm to carry the table, is added. A 4 by 4 by 2-in. tee serves as the body; it is chucked in the lathe, and the threads bored out to $3^{15}/_{16}$-in. inside diameter,

making it a neat sliding fit on the turned pipe column. Ears, or lugs, are then welded to the rear side, as shown; these are drilled and tapped for the clamping screws, after which the lugs and tee are split, to make a clamp for holding the support at any position on the column. A section of 2-in. pipe is screwed tightly into the side of the tee; this horizontal piece of pipe is turned down to $1^{15}/_{16}$-in. outside diameter. This arm must be perfectly square with the main column, when assembled, as it supports the pillow-block base of the pivoted worktable.

The worktable is made from a slab of flat steel, with pivot lugs welded to the underside of the rear end; the pivot arrangement for tilting the table is clearly shown. Holes are drilled and tapped through the lugs for taper-pointed screws, the points of which fit into 60° countersunk holes in the pillow-block base. Locknuts hold the screws, when tightened. This pivoting arrangement, together with the elevating screw shown, makes an accurately working mechanism. The weight of the table keeps it down tight and firm while grinding. The horizontal arm is made sufficiently long to allow the work to be moved laterally; the height of the pedestal is also sufficient to permit the use of jigs and fixtures. Since the table has no longitudinal travel, it is necessary to move the work itself, passing it back and forth under the wheel, feeding it in or across with each pass, until the whole area has been surfaced. Bent-wire frames are used to hold work that is too small to be fed by the hand, and on thin, flat stock, masks made of thin metal are used. Large work can be held and moved by C-clamps, as in Fig. 4, while a small toolmaker's vise comes in handy for holding many odd-shaped pieces of work.

As the work is slid back and forth under the wheel, it can readily be seen that the parallelism of the two surfaces must be exact. This feature is the most valuable characteristic of the machine, and makes for accurate quantity work.

For properly dressing and truing the grinding wheel, a diamond dressing tool is clamped in a small vise, held on the table, and brought against the wheel. The diamond point can be guided parallel at a speed of about 2,500 r.p.m., which may be considered an entirely safe and efficient one.

An addition to the machine, which may be looked upon as a refinement,

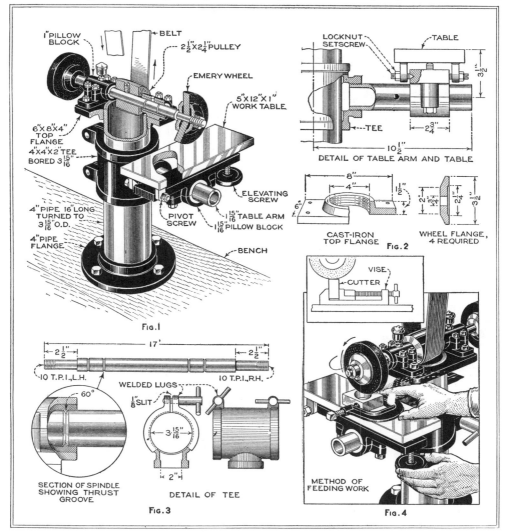

A Small Bench Grinder of a Very Convenient Type for the Small Workshop: All the Parts are Easily Obtained, and the Finished Grinder Is Capable of Accurate Work

with the wheel by clamping a steel square to the table.

Work must always be fed under the wheel from the rear, against the direction of rotation, as in milling-machine practice and for the same reason—to prevent the wheel or cutter from pulling the work in. A 6 by 1-in. grinding wheel is a suitable size for use with this machine.

The spindle or arbor should be driven

would consist of a vertical screw for adjusting the height of the table accurately. This would operate in exactly the same manner as those used for elevating the bed of a drill press. The addition of the screw would, of course, require that a lug be welded to the side of the tee and another to the flange base, the lug on the tee being drilled and tapped to serve as a nut for the screw.

Machine Anneals Parts Rapidly

The machine illustrated is used for annealing the ends of casehardened shackle bolts, which are afterward inserted into

A Machine for Annealing the Ends of Casehardened Shackle Bolts Used in Automobile-Spring Suspensions: The Bolts are Placed on the Radial Pins of a Slowly Revolving Disk and Pass between Gas Flames

the shackles and headed over in a punch press. The operation is practically automatic, and it is only necessary for the operator to place the bolts on the projecting pins of the revolving disk.

This disk is a casting, into the rim of which the pins are driven radially; these pins are just large enough to fit inside the hole drilled through the center of the parts to be annealed. The disk is driven at a slow speed by the worm reduction gear seen at the left in the illustration. Gas and air pipes are arranged at each side of the disk so that an intensely hot flame is directed against the ends of the pieces as they slowly revolve. The operator places the parts on the pins at the front of the disk, and only a few seconds are required to bring the parts to be annealed to a red heat, which is maintained for the period it requires to pass between the double flame.

As soon as the parts have passed below the center of the disk, at the rear, they drop off into a box, where they are allowed to cool.—J. Brandstetter, Chicago, Illinois.

Miscellaneous Uses for Linseed Oil

In the spring, before putting up the door and window screens, give the screens a very light coat of linseed oil on both sides. This treatment will add to the life of the screens by preventing them from rusting.

When there are so many coats of paint on tin roofs that the heat causes it to blister and peel, discontinue the painting and apply an annual coating of linseed oil; this applies also to tin valleys and gutters.

Galvanized-iron downspouts from the gutter troughs begin to rust first on the inside. To prevent this, pour a small amount of the oil into the top of each spout once a year, just after a rain and while the inner surface of the spout is still wet. The oil will distribute itself quite evenly over the wet surface and provide a rustproof coating.—Arthur Thornton, McKeesport, Pa.

Perforated-Pipe Lawn Sprinkler

Along the edge of the pavement, in front of the city hall of a small town, runs a ½-in. pipe that is practically invisible, being half buried in the earth of the parkway. Holes, at intervals of 1 ft., are drilled through the wall of the pipe at an angle of 45° to the pavement. The first

The Grass Plot along the Walk in Front of a City Hall is Kept Sprinkled during the Summer by a Perforated Pipe, the Water having First been Used to Test Water Meters

impression is that the arrangement is installed primarily for watering the lawn but the sprinkling system has another use. A pipe line runs from the basement of the building, where the water meters used within the municipality are tested. When a meter is to be tested it is inserted in the line, the connections tightened, and the water, which would otherwise be wasted, is used for sprinkling. During the winter months, the water from the meter-testing bureau is run into the sewer.—Dale R. Van Horn, College View, Neb.

Hardening Small Coil Springs

Small coil springs made of annealed steel wire should be hardened and tempered while held on an arbor. A process successfully used by jewelers is the following: The soft wire is wound on a threaded arbor of the proper diameter; two small holes are drilled through the arbor, at a distance apart equal to the length of the spring to be wound, and tapped and fitted with large-head screws. One end of the wire is fastened under one screw head, the wire wound on the arbor, and the other end is fastened as the first. The assembly is heated to a cherry red and quenched in cottonseed oil. To temper, the assembly is removed from the oil, held over a flame until the oil on it ignites and burns off, then quenched again.

To blue a spring after hardening, it should be polished thoroughly, and be free from grease or finger marks. It should then be placed, while on the arbor, on a small metal plate, copper being best for the purpose, and the plate placed over a flame. The spring is rolled back and forth until a deep-blue color appears, then quenched in water. The finished spring is removed from the arbor, washed in soap and water, and rinsed and dried in hot sawdust.

Case for Small Drills

Twist drills, especially those of the smaller or numbered sizes, are difficult to keep in proper order when dumped into a compartment of a tool box; besides, time is consumed in hunting for the size wanted, and the drills are liable to injury from contact with other tools. To make all the drills readily accessible, so that the proper size can be selected without hesitation, and prevent them from damage, the case illustrated provides a neat addition to the mechanic's tool kit.

It is made of sheet metal, to any dimensions desired, although the size indicated is convenient for the tool chest. The top and front flap of the case are hinged and provided with a small hasp so that a split ring, or lock, can be used to keep it closed. Two angle pieces are fas-

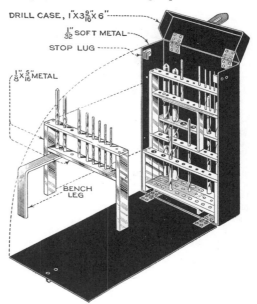

DRILL CASE, 1"X3 9/16"X 6"
1/32" SOFT METAL
STOP LUG
1/8"X 5/16" METAL
BENCH LEG

The Numbered, or Smaller, Sizes of Twist Drills are Kept in Order, So That the Proper Size can be Selected without Delay, and the Tools are Protected against Damage

tened to the sides, inside and near the top, to serve as stop lugs for the flap cover.

The drills are held in their proper order in a series of graduated drill benches, made of flat stock. Each of these benches is provided with a leg that folds underneath, so that a series of drill sizes can be taken from the case and stood on the bench. Five benches, as shown, will hold drills from No. 1 to 80, although the last bench, which holds the sizes from 56 to 80, can be dispensed with if extremely fine work is not done. The size of the drills may be stamped on the upper crosspieces of the holders, or the numbers may be stamped on a piece of sheet metal to be attached a little below the top shelf.—P. A. Daschke, Astoria, L. I.

¶As a rule, timothy should be harvested for hay after the plants have passed out of full bloom, before any of the heads of the earliest plants have begun to turn brown, and before the seed has begun to mature.

Pinch Dogs Made from Nails

Inexpensive pinch dogs can be made from common nails by cutting off the head and end with a hacksaw, and bending them into the desired shape and distance between the prongs. The prongs are filed on the inside to a flat sharp edge. Most pattern-makers desire their pinch dogs to be interchangeable, and in this case, a simple forming fixture can be made from a piece of flat steel. Two holes are drilled the desired distance apart and a little larger than the nail or rod used. The pinch dogs are then bent to the approximate size in a vise, after which the ends are placed in the holes of the fixture and driven down with a hammer.

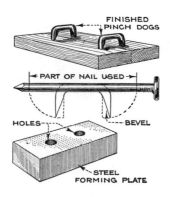

FINISHED PINCH DOGS

PART OF NAIL USED

HOLES

BEVEL

STEEL FORMING PLATE

Proper Angles and Dimensions for Steps and Stairs

Even the most casual observers have noticed that some stairways are much easier to ascend or descend than others, but why this is so, is not easily discovered. A stairway is only a man-made hill used to connect planes at different levels. By referring to the lower part of the accompanying drawing, it will be seen that the human leg swings in an arc, which necessitates a certain amount of "clearance" or drop to the incline or hill the person is ascending or descending. This principle, if applied to the building of steps, makes them easy to climb. A slant of ⅛ in. given to the individual steps will be sufficient, and this is the secret used by expert stair-

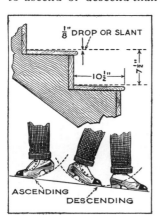

⅛" DROP OR SLANT

10½"

7½"

ASCENDING

DESCENDING

builders for producing what is known as an "easy tread." A flat, or perfectly level, step, or one having a slant toward the back, compels the person to lift the foot high to clear the front edge, and then lower it again to make contact for support. Besides being tiresome to climb, such a stairway is the cause of accidents due to tripping. Tripping is usually experienced on the descent, and the feeling of unnecessary fatigue on the ascent. The height of the steps is another important feature of a properly designed stairway. To be at their best, the steps should not be lower than 7½ in. nor higher than 7⅞ in. The width of the step, or tread, should be approximately 10½ in. The pitch of all stairs should be governed by these dimensions when the layout or design is made.

Powerful Shear Made of Bar Stock

The shears shown in the drawing were made in a sheet-metal shop, for cutting material too heavy for the usual cutters. The design is of special interest, as the method of supporting the fixed cutter blade, and that of providing a powerful leverage with a simple linkage, are quite novel. The main frame is made from a triangular piece of structural plate, cut out to leave a diagonal support for the outer end. The long side of the frame is bent at right angles, and drilled for lag screws, by means of which the device is attached to a post or other support. The movable blade is attached to a lever pivoted at the rear of the frame, while the hand lever is attached to the outside corner of the triangular frame; a link to connect the hand and blade levers completes the shear. The blades are made of tool steel, hardened and tempered, and are removable, so that they can be sharpened or replaced easily.— G. A. Luers, Washington, D. C.

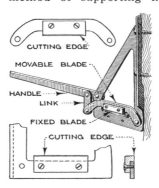

CUTTING EDGE

MOVABLE BLADE

HANDLE

LINK

FIXED BLADE

CUTTING EDGE

❡Blueprints that have been slightly "burnt" can be brought out clearly by light sponging with peroxide of hydrogen.

Chucking Thin Tubes without Distortion

Thin brass or copper tubes are often distorted when held in a three-jaw chuck for facing or threading the ends. For this reason many lathe operators turn up pieces of scrap stock to fit the bore of the tube; this takes the thrust of the jaws, but a better method is shown in the drawing, whereby tubes of any diameter, from 1 in. up, can be adequately supported with very little extra work.

The body of this support is a piece of 1-in. steel turned on one end to fit the taper in the headstock spindle. The front end is tapped for three ⅜-in. headless screws, the holes for which are tapped clear through the piece and are equidistantly spaced around the circumference, to suit the position of the chuck jaws. The device is set in the following manner:

A piece of tubing of the size to be turned is first gripped lightly in the chuck. The support is then held in the tailstock and advanced, each screw being set in turn to touch the inside wall of the tube. The piece is then removed

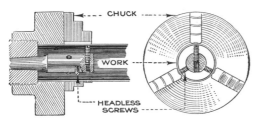

Support for Preventing the Distortion of Thin Tubing When the Jaws of the Lathe Chuck are Tightened Up

from the chuck, and the supporting device is placed in the headstock, after which it is necessary only to slip the work over the screws and tighten the chuck firmly. Care should be taken to have the three screws beyond the face of the chuck, so that large-size tubing, that will not enter the chuck bore, can be handled. Longer screws are used to support tubing of larger diameters.

Lathe Used to Saw Logs

A lot of back-breaking labor in sawing logs can be saved by harnessing the end of the crosscut saw to the faceplate of a lathe. The necessary attachment for the one-man saw is made by forging an eye on the end of a ¾-in. rod, the opposite end of which is flattened and drilled to fit bolts for attaching it to the saw. A ⅝-in.

bolt is used to fasten the rod to the lathe faceplate, the bolt being an easy fit in the eye, to allow it to serve as a crankpin. The stroke of the saw can be adjusted by sliding the bolt closer to or away from

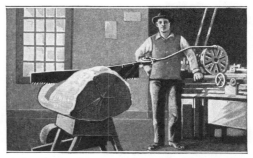

A Log-Sawing Attachment for the Engine Lathe That Relieves the Owner of a Lot of Back-Breaking Labor

the center, and its speed regulated in the ordinary manner; a weight, hung on the connecting rod, may be found necessary for rapid cutting.—Harry J. Bernhard, Pasadena, Calif.

Skid Used to Remove the Soil from Unbraced Excavation

When excavating material from a deep, unbraced sewer trench, two inclined poles were used to remove the soil to the surface. Planks were placed between the poles to form a smooth sliding surface for the drag scraper. The power for hauling the scraper was supplied by a team of horses hitched to the end of a rope; the poles served as guides for the scraper and supported the plank runway.

Skid Arrangement Used to Remove Excavated Material from an Open Sewer Trench: The Soil was Wheeled to the Bottom of the Runway and Dumped into a Drag Scraper, Which was Drawn to the Surface by a Team of Horses

The earth was wheeled to the foot of the skid in wheelbarrows and dumped into the scraper.—Allen P. Child, Kansas City, Missouri.

Blueprinting without a Frame

Good blueprints can be made without the use of a regular printing frame. It is

advisable to have at least one sheet of glass a little larger than the print, and another sheet of the same size for backing will make the job easier, although in its absence a piece of stiff cardboard can be used. A few paper clips around the edges of the glass will hold the improvised frame together and the blueprint paper in close contact with the tracing, or negative, whichever is used.—H. K. Randall, Chicago, Ill.

Disk-Grinding Pulleys

Instead of the slow method of turning flat-faced pulleys in the lathe, the drawing

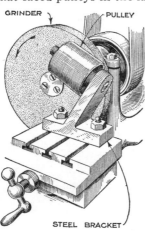

shows a quick and satisfactory method of doing the work that will equal the results obtained on the lathe. Place a steel bracket of the type shown, with a spindle onto which the pulley fits, upon the grinder table, fastening it so the pulley cannot come off but can revolve freely in contact with the face of the grinder. When the machine is started, the table is fed in until the pulley makes contact with the wheel. The result is that the pulley revolves according to the speed of the abrasive disk and in a few minutes the work is done.

Loosening Sticking Screw Caps

The screw tops on cans, jars, and similar receptacles, have the bad habit of sometimes becoming so firmly stuck that force sufficient to damage the cap is necessary in order to remove it. If it is desired to take off the cap easily and without damage so that it can be used again, a simple method consists in soldering two pieces of wire, or nails with points and heads cut off, across the center of the cap about ⅛ in. apart. This will produce a channel or groove, into which any straight-edged piece of metal can be inserted, so that sufficient pressure can be exerted to start the cap.—Leighton Powell, San Francisco, Calif.

Securing a Loose Valve Wheel

The usual method of fastening the valve wheel to a cast-iron valve is by means of a nut and washer, or a single screw on the end of the stem, but when either is ac-

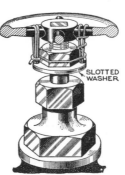

cidentally broken off or lost the wheel may roll off and possibly become lost when urgently needed. To make a proper repair, the valve should be taken down and the broken part machined, but as this is impracticable in many cases, the valve is either left "as is," or some effort made to fasten the wheel. As shown, a nut and washer, and piece of wire can be used to make a serviceable repair. Run a thread-cutting die down the stem for a short distance; then file a slot on opposite sides of the washer and slip it on, followed by the nut. The wire is now twisted around one of the handwheel spokes, brought down through the slot on one side of the washer, up through the slot on the opposite side, and around a spoke on the other side of the wheel. These operations are then reversed, the wire pulled tight and twisted, after which the nut is given a turn or two to stretch the wire. The nut is then locked by a turn of wire around it.

❡To find the pressure in pounds per square inch of a column of water, multiply the height of the column in feet by .434.

A Convenient Folding Drawing Table

By EUGENE F. DAWSON

ARTISTS, draftsmen, and students of mechanical drawing, who find it necessary to do more or less of their work and study at home, will appreciate the desirable features combined in the folding drawing table illustrated. Unless can be folded and stored away in little more space than that required for an ordinary drawing board.

When the table is folded, the legs fit snugly underneath the top, making the whole 5½ in. deep. The legs are about

Upper Left: The Complete Table. Upper Right: Constructional Details. Lower Left and Lower Right: The Height of the Table Varied to Conform to the Posture of the User by Lengthening or Shortening the Chains That Hold the Legs Together. Center: Table, Folded

the amount of work done is great enough to justify it, the standard drawing table cannot be used, as it occupies considerable room—usually at a premium in the home. The table described, however, is light, but strong, and when not in use, 36 in. long, and are cut and hinged, 12 in. below the thumbscrew bolts, by which they are pivoted to the top.

The table top is made from an ordinary drawing board, 25 by 33 in., which is large enough for most purposes. The legs are fastened to battens with bolts and thumb-nuts, the battens also helping to prevent warping of the top. It will be noted that the legs are hinged on the inner sides, and that hooks are provided to make a rigidly locked joint. The working height of the table can be varied to conform to the posture of the user, either sitting or standing, by lengthening or shortening the chains between the legs. The top can be tilted to any angle desired, by manipulation of the thumbnuts on either side.

When completely folded, the table occupies a space 33 by 25 by 5½ in.; this, together with the fact that it can be lifted and carried with one hand, makes it most convenient for the purpose intended.

Renewing Locomotive Piston Heads

A western railroad has solved the problem of renewing locomotive piston heads, which had previously been one of their most troublesome and expensive repairs. The worn piston heads are now placed

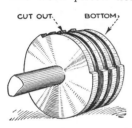

on the slotter and a small cut, generally about ¼ in. deep, is taken across, as shown, for about two-fifths of the diameter, on the bottom side; the ribs are then filled in with bronze by means of an acetylene torch, and the piston is made as good as new, after it has been re-turned in the lathe. The cost and delay of making a new piston head are avoided, and the time required to overhaul the engine is greatly reduced. —A. A. Strafford, Reno, Nev.

A Handy Split T-Bolt

Most machine operators have experienced the annoyance of having to take

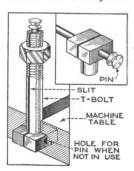

down all or part of an elaborate set-up in order to slide an extra bolt, the use of which has been found necessary, along the T-slot. This, of course, may happen on any machine having a slotted table, but more especially on milling machines, where an extra bolt is often needed and the slot is blocked at both ends. A pair of split T-bolts, such as that shown in the drawing, will make it possible to avoid disturbing the set-up in practically every case. The heads on these bolts should make a good fit in the slot. A hole is drilled lengthwise through the bolt to take a pin, and another, of the same diameter, is drilled through the head, in which the pin is placed to hold the parts together when not in use. To insert the bolt, it is only necessary to drop the halves into the slot, slide them to a position opposite each other, and insert the pin, as shown in the drawing.

Putting on Tight Belts

The problem of how to get a tight belt onto a pulley is one that is met with in every shop at some time or another. New belts are generally cut short to allow for the inevitable stretching that takes place when in use, and, while a belt will soon accommodate itself to the length of drive, considerable force is required at first to place it on the pulley. Various devices are used to do this, but the drawing illustrates a method difficult to surpass for simplicity. A short piece of rope is passed through a hole in a flat board and knotted on one side. The board is placed against the belt, and the rope

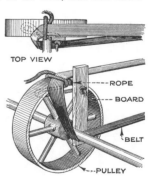

looped around the nearest arm of the pulley, then brought back and passed once around the outside of the belt and inside of the pulley, after which it is passed between the face of the pulley and the underside of the belt, and pulled tightly. When the shaft is turned, the pulley arm pulls the board around, while the belt binds the loose end of the rope tightly between it and the face of the pulley until the belt is properly placed. The board will fall away when the rope is released by the belt. Of course, the shaft should be revolved as slowly as possible.

A Novel Wire Gauge

A peculiar form of wire gauge, especially useful to electrical workers, is a card or piece of metal having mounted on it short straight pieces of wire of every size within the range desired, each size being marked with the proper number. The wires should project for a short distance beyond the edge of the card. By holding this gauge close to any other piece of wire, it is easy for the eye to pick out the wire on the card which has the same diameter as the piece to be gauged. —Curtis Ralston, Chicago, Ill.

An Oil Dropper for the Oilstone

Using kerosene as a lubricant on the modern sharpening stone makes it a very fast and free-cutting tool, but, unlike the old-fashioned stone sprinkled with thick oil, fresh oil must be applied each time it is used.

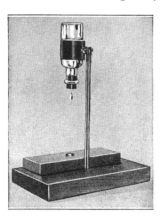

In most cases the oil is applied from oil-cans or even open cans; this is wasteful, as much of the oil runs off the stone altogether. A certain definite feed can be obtained in a simple manner, as shown in the illustration, where the oilstone is held on a wooden stand, and a glass bottle used to hold the kerosene. The ends of a piece of tin wrapped around the bottle are secured by a nut and screw, and the bottle is held at a convenient height, out of the way, by passing some ⅛-in. wire through a hole in the tin and bending it double, afterward driving the ends into the wooden stand. Above and below the hole in the tin, the ends are bent at right angles to form a stop that holds the bottle in a vertical position. A cut is made in one side of the cork stopper, and the feed is regulated by pushing in the cork more or less tightly. No oil is wasted by this device, as the drops fall on the center of the stone, and the oil is evenly distributed over the surface by the movements of the tool being sharpened. When not in use, the bottle is turned right side up in the clamp.

Knife for Cutting Sheet Metal

Those who have difficulty in cutting tin, or other thin sheet metal, straight and without curls, will appreciate the tool il-

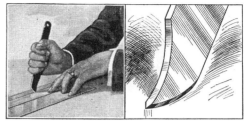

Cutting Sheet Metal Straight without Curls by Means of a Simple Tool Made from a Discarded Power-Hacksaw Blade

lustrated. The knife is made from a part of an old power-hacksaw blade; one end of the blade is ground as shown, and the teeth are also ground off. In cutting sheet metal with this tool, a straightedge is placed on the line to be cut, and the cutter, with its point in contact with the metal and against the straightedge, is drawn toward the body. If a single stroke is not sufficient to cut the metal, the cut can be repeated, care being taken that the point of the cutter is always placed in the same groove. When the score is deep enough, the metal can usually be separated by bending it back and forth once or twice. When the point becomes dull it can be resharpened by grinding the face.

Quick-Reading Micrometer Attachment

A circular clip, that fits closely around the thimble of a micrometer, will be found very useful when turning or grinding a number of pieces to the same size; by means of this, the mechanic is enabled to read the instrument at arm's length, avoiding the usual bending over the machine. The

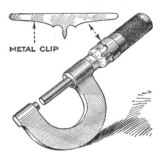

clip is made of sheet metal, and is formed so that it will have enough tension to grip the thimble of the caliper tightly. The pointer is set at the proper graduation on the thimble, making the subsequent reading of the caliper a very simple matter.—Percy W. Thomas, Beloit, Wis.

Settling Chamber for Water System

At one time the water from the city mains contained so much fine sand that pump valves, washers, and other parts, suffered considerable damage. To overcome the trouble, I tried out, with success, a simplified settling chamber. The tank used was a 100-gal. range boiler, connected to the water pipes as shown. The inlet and outlet pipes were made of different sizes, in order to reduce the force of a jet

¾" OUTLET PIPE

1" INLET PIPE

TANK — DRAIN

of water entering the tank, which would have tended to keep the water agitated, and prevented the suspended matter from settling to the bottom. The dotted lines show a pipe usually supplied with a range boiler, which should be removed when the boiler is to be used as a settling tank. A valve is provided at the bottom of the tank for blowing out the sediment.— James E. Noble, Toronto, Can.

Radiator Guard for Tractor

When plowing in brush land, or fields of heavy-growth cornstalks that have not been broken down, I have several times injured the radiator of my tractor. At one time a stick about 4 ft. long was thrown by one of the guide wheels so one end caught the radiator just as the other end struck the ground. The result was that, before the machine could be stopped, a hole was made through

the radiator, breaking five of the tubes and bending many of the cooling fins. To prevent a recurrence of this, and also to prevent trash and corn husks from collecting over the front of the radiator when cutting or husking corn, the protector illustrated was fitted. It is

placed far enough ahead of the radiator not to interfere with the functioning of the cooling system.

Two pieces of wagon tire, 40 in. long, were bent so that the lower part extended forward horizontally about 12 in., the rest of the stock being bent at an angle to meet the top of the radiator. One end of each iron was fastened to the tractor frame at the lower corners of the radiator, and the frame covered with a piece of heavy ¼-in.-mesh screen, attached with rivets. A board was fastened across the space at the bottom to prevent anything from striking the radiator from below. The trash which would formerly collect on the radiator and hinder cooling is now caught by the screen, and ample space is left back of this for the circulation of the air.—G. G. McVicker, North Bend, Neb.

Transferring Pinholes in Shafts

Trouble is often experienced with pinholes in worn shafts that are being replaced. Generally, only the shaft is sent to the repairman, with instructions to make an exact duplicate, which is easy enough so far as the diameter and length of the shaft are concerned, but, should the shaft carry collars or flanges pinned to it, a mistake is easily made, as pinholes are as likely as not to be off center. Unless the hole in the shaft matches up with the hole already drilled in the collar, or other part to be pinned to it, the pin will not enter unless it is filed away or otherwise fitted, the result invariably being an unsatisfactory job.

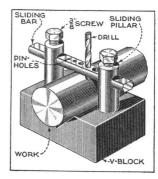

SLIDING BAR — ⅜" SCREW — SLIDING PILLAR — DRILL — PINHOLES — WORK — V-BLOCK

The special V-block shown in the drawing is very handy in cases of this kind, as it enables the operator to reproduce the exact position of the pinholes at once. On each side of the "V" a ¾-in. hole is drilled to take two pieces of cold-rolled steel, these pieces in turn being drilled through for a piece of ½-in. tool steel. This forms a sliding bar that is flattened on the top and bottom and drilled, as shown, for standard-size pins.

The method used in transferring holes is as follows: Place the old shaft in the

V-block, the other end being supported by another V-block, or by packing; then, with the sliding bar loose, insert the drill required in the chuck, and bring it down through the corresponding hole in the bar and through the pinhole in the shaft. Tighten the screws provided for clamping the sliding bar, which is now lined up exactly with the pinhole in the old shaft; the latter is removed, and the new one put in place, clamped down, and drilled. The uprights are not clamped in any way, but are pushed down until the sliding bar touches the shaft.

Knot for Wiring Electrical Fixtures

In order to relieve the terminals of lamp sockets, etc., of the weight of the shades, the ends of the wires should be knotted as shown in the drawing. The knot should be made so that the socket cap will bear against it and support the entire weight, or strain, which prevents the connections from being pulled loose. This knot is simple, and brings both ends of the wire out even. It should be pulled as tightly as possible, so that it will fit easily inside the cap.

ATTACHMENT CAP

Holder for Short Nails

Cabinetmakers, and others required to drive small nails in difficult positions, will lessen the chances of pounded fingers and marred work by use of the nail holder shown in the drawing. A piece of ¼-in. rod of suitable length is bent to the desired form, and the short end is flattened on opposite sides. A piece of spring brass or steel is riveted to one of the flat surfaces, to serve as a clip for holding the nails.

NAIL
SQUARE ROD
RIVET SPRING

A Handy Saw Oiler

Oiling handsaws before storing them away for any length of time is essential if they are to be kept in good condition and free from rust, and if means are provided for doing this quickly and easily, the chances of neglect are materially lessened.

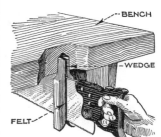

BENCH
WEDGE
FELT

Cut two strips of pine, 1½ in. square by 10 in. long, and glue strips of felt to one side of each strip. Bore a hole in the underside of the workbench and secure the strips in the manner shown, with a wedge between them. The felt is saturated with a good grade of lubricating oil, and, by inserting the back of the saw in the slot, and drawing it back and forth several times, the tool will be covered with a thin film of oil.—G. E. Hendrickson, Argyle, Wis.

Gauge for Setting Lathe Tools

To give the best results, a lathe tool must be used with its cutting edge exactly on, or a little above, the horizontal center line of the work being turned. After years of machine-shop experience, the machinist is able to set his tool without measurement, but the beginner will find the gauge illustrated useful for setting the cutting edge of the tool at its proper height. A piece of mild steel, about ¼ by 1 in., is bent to make a right angle, one side of which is left considerably longer than the other. The short leg of the gauge is carefully ground, until its length exactly equals

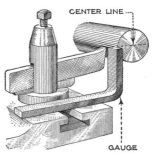

CENTER LINE
GAUGE

the vertical distance from the top of the toolpost block, or compound rest, to the center line of the lathe. The gauge is laid on the rest beside the toolpost, and the operator sets the edge of the tool even with the top of the gauge.—Lowell R. Butcher, Des Moines, Ia.

Preventing Rolls of Roofing Paper from Crushing

It is no longer necessary to crate rolls of prepared roofing paper for transporta-

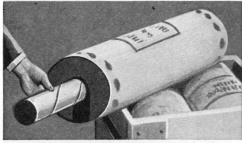

Cardboard Mailing Tubes, Inserted in Rolls of Roofing Paper, as Shown in the Upper Photo, Prevent Crushing During Transportation, as Shown Below

tion in order to prevent the rolls from being crushed flat. One manufacturer of this product inserts two 18-in. cardboard mailing tubes into the center of each 36-in. roll of roofing paper. This arrangement has been found to give adequate protection against crushing, and as a result, the firm is able to quote more attractive prices on export shipments, because it is no longer necessary to crate the product.—Chas. W. Geiger, San Francisco, Calif.

Removing Stains from Ivory

To remove brown spots from ivory, a bell glass or similar cover is required. Place some chloride of lime on a shallow dish, drop some hydrochloric acid on it, and put it underneath the inverted cover together with the object to be cleaned. The work should all be done in the open and in bright sunlight. The combination of the chlorinated lime and acid will generate chlorine gas, which should not be breathed, as it is highly irritating to the air passages. The powerful bleaching action of the gas will remove all discolor-

ations due to age and many other causes. Any spots or stains not removed by the treatment should be rubbed with a lump of tripoli, finishing with fine-powdered rouge. After bleaching the ivory in the chlorine gas, the piece should be washed in a solution of baking soda and water, rinsed in clean water, and dried with a piece of clean linen.

Replating Worn Spots

It is sometimes necessary to plate worn spots on an article so large that it would be a quite expensive item to replate the whole surface. A quick and satisfactory method of plating such worn areas is to fasten the cathode wire to the article to be plated, and the anode wire to a piece of sponge, about 2 in. in diameter. The sponge is dipped into the plating solution, the current turned on, and the metallic deposit is painted on the worn spots by passing the sponge over them. If a slight ridge is created on the line of the old and new deposits, a good burnisher should be used to work down the irregularity.

Fence Made from Discarded Porch Railing

A few years ago architectural styles demanded the addition of railings wherever they could be tacked onto a frame

The Owner of a Suburban Home Removed the "Ornamental" Railing Which Style Demanded When the House was Built, and Used It to Make a Neat Fence

house. Besides being of questionable decorative value, the railings added to the cost of painting. The illustration shows a railing which was removed from a suburban residence and used to make a fence around the yard. The square posts, being hollow, were slipped over stout stakes driven into the ground, holding the whole structure erect. Before driving, the stakes were given a coat of asphaltum paint, to serve as a preservative.—Walter C. Harris, Brooklyn, N. Y.

A Handy Drag-Saw for the Farm

By A. R. FERGUSON

MANY farmers still use the old hand methods of cutting up cordwood for storage, in spite of the fact that there are engines on their farms that can be harnessed to the work, with a very considerable saving in time.

In cases where the wood to be cut into stove lengths is too large for sawing on an ordinary buzz saw, the type shown in the drawing can be built on the side or end of the woodshed in a few hours, at practically no expense, as the materials required are usually at hand. All that is necessary for such a saw is a drag-saw blade, a piece of shafting about 5 ft. long, two pillow blocks, a pulley and flange to fit the shaft, two pieces of 2 by 8-in. plank, each 20 ft. long, and some short lengths of 2 by 6, 2 by 10, and 2

that the smallest type of farm engine can be successfully used to drive it.

The piece of shafting referred to and its pulley are mounted on the pillow blocks, as shown in the drawing, so that the engine can be connected to it. One end of the shaft projects beyond the side of the building, and a second pulley, or a flange, keyed to the shaft at this end, will simplify the attachment of the wooden crank, which is bolted to the shaft; this arrangement makes it unnecessary to provide a steel crank.

The crank is made from a short length of 2 by 10-in. plank, fastened to the pulley or flange on the outer end of the shaft with bolts. A bolt is used for the crankpin. The distance of the crankpin from the center of the shaft will determine

A Homemade Power Drag-Saw for Farmers. Upper Left: A Close-Up, Showing the Crank and Connections of the Pitman, Swinging Crossarm, and Saw Arm. Right: General View of the Outfit. Lower Left: Dog and Saw in Position, the Saw Being Nearly through the Log. Right: The Saw and Dog Lifted at the Completion of a Cut

by 4-in. lumber. If the shafting and pillow blocks are not already at hand, it is possible that their cost can be saved by borrowing them from some of the farm machines, which, as a rule, are in storage when wood is being cut.

A common one-man saw blade may be used in place of the drag-saw, and when a small engine is used, is preferable. However, the light saw must be run slower, and given a lighter feed, or it may buckle, particularly if green wood is being cut. The machine itself has so few parts, and so few sources of friction,

the length of the saw stroke. For engines of 2 hp. or more, the proper stroke will be about 34 in., which means that the bolt used for the crankpin should be located 17 in. from the center of the shaft. Small holes are drilled through the bolt that serves as a crankpin; these are for cotter pins; if locknuts are used on the pin, these cotters are unnecessary. Steel washers should be placed on each side of the pitman on the crankpin, and between all other moving wooden parts, so that the friction of wood against wood will be reduced. The end of the pitman farthest from the crank is supported by a swinging crossarm, as shown in the drawing. The upper end of this arm swings on a bolt in a slotted wooden bracket, fastened to the side of the building, and the lower end on a bolt in a wooden clevis, screwed to the end of the pitman. The open end of the clevis receives the end of the saw arm, which should be long enough to clear the corner of the building. Sidewise movement of the saw arm and saw is prevented by a guide placed about 3 ft. back of the corner of the

the saw from dropping onto the ground. A catch can be provided for holding the saw arm in its elevated position, when a new log is being placed on the carriage, or when it is fed forward for another cut. The saw arm should just move freely inside the guide, while the swinging crossarm should not be less than 6 ft. long and the pitman about 5 ft. The sides of the clevis extend past the swinging crossarm far enough to take the saw arm; this arrangement gives the slight rocking motion to the saw which is es-

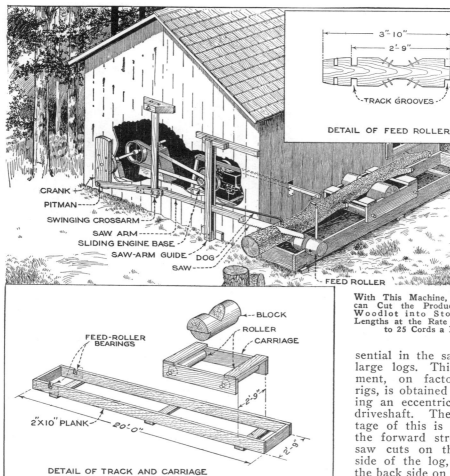

DETAIL OF FEED ROLLER

TRACK GROOVES

3" 10"
2'-9"

CRANK
PITMAN
SWINGING CROSSARM
SAW ARM
SLIDING ENGINE BASE
SAW-ARM GUIDE   DOG
SAW
FEED ROLLER

With This Machine, a Farmer can Cut the Product of His Woodlot into Stove-Wood Lengths at the Rate of from 5 to 25 Cords a Day

FEED-ROLLER BEARINGS
BLOCK
ROLLER
CARRIAGE
2'-9"
2"X10" PLANK   20'-0"
2'-9"

DETAIL OF TRACK AND CARRIAGE

sential in the sawing of large logs. This movement, on factory-made rigs, is obtained by placing an eccentric on the driveshaft. The advantage of this is that, on the forward stroke, the saw cuts on the front side of the log, and on the back side on the back stroke. The driveshaft must revolve from left to right, or counterclock-

building; this guide should be long enough to allow the saw to be raised clear above the largest logs to be cut. Also, the guide should be so arranged that, when the cut is completed, it will prevent

wise, else the sawdust will be pulled to the center of the saw cut or kerf, instead of being thrown out at the sides. Both the saw arm and pitman must be in a straight line and parallel with the side of the building, and the shafting must be level and at right angles to the pitman and saw arm.

If the engine is a small one, a 3-hp. or less, it can be placed on a sliding base in the manner suggested in the drawing, so that by moving it backward or forward the belt will be tightened or loosened for controlling the operation of the saw. The sawyer is thus able to start and stop his saw by means of a lever extending through the side of the building and located near his post; the lever is pulled out to start the saw, and pushed in to stop it. A notch cut out of the underside of the lever forms a catch to prevent movement of the engine while the saw is running. If the engine is too large to be moved readily by this means, an ordinary belt tightener can be used, unless a countershaft with a tight and loose pulley is available.

The carriage track is made 3 ft. wide and 20 ft. long, 2 by 8-in. material being used for the sides and ends, the other crosspieces being made from 2 by 6-in. plank. The end of the track is placed even with the end of the building; the track should be exactly at right angles to the saw, and must be level and solid. The feed roller is made from a piece of log,

about 10 in. in diameter by 3 ft. 10 in. long. Its journals, or track grooves, are 3½ in. in diameter, and just wide enough to turn freely in the notches provided in the forward end of the track. The spikes are made of ⅜-in. steel sharpened on each end and driven into holes drilled about 3 in. deep, after which they are hammered for another inch into the solid wood, to hold them firmly. Four large holes are drilled opposite each other in the outer end of the roller for the insertion of the bar that feeds the log forward.

The log carriage is made as shown in the drawing, with the centerpiece saddled down to match the height of the feed roller, and prevent the log from moving sidewise; a few spikes set into the sides of the notch will prevent the log from slipping off as the feed roll is being turned. While the weight of large logs will be sufficient to prevent them from rolling, the smaller ones must be held by a dog. The latter is made from a piece of flat iron, the end of which is bent at right angles and sharpened, so that it can be driven into the log; this part of the equipment is bolted to the side of the building so that it can be swung up and down as desired. It should be heavy enough to stand a good blow.

Putting Rubber Sleeving on Wire

In electrical work, it is sometimes either necessary or desirable to slip rubber tubing over wire, in addition to the regular insulation, to make sure that there will be no short circuits. To get the sleeving on is rather difficult, as the insulation will slide along with the tubing unless the latter is oversize. One method of simplifying the work consists in waxing the insulation and heating the tubing slightly; another is to soak the tubing for a while in water, which causes it to swell enough to slip on easily. When dry, the sleeving will contract to its original size.—Frank Jablecnik, Chicago, Ill.

Self-Locking Drill Bushing for Slot Jig

In all cases where holes are drilled with their edges close to each other, the novel method of locking a drill bushing shown in the drawing will be found of great assistance. It is shown applied to a box jig used to drill the cores of boring-bar slots, but, of course, can be used in any work of a similar character. A slot is cut in the top plate of the jig, wide enough to

take the drill bushing snugly. In line with this slot a pin is driven in the plate;

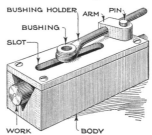

this carries a square steel arm, which in turn, carries the bushing holder, the latter being a piece of drill rod flattened at one end and drilled for the bushing.

It will be seen that, when the bushing is in the slot, it is impossible to move it backward or forward. When it is desired to change the location of the bushing, the holder is lifted, bringing the bushing out of its slot; the arm slides up the pin at the same time. The bushing holder is then pushed farther in or out of the arm, as required, and pushed down again until the bushing enters the slot. Holes can be drilled very closely together in this manner without danger of breaking through, or, if it is desired that they break into each other, no fear need be entertained that the drill will break.— Harry Moore, Montreal, Can.

A Simple Corn Harvester

The contrivance shown in the drawing was devised to supplant the slow and

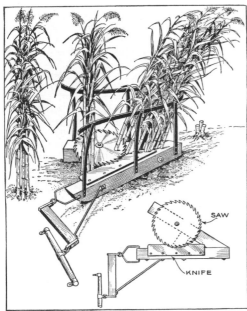

SAW

KNIFE

A Simple Corn-Harvesting Machine, Built by a Farmer to Overcome the Tediousness of Cutting the Corn by Hand

tedious method of cutting corn by hand. A stout wedge-shaped timber frame was made, as indicated. A piece of flat steel was sharpened along one edge to form a knife, and this was bolted to the top side of one part of the frame in such a manner that about 1½ in. projected over the edge of the timber. On the opposite side of the frame an old circular saw was mounted so that it overlapped the knife for an inch or so. Discarded wagon tires were used for making the carrier, which is bolted to the frame, as shown.

In operation, a horse hitched to the device walks just outside the row, causing the cornstalks to strike against the teeth of the saw. As the stalks are carried between the saw and knife, the former revolves and cuts off the stalk, which falls into the carrier. When the carrier is filled, the stalks are removed, ready to be tied and shocked. On account of the unprotected knife arrangement, the operation of such a machine should not be entrusted to a youngster, who might become careless.

¶A tire pump can be used for blowing lamp burners.

Quick Method of Making Blueprints

In small shops, and other places where the facilities for making blueprints are lacking, the following method can be used to produce satisfactory results: Instead of making the original drawing on tracing cloth, use a piece of paraffined tissue paper which is backed up with a piece of new carbon paper. The waxed paper is placed over the carbon, so that pencil marks on it will be intensified by the carbon reproduction on the under-side. The sketch is made in pencil, and the lettering can be printed in on a typewriter, still using the carbon. When finished, a print can be made from either the sketch intensified by the carbon backing, or from the carbon sheet itself. Blueprints made from the sketch will show white lines on a blue background, while prints made from the carbon copy will have a blue line on a white ground.

Coppering Brass for Laying Out

Copperplating brass with a solution of copper sulphate (blue vitriol or blue-stone) and water is not so easily done as on steel. To enable the mechanic to lay out or scribe the work so that the lines can be easily seen, scatter a light coating of steel chips over the surface to be plated, and then apply the liquid. By using this method, brass can be given a thin coating of copper as easily as steel.

Table for Computing English Exchange

The usual printed tables for computing the exchange rate of English currency can hardly be used where the rates fluctuate

POUNDS		SHILLINGS		PENCE	
1	$ 1.00	1	$ .05	1	$.004166
2	2.00	2	.10	2	.008332
3	3.00	3	.15	3	.012498
4	4.00	4	.20	4	.016664
5	5.00	5	.25	5	.020830
6	6.00	6	.30	6	.024996
7	7.00	7	.35	7	.029162
8	8.00	8	.40	8	.033328
9	9.00	9	.45	9	.037494
10	10.00	10	.50	10	.041660
		11	.55	11	.045826
		12	.60	12	.049992
		13	.65		
Useful Table for Quickly and Accurately Converting Pounds, Shillings, and		14	.70	Pence, Quoted at Any Rate of Exchange, into Its Equivalent Value in Currency of the United States	
		15	.75		
		16	.80		
		17	.85		
		18	.90		
		19	.95		
		20	1.00		

as they have done at periods during and since the World War. The table shown herewith is good for all exchange rates, and is used as follows:

Supposing it is desired to convert £16 3s. 4d. into its equivalent in currency of the United States, and assuming that the rate of exchange is $3.62 per pound sterling, add the totals of the following, which have been obtained by reference to the table:

£ 16 ....$16.00
3s. .... .15
4d. .... .016664
                                ————————
                                $16.166664

Multiply the sum obtained above by the exchange rate per pound sterling, or $3.62, the result of which is $58.52332368 or $58.52 in currency of the United States. Any other exchange rate is used in the same manner.

A Ratchetless Windlass

A windlass or hoist that is specially handy around the farm is very simply made by mounting a wooden roller or pulley as shown in the illustration. The wooden roller, shown in Fig. 1, is bored along the axis, an iron rod of the proper diameter driven into the hole and bent to the shape indicated, to form the axle and crank;

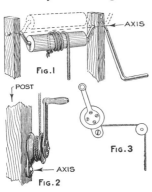

this rod is journaled in two posts, and the crank should be long enough to furnish the proper leverage. A hole, through which the rope is threaded, is bored through the roller as indicated. The rope cannot unwind from the roller when the latter is on the bottom center. It is true that this arrangement has a considerable up-and-down movement, but the usual ratchet is eliminated, a factor of importance when a winch must be improvised from materials at hand. The same principle is applied to the design shown in Fig. 2, in which a small pulley is used. By the use of additional pulleys, as in Fig. 3, the windlass can be arranged to pull a load in any direction, or from any reasonable distance.—W. G. Partin, La Grange, Ga.

❡Do not tamp cinder concrete too much, as the cinders will crush and the surface to be covered by the cement will be increased considerably.

Armrest for Draftsmen

In cases where the draftsman must do a lot of lettering or fine detail work near the bottom of his drawing, there is not,

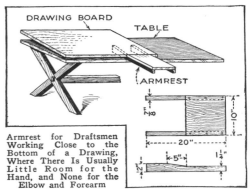

Armrest for Draftsmen Working Close to the Bottom of a Drawing, Where There Is Usually Little Room for the Hand, and None for the Elbow and Forearm

as a rule, enough space on the board for placing the hand, and no support at all for the arm. The armrest illustrated was designed to overcome conditions of this kind. The construction of the rest is amply described by the drawing, and, in use, the projecting ends of the side members are placed underneath the lower edge of the drawing board as shown.

Fixture for Dressing Angular Grinding Wheels

When grinding straight-type formed cutters, it is sometimes necessary to dress the wheel to the exact angle, frequently a difficult thing to do. The drawing shows a fixture for dressing the grinding wheel that can be used to produce accurate results. A hardened and ground slide is attached to the angle plate by a stud; this can be adjusted to any angle by setting

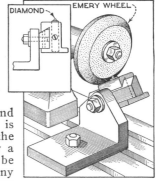

with a protractor from the base. The diamond-tool holder fits on this slide, and is moved back and forth on it to dress the wheel. The fixture may either be clamped to the table of the grinding machine or held on the magnetic chuck. The diamond holder is held in place by a setscrew, as shown in the insert.

Emergency Shank for Farm Implements

On farming implements using disk wheels, the shanks holding them are often broken, or so badly worn that they cannot be used.

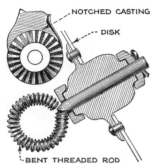

NOTCHED CASTING
DISK
BENT THREADED ROD

New shanks are easily made in the farm workshop, but the teeth for holding the adjustable shank tightly against the notched casting are difficult to form with the file or chisel generally used. An easier method is to use a threading die that will cut threads corresponding as accurately as possible to the notches in the casting, and thread the end of the shank before the eye is formed. Although the threads may not coincide exactly with the notches in the casting, the parts can be bolted together tightly enough to hold.

Screwdriver for Rapid Work

The novel screwdriver shown will be found a handy tool, in cases where a large number of screws are to be turned down, as in assembling operations of different kinds. Starting the screws by hand, as usual, they can be quickly spun into place and tightened. The blade is made of ½-in. stock, and is ground with a concave edge. The upper end of the stock is drilled out and flat-bottomed, leaving a small center only. Next, a recess is cut near the end, and a small hole is drilled through its center, as shown. Another

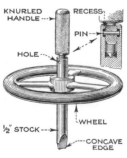

KNURLED HANDLE
RECESS
PIN
HOLE
WHEEL
½" STOCK
CONCAVE EDGE

piece of ½-in. stock is used for the handle, one end of which is turned down to fit loosely into the hole in the blade section. The small end of the handle is turned to a taper point, which runs in the center provided. A pin, a little shorter than the diameter of the recess, is driven into the handle and prevents the parts from becoming separated. An old valve wheel, or any wheel of suitable diameter,

is then driven tightly onto the driver section of the tool, and, if necessary, further secured by a pin. With the screws all started in one or two threads, the screwdriver is placed on each in turn, a slight downward pressure being applied on the handle; this, together with the concave edge, holds the tool in place while the wheel is given a quick twirl which sends the screw home rapidly. A slight pull on the wheel seats the screw tightly.

Double-Faced Finishing Tool

Many turning operations demand that the cut be taken to a shoulder at each end of the work, and ordinarily a change from right to left-hand cutters is necessary, which, unless some form of a turret tool holder is used, requires a separate operation or else a delay while the operator

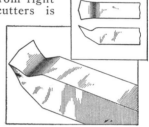

changes from one tool to another. In order to speed up work of this character, the tool illustrated can be used. As will be observed, the tool is made with a clearance and slight bevel from the center, thus adapting it for either right or left-hand cuts without change.—John Harger, Kaimuki, Honolulu, T. H.

Removable Jaws for Machine Vises

The narrow depth of milling-machine vises requires the use of some kind of false jaws when it is necessary to hold work with a bearing point above the fixed jaws; a shaft of such a diameter that the center is higher than the top of the vise jaws is a familiar example. Removing the regular jaws

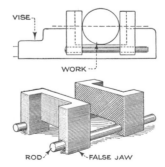

VISE
WORK
ROD
FALSE JAW

and attaching false jaws by means of screws and dowels, may take more time than the job warrants, but the removable jaws illustrated can be slipped into place or out again in a second or two. Two pieces of flat stock are shaped as illustrated, to fit the vise, and cut away in the center to allow the sides to hang down against the sides of the vise. Two tool-steel rods are then driven tightly into holes drilled in one of the jaws, the holes in the other jaw being large enough to allow it to slide on the rod guides. The jaws provide a good bearing for the guide rods and are held in line by them when the vise is tightened on the work.

Testing for Electrical Grounds during Winding Operations

Even the most skilled armature or field-coil winder often finds, on completing his work, that the final electrical test indicates a ground. Should this ground be at the bottom of a slot, where it is difficult to repair, it may be necessary to rewind the entire job. It is quite possible to save this time and expense by testing for grounds during the winding. As will be noted, the iron of the core or field, as the

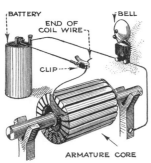

ARMATURE CORE

case may be, is connected electrically through a bell or low-voltage lamp to one terminal of a battery. A flexible lead, with a snap clamp attached, runs from the other battery terminal. When a coil is about to be placed in position, the clamp is clipped to the end of one of the coil wires. By this method, if a ground is made at any time while the coil wires are being placed in the slots, the bell will ring or the lamp light. After one coil has been placed in position, the clamp is fastened to the second coil, and so on, until the job is finished. If it is not convenient or possible to use a snap clamp of the type shown, it is suggested that the battery wire be fastened to the pliers; then, when the wires are being connected or pulled into place, the grounds will be indicated as they are made.

¶A four-per-cent solution of soda and water will lighten overexposed blueprints, or will bleach them nearly white if desired; add more soda to bleach completely.

Handy Type of Scaffold Dogs

The dogs shown in the illustration will prove of value when erecting a scaffold for painters and carpenters, and for other purposes, as they eliminate the necessity of nailing the timbers together, and yet provide perfectly secure structure. The supporting arms are made of iron rod, bent to fit the 2 by 4-in. material commonly

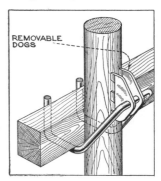

used for scaffolding. The toothed dogs are forged from steel, and bite into the uprights as soon as weight is applied. These dogs can be used with either round or square timbers. — Henry S. Laraby, New Haven, Conn.

Water-Tight Pipe Connection for Concrete Tank

For some time, the making of pipe connections in the walls of concrete tanks has proved a troublesome problem, especially if the connection is to be made below water level, where it must be tight. The drawing shows a simple method of making a water-tight joint that can be easily disconnected. Make up a short nipple, with both ends threaded, so that the flanges can be screwed up to be flush with the inner and outer surfaces of the tank. The flanges are equipped

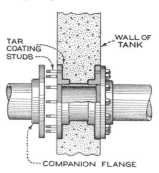

with studs, and the flanges and nipple should be coated with tar before assembling. It should be understood that a sleeve of the same diameter as the outside diameter of the nipple used should be placed in the form before the concrete is poured. After the concrete has set, and the nipple and flanges have been screwed in place, companion flanges are bolted in place.

Driving Pulleys for Magneto Testing

Magnetos are driven from the timing gears of an automobile engine through a coupling, and, when testing the magneto after being repaired, it is usually found unsatisfactory to drive it by running a belt over this coupling. Many repairmen try to use makeshift devices when testing, but the only fitting by which satisfaction can be obtained is a V-groove pulley, the bore of which is tapered, and having a keyway to suit the Woodruff key in the shaft. These pulleys can be made of cast iron, and a set of four or five should be made up at one time. Machined all over, they will have perfect balance, this being necessary, as they must turn at high speed. As the spindles of various magnetos are different in taper as well as in size, one pulley should be made for each of the most commonly encountered types. Some of the older makes use a straight shaft, holding the coupling with a taper pin through shaft and coupling.

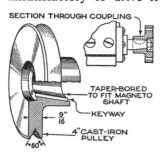

SECTION THROUGH COUPLING

TAPER-BORED TO FIT MAGNETO SHAFT

KEYWAY

9/16

4"CAST-IRON PULLEY

60°

A Brace for Doubletrees

The tendency of a doubletree to wobble and teeter, with the tongue of the implement as a fulcrum, is always an annoyance, causing unnecessary rattle, and a hardship on the team. The brace illustrated overcomes the troubles mentioned, holding the doubletree steady and without interfering with its swiveling movement. A piece of old wagon tire is used for the brace, which is bent in the manner shown. Three holes are drilled in the brace, one at each end for the clevis pins of the doubletree to pass through, and one hole at the middle for the doubletree pin through the tongue.—G. H. Glitzke, Kansas City, Mo.

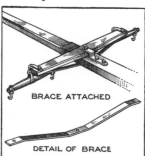

BRACE ATTACHED

DETAIL OF BRACE

To Color Aluminum Black

A solution for coloring aluminum black is made up as follows: Dissolve 1 oz. white arsenic (poison) and 1 oz. sulphate of iron in 12 oz. hydrochloric acid, and add 12 oz. of water. The aluminum to be blackened is well cleaned with fine emery cloth and washed, before immersing it in the blackening solution. It is allowed to remain in this until the color is deep enough, when it is removed, washed in clean water, and dried in fine sawdust, after which a coat of lacquer is applied.

Cutting Keyseats in the Shaper

When no milling machine is available, the work of cutting a round-ended keyseat is awkward. Drilling a hole at each end of the keyway and cutting out the intervening metal on the shaper is the method generally adopted, but as only a very slender tool can be used, breakage is naturally frequent. If the number of keyseats will warrant, the tool and holder shown will be well worth the time spent making them. The holder is simply a piece of rectangular stock, slotted at one end, and drilled and tapped for a long-head screw. The tool is as thick as the width of the keyseat to be cut and as wide as the holder, as will be explained. When assembled, there should be a small clearance at the top between tool and holder, to allow the tool to rock. The keyseats are drilled at the ends in the ordinary way, and a hole is drilled in the middle, the length of the tool being equal to the center-to-center distance of the holes. In operation, the holder is gripped in the toolpost and the clapper box blocked up. The shaper is set to a stroke slightly longer than the length of the tool, which cuts away from the center hole on both forward and backward strokes, the clearance between the top of the tool and bottom of the slot allowing the noncutting end to clear the work. It will be seen that a substantial tool can be used by this method, and that the time required to cut the keyseats is reduced to almost half that required for the older method.

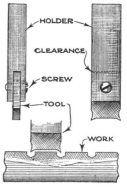

HOLDER

CLEARANCE

SCREW

TOOL

WORK

Making Electrolytic Rectifiers

By CHAS. E. MULLIN

MOST experimenters feel the lack of direct current for recharging small storage batteries, such as are now widely used with radio apparatus; and for running small direct-current motors, electroplating, and such other purposes for which alternating current cannot be used. The residence zones of nearly all cities are, with but few exceptions, served only with alternating current. It is a very simple matter to transform the alternating-

all that might be desired from the standpoint of efficiency, but the power demand for experimental work is not usually very heavy, and therefore the technical efficiency becomes of minor importance when compared with considerations of low cost and convenience.

The rectifier here described utilizes both sides of the alternating-current wave, which makes it just twice as efficient as the single-cell type sometimes used. The

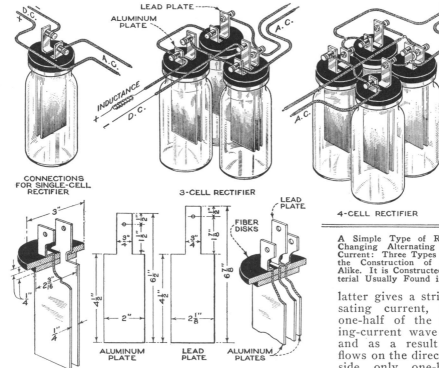

A Simple Type of Rectifier for Changing Alternating to Direct Current: Three Types are Shown, the Construction of All Being Alike. It is Constructed from Material Usually Found in the Shop

latter gives a strictly pulsating current, as only one-half of the alternating-current wave is used, and as a result current flows on the direct-current side only one-half the time.

The three and four-cell rectifiers utilize both sides of the alternating-current wave, and, while the direct current from this type of rectifier is also pulsating in character, current is flowing through the output side practically all the time, and these pulsations may be greatly damped or smoothed by means of an inductance, as will be described later on.

current voltage to almost any other voltage, up or down, by using suitable transformers, but this does not change the character of the current. Rectification of alternating current into direct current is an entirely different matter, and is accomplished by various forms of rectifiers, or by a motor generator, all of which are rather expensive.

For the ordinary requirements of the small-shop man, experimenter, or radio-set owner, a three or four-cell electrolytic rectifier provides the cheapest and most satisfactory method of rectifying the alternating current. Such a rectifier is not

Direct current produced by rectification cannot be used in place of a storage battery for radio receiving on account of its pulsating character, but may be used for recharging the storage battery if it is of small size.

Either the single or multiple-cell type

electrolytic rectifier may be readily constructed from materials usually at hand in the shop or laboratory, or which can be easily bought at very small cost. From my own experience I prefer the three-cell type of rectifier, but the four-cell combination gives a direct current that is slightly steadier. The instructions given apply to the construction of the three-cell type for use on 110-volt alternating circuits, but they may be readily adapted to either the single or four-cell rectifiers. This rectifier will give as much as 5 amperes for very short periods, but heats up under continuous service at even much lighter loads. However, by increasing the surface area of the plates, using larger jars, or by water-cooling the outside of the jars, the current capacity of the rectifier may be increased as desired.

For the three-cell rectifier the following materials will be required:

    2 pieces of sheet lead, 6½ by 2 by 1/16 in.
    1 piece of sheet lead, 6⅞ by 2⅛ by 1/16 in.
    4 pieces pure sheet aluminum, 6½ by 2 by 1/16 in.
    3 pint fruit jars.
    Bakelite or fiber board, about ⅛ or 3/16-in. thick, sufficient to make three disks, 2 3/16 in. in diameter, and three, 3 in. in diameter.

A good grade of sheet iron, or carbon rods or plates, may be substituted for the lead plates. The four aluminum and two of the lead sheets are cut into plates of the same shape and dimensions as indicated by the detail drawing marked "aluminum plate." The larger lead plate is formed to the measurements shown in the other plate-detail drawing. Three disks are cut to fit neatly inside the mouth of the jars, and three larger ones are provided to form covers. Ordinary wood may be used instead of the bakelite or fiber board, but it must first be boiled in paraffin, to prevent warping, and to increase its dielectric properties. One each of the large and small disks are fastened together to form single covers, and slots, about ¼ in. apart, are cut in them; these slots should be just large enough to make a tight fit on the plate lugs. Two of the cells are arranged with one lead and one aluminum plate in each, while the third cell has two aluminum plates, one on each side of the larger lead plate. The plate lugs are offset slightly, as shown in the drawing, in order to hold them securely in place. If desired, holes can be drilled through the plate lugs and the lugs fitted with binding screws or posts to facilitate connecting.

The mouths of the jars should be dipped into melted paraffin for about ½ in.; this will prevent the electrolyte solution from "creeping." The jars are then filled to within about ½ in. of the top with a 5 or 10-per-cent solution of sodium bicarbonate (ordinary baking soda). The covers are then placed on the jars with the plates extending down into the electrolyte. Make certain that no two of the plates touch each other, and connect them as shown in the several drawings with No. 14 insulated copper wire. Suitable fuses and a switch should be provided on the alternating-current side, between the line and the rectifier, as a protection against accident. This switch should always be open when the rectifier is not in use.

To start the rectifier, switch on the alternating-current and close the direct-current circuit for a few minutes through about 100 ohms' resistance, such as a 100-watt lamp; this is only necessary when starting a new rectifier for the first time, but must be done in all cases, or else the device will not work.

In case a smoother current wave is desired than that furnished by the rectifier alone, an inductance may be introduced into the circuit in the manner shown. A suitable inductance is made by winding 200 or more turns of No. 16, or larger, insulated copper wire around a 1 by 1 by 6-in. laminated-iron core. Of course these inductance specifications can be changed, and the larger the core and the more turns of wire upon it, the smoother the direct-current wave will be, but this will cut down the power available.

Chucking Narrow Work

Every mechanic knows the necessity of backing up work against the chuck jaws whenever possible, as this enables heavy

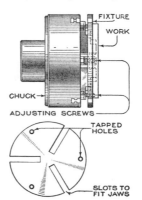

FIXTURE
WORK
CHUCK→
ADJUSTING SCREWS
TAPPED HOLES
SLOTS TO FIT JAWS

cuts to be taken and also greatly facilitates the setting up of the job. A handy fixture that can be instantly attached or detached to a three-jawed chuck is shown in the drawing; it is designed to be used when facing rings, flanges, or covers that are too thin to be backed up against the step of the chuck jaws and still allow the surface to be clear. The supporting piece is made from stock about the same diameter as the chuck, and thick enough to insure strength for the size of chuck used. Three slots are milled in this piece, 120° apart, and wide enough to form a sliding fit over the chuck jaws. Three holes are tapped in this piece, to take a corresponding number of hexagon-headed screws. When a number of pieces require to be faced, the fixture is slipped over the jaws, and the screws are adjusted until the piece is held in the proper position and is running true. The work is then held back on the fixture with one hand while the jaws are tightened. Very thin work can be securely held in this way, supported as it is all the way around. Furthermore, no time is wasted in tapping the work true, always an annoying operation on thin work and, if the job is a light casting, the danger of breakage is avoided.

Flooring Clamp

Flooring clamps of some sort are a necessary part of the carpenter's equipment for laying floorboards, unless he clings to

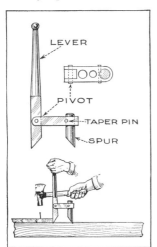

LEVER

PIVOT

TAPER PIN

SPUR

the primitive method of nailing a piece of 2-by-4 stuff to the joist and wedging the warped stock against the rest of the floor.

The lever part of the clamp shown is made of 1-in. square steel, and the connecting link is made from a piece of ¾ by 1¾-in. flat stock; it is slotted at the front, for the lever, and drilled at the rear, for the spur. The spur is a piece of ¾-in. round tool steel, beveled at its lower end. A taper pin is used to hold the spur and link together. One or two holes can be drilled in the link in order to lighten it.

In use, the tool is brought up against the board, and the spur is driven into the joist with a blow of the flooring hatchet or hammer; this being done, pressure is exerted on the lever to bring the board into position for nailing.

Grinding Plane Bits

A practical way of grinding a plane bit at the proper angle is to reverse the plane clamp on the back of the bit and then reverse the grinder tool rest, which will serve as a guide. By placing the edge of the clamp against the straight edge of the rest, and lowering the edge of the bit against the face of the grinding wheel, the proper bevel will be found. Then tighten down the clamp screw,

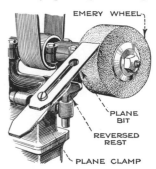

EMERY WHEEL

PLANE BIT

REVERSED REST

PLANE CLAMP

and, by sliding the bit and clamp back and forth across the face of the wheel, a good, straight edge and hollow grind will be obtained. It goes without saying, that the face of the wheel should be perfectly true.—Glen W. Noble, Jesup, Ia.

Method of Mounting Window Sash

In doing some work where it was impracticable either to slide a window sash upward or sidewise, or to hinge it at the top and swing it to the ceiling, the arrangement illustrated was found very satisfactory. The window was hinged to two short iron straps as shown. When the window is closed these straps fit into a mortise cut into the edge of the sash. Wooden dowels, driven into the edges of the sash

GROOVE

FLAT-IRON HINGE

a short distance above the hinges, fit into the grooves on the sides of the window casing. Notches, cut in one side of the grooves as shown, allow the window to be held open at several angles.—Rufus E. Deering, Ottawa, Kan.

¶When cutters do not run true, when the work springs, or when the arbor of the milling machine is too light, wavy lines will show on the surface of the work.

Flooring Saw for Wiremen

An electrical contractor, making a specialty of wiring old houses, devised the saw shown in the drawing for cutting neat openings in the flooring. It was found that this saw saved a great deal of time and labor, and made a much neater cut than could be obtained by any other method.

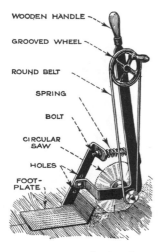

WOODEN HANDLE

GROOVED WHEEL

ROUND BELT

SPRING

BOLT

CIRCULAR SAW

HOLES

FOOT-PLATE

A small circular saw was fastened to a ⅜ by 1¼-in. flat iron bar, bent to the shape shown and provided with a handle. A handwheel, with a groove for the round leather belt used, was fastened to the upper part of the bar, and a smaller grooved pulley was fixed to the arbor on which the saw was fastened. This arbor was made from a bolt, and was supported and held rigid by a long bushing, forced into a hole in the supporting bar. A lug was welded at right angles to the upright bar. A similar lug was provided on the member to which the footplate was fastened, and a bolt and spring connected the two lugs. The spring was open-wound, to give it resistance to compression or expansion, as the pressure on the handle demanded. The bar to which the footplate was fastened was made of the same material as the longer one, and several holes were drilled in it for the purpose of raising or lowering the saw when cutting flooring of different thickness.

Yellow Stain in Hardwood

A troublesome defect often found in hardwood lumber is that known as yellow stain. It is usually distinguished by a pale-yellow color, generally occurs in streaks, and is detected most easily when the wood is surfaced, although it is present at times without discoloration of the wood. Its first symptom may be a moldy appearance of the wood.

The only damage yellow stain is positively known to do, is to mar the finish of the product, since it usually penetrates the wood so deeply that it cannot be surfaced off. It is probable, however, that the fungus actually weakens the wood, and the use of yellow-stained lumber for airplane construction and similar purposes where strength is important, is to be discouraged, until a more definite knowledge is obtained about its action on wood structure.

Lumber can be protected from attack of the yellow-stain fungus by seasoning the stock without delay after it is cut, storing it in a dry place, or treating it with preservatives.

Improving Cutting-Off Tools

The only fault that can be found with ready-made cutting-off tool bits is that there is no taper to the blade, so that clearance is only obtained at the bottom. If a quantity of such bits are on hand in the tool room, they can be taper-ground, to the dimensions shown, on a common surface grinder. This grinding should be done on both sides of the tool, as it is a good idea to remove the oxidized surface of the hardened steel. Tools ground with a taper from front to back will, when set square with the job, cut without tendency to dig, and only require grinding on the front face to resharpen them. It is best to buy the ready-made kind and regrind, as the steel used by the makers is of the best and is properly hardened and treated.

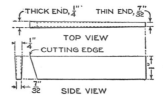

THICK END, ¼" THIN END, 7/32"

TOP VIEW

¼" CUTTING EDGE

7/32" SIDE VIEW

Making Concrete Bases for Steel Posts

The increasing scarcity and cost of wooden fence posts are gradually forcing the steel post into general use. It is well known that steel posts, when set in concrete, will stand firmer and last longer, but the common system of digging the post hole first, setting the post, and then filling the hole with concrete, is a slow and tedious job. I have found the following method much better: Make tubes 6 in. in diameter and 20 in. long from building paper; strengthen the splice by driving a few tacks through the double thickness of paper into a piece of lath placed on the outside. Drive the tacks from inside the tube. Place these tubes in rows on the ground, about a foot from the barn wall and slanting a little toward it. Then drop a little sand or loose dirt into each tube to prevent the concrete from running out at the bottom. Place the lower ends of the posts in the tubes, leaning the upper ends against the barn wall so that they will be approximately centered in the tubes, and fill the latter with concrete. The mixture should be in the proportion of 1 part of cement to 5 parts sand. After the tubes have been filled with the cement and sand mixture, they should be allowed to remain undisturbed until thoroughly dry. When ready for use, the posts and their concrete bases can be loaded onto a wagon and hauled to their destination.—Ed Henderson, Lake Mills, Ia.

Strap Handle for Pounding Block

The common lead block, used in every shop for the purpose of pounding different materials without marking or marring, can be more conveniently handled if a leather or thick-felt strap is attached in the manner shown in the illustration.

As a rule, no particular attention is paid to the shape of the block, weight being the only consideration, but it will be found that blocks molded in the end of a tube are both easy to make and handy to use. To attach the handle, a hole is drilled through the lead, near one end, to take a stud about ¼ in. in diameter. The strap is cut out in one piece, and one end is passed over the stud on one side, then brought over the top and over the stud on the opposite side, doubled and brought back to the first side again, leaving enough space between the parts of the strap to insert the hand easily. Then the nuts are screwed tightly. In this manner the bottom part of the strap forms a pad that lessens the shock of the blows, and the top piece enables the workman to lift the weight without gripping the sides all the time. The advantage of making the handle in one piece is that the top portion cannot fall out of an upright position.

Filling Can for Auto Engines

The breather pipe through which oil is poured into the crankcase of automobile engines is usually so located that a funnel is required when the oil supply is to be replenished, if some of the lubricant is not to be spilled. A convenient filling can for this work can be easily made from an empty oil tin in the manner illustrated. The top and handle of the can

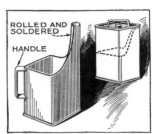

are removed, and the sides are cut away as shown by the dotted lines, leaving a section in one corner; this is rolled over and soldered to form a spout. The handle is soldered to the opposite corner. If made from a 1-gal. can, the filler will have a capacity of about one-half gallon.

Eaves Trough Made Removable

Eaves troughs can be made so as to be easily removed from the house for painting and cleaning. A great many persons are under the impression that, because the material from which the eaves troughs are made is galvanized, it will last more or less indefinitely, with little or no painting. This is a wholly erroneous and expensive notion. Painting the troughs on the building is a laborious undertaking, and the work cannot be done as well from a ladder as it can on the ground. The drawing gives a clear idea of a hanger that makes it possible to remove the trough, and apply the

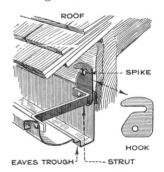

paint thoroughly and comfortably. The hook is made of sheet iron, and is riveted between the Z-shaped brace and the side of the trough, so that it can be swung back. If a large quantity of such fasteners is to be made, a simple blanking die could be used. A short spike, or heavy screw, driven into the side of the building, is used for attaching the hook.

An Adjustable Rest for the Workbench

The manual-training department of a school uses the adjustable work rest shown in the drawing on the work-

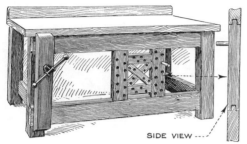

SIDE VIEW

A Support or Rest for the Workbench That Accommodates Work of Any Width or Shape

benches. The rest is provided with a tongue and groove on its upper and lower edges, as shown at the right; these fit corresponding guides in the horizontal braces of the bench. The frame, or rest, is drilled with irregularly spaced holes so that work of any shape, held in the vise, can be supported by inserting pins in the proper holes. It will be noted that the groove is cut on the upper brace of the bench; this prevents its becoming choked with sawdust and other débris of the shop.—Irwin L. Morrow, Muncie, Ind.

Neat Drill-Press Stop Collar

For the smaller sizes of drill presses, the split stop collar shown in the drawing will be found much more convenient than the type commonly used, as no screwdriver or wrench is required to fasten it to the spindle. Furthermore, this stop collar presents a neater appearance and is less likely to catch the operator's clothes than the common type. It is made in two pieces, the split collar itself and a knurled ring that screws onto it. The collar is bored to make a close fit around the drill spindle, and a slightly tapering, fine-pitched thread is cut on the circumference. The thread is turned down on both ends, only the center portion being left, the width of this being slightly greater than the width of the knurled ring. A hole is drilled through the side of the collar for a pin that fits

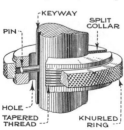

KEYWAY
SPLIT COLLAR
PIN
HOLE
TAPERED THREAD
KNURLED RING

into the keyway of the drill-press spindle. To complete the stop, a hole is drilled through the collar, in line with the saw slot, to provide further spring, and the knurled ring is fitted. When slipped onto the spindle of the machine, the collar can be loosened or tightened in a second, the pin in the side preventing it from turning on the spindle while this is being done. Care should be taken to use a fine-pitch thread and turn down the ends to suit the narrow ring, as otherwise the collar will be difficult to adjust.

Magneto Magnets Used for Clamps

Old magnets from the magneto of a well-known light automobile, which are obtainable at garages and service stations, can be used to make serviceable clamps for bolting work down to machine tables. What magnetism there may be remaining in the parts can be removed by heating them to a bright red, and quenching in water.—J. H. Rouse, San Francisco, Calif.

Filling the Grease Gun

Filling the grease gun is a messy job, especially when one is in a hurry. A very convenient and easy way to fill the cylinder of the gun is illustrated in the drawing. Cut a disk of wood, slightly smaller in diameter than the inside of the grease can, and bore a hole through the center of the wood a trifle smaller than the end of the grease gun. Then glue or tack a strip of felt around the circumference of the wooden disk, so as to make a snug fit inside the can of grease. By placing the disk inside the can, with the end of the grease-gun cylinder over the hole in the center, and applying pressure, the lubricant will be forced upward through the hole into the barrel of the gun. The disk can be left in the can, until empty, to serve as a cover.—Rudolph H. Kasper, Philadelphia, Pa.

WOOD　FELT
GREASE GUN
GREASE

Shop Notes

How to Make Concrete Tile

By HJALMER LINDQUIST

FLOORING, wall facing, garden walks, etc., are some of the common constructions in which concrete tiles are used. These tiles are not at all difficult to make, and the results of their use are well worth the time expended.

When only a few tiles are wanted, the forms can be made from two pieces of board, tacked flat to a wide plank, with other pieces tacked between them at right angles, to divide the individual tiles. The nails with which the boards

of tiles are to be made, it will, of course, pay to have good forms ready beforehand so that the work can be done quickly.

The forms are filled with a wet concrete mixture of 3 parts sand and 1 part cement. Some kind of reinforcing wire should be placed in the center of each tile to strengthen it; a coarse wire mesh will serve the purpose. The form is half-filled with concrete, the reinforcing put in, and the rest of the cement applied until the

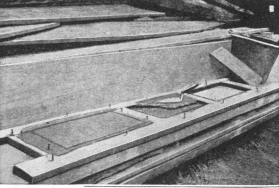

Upper Left: Coating the Tile Surface with Neat Cement. Upper Right: Simple Forms for the Production of the Tile. Lower Left: A Group of Finished Concrete Tiles

mold is filled. A little care will be required to get the corners of the work square and sharp; all corners should be well tamped with a short wire. The concrete is "struck" off flush with the top of the forms by drawing a straightedge over them. The top surface of the tile is left rough. Cleaning the top edge of the form, next to the tile, with the point of a trowel, will help give the tiles a better appearance when they are dry.

When finished, the tiles should be allowed to dry, before they are taken from

are fastened are only partly driven in, so that they can be easily pulled when the tiles have set. These forms should be squared, and the lumber from which they are made should have straight, smooth edges. If a considerable number

the forms, preferably in the shade, as rapid setting is not advisable. They should then be soaked in water for about two days to harden them. After being removed from the water, they are allowed to dry overnight, and the top surfaces are coated with a neat cement, which is a mixture of cement and water, a little thicker than cream. Whipping the cement while mixing it seems to give a slight gloss to the work. A little of the neat cement mixture is spread over the tile surface and shaken into contact and smoothness by rubbing the bottom of the piece over a thin layer of sand sprinkled on a smooth surface. When the top coating has set for a day, the tiles should be placed in water for a day or two, then allowed to dry for a day before coloring.

Coloring of the tiles is effected by inexpensive chemical solutions. A saturated solution of copper sulphate, or bluestone, gives a bluish-green color,

while a solution made from sulphate of iron or copperas produces a rust-red. By using a solution of either of these salts as a mordant, any of the dry cement colors can be used. The dry cement color is mixed with water to the desired shade, and then about ⅟₂₅ part, liquid measure, of either copperas or bluestone solution is stirred in. A syringe should be used in applying the colors; with this the colors can easily be varied and blended together on the surface of the work.

The tiles should be set in soft mortar, on a solid base, and the appearance of the work is often improved by spacing the tiles about ½ in. apart and filling this space with colored mortar. To color the mortar, the dry colors can be mixed with it directly. The tiles shown in the illustration are about 7 by 14 in. and ¾ in. thick. Other sizes, of course, can be made in the same manner.

Gas Burner for Heating Furnaces

The high cost of gas-furnace burners led a householder to devise a burner that

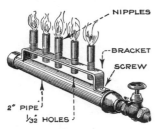

is very easily made, and at the same time cheap and efficient. The burner consists simply of a flat-iron bracket fastened to a 2-in. pipe by a machine screw at each end. The burner tips screw into holes in the bracket, so that they can be adjusted individually to the proper distance from the small holes that serve as outlets for the gas.—John H. Schalek, Pittsburgh, Pa.

Strength of Douglas Fir and Southern Pine

There is little difference between the strength of the southern pines and that of Douglas fir from the Pacific Northwest, as government tests show. True long-leaf yellow pine averages heavier, stronger, and tougher than Douglas fir. True short-leaf pine averages heavier and tougher than fir, but is about equal to it in strength when used as a beam or post. Loblolly pine, though averaging heavier than the fir, is somewhat weaker. The difference in strength between any of these pines and Douglas fir, however, is

not so great but that low-density pieces of the one species are weaker than the average for the other species.

As far as strength is concerned, the choice between any of two lots of southern pine and Douglas fir will depend upon the grade and density of each lot. The mountain type of Douglas fir averages considerably weaker than the Pacific-coast type.

Runner for a Plowshare

A shoe or runner, such as that shown in the drawing, will save a lot of time

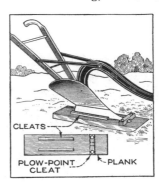

and energy when the plow is being taken to and from the field. A thick plank of oak, or other hardwood, is provided with a cleat in which a notch is cut; this is fastened to the forward end of the shoe and the point of the plow inserted into the notch. Cleats nailed on either side of the share serve to prevent it from slipping off to one side. The front end of the shoe is beveled or rounded off, so that it will ride over any obstruction in its path.— F. H. Hanford, Detroit, Mich.

Antique Color for New Parchment

New parchment can be given the appearance of great age by soaking it in a 5-per-cent solution of potassium permanganate and then washing in clean water. The solution acts very quickly, and care must be taken that the parchment is not allowed to remain in it too long, or the color will be too dark. If the parchment should be a little greasy, wash it with soap and water, and rinse before placing in the permanganate solution. If the parchment is to be pasted to anything, as, for example, the covers of a book, fasten it to a board with thumbtacks and allow it to dry slowly.—Jean L. Martin, Paris, France.

Removing Bushings from Blind Holes

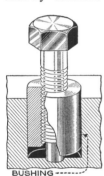

Although it is easy to install a bushing in a blind hole, its removal is an entirely different matter. The shopman is frequently called upon to remove such a bushing, and the method described may help when he meets with an obstinate case. The bushing hole is first tapped, using a bottoming tap, and running it down to the bottom of the hole; this will thread all but a very small length of the bushing. An ordinary bolt with the same size thread as the tap is turned down or filed so that a portion of the end is smaller than the bore of the bushing. By screwing this bolt into the threads cut on the inside of the bushing, the end of the bolt strikes the back of the hole and the bushing is forced out. If the bolt screws into the end of the thread before the bushing is entirely out, the bolt may be removed and a small block placed below; this will usually give enough additional purchase to finish the job.

Fuse-Wire Gaskets for Tight Joints

Cutting gaskets from sheet lead, as usually performed, is wasteful, and it is also difficult to cut them uniformly without special tools. In addition to this, if the surfaces to be jointed are not true at all points, great pressure will be required to make the joint tight. On a small ice

machine, 40-ampere fuse wire was used instead of sheet lead, with entirely satisfactory results. A step was cut in the cover of the machine, as shown, and the wire laid in this step and cut so that the ends just met. A groove was then cut

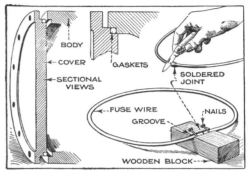

Fuse Wire Used Instead of Sheet-Lead Gaskets, in Ice-Machine Cylinder Heads: The Method of Jointing the Ends of the Wire is Shown at the Lower Right

in a small block of wood, and the ends of the fuse wire held together, in the groove, with small nails. Soldering paste was applied and the ends soldered, after which the joint was trimmed smooth with a pocketknife. With the lead ring in place, very little pressure was needed to make a gas-tight joint, as the wire squeezed out against all four sides of the joint.

Adjustable V-Blocks from Pipe Fittings

One of the handiest sets of V-blocks for use on the drill press or milling machine can be made with a minimum of machine work, from standard pipe fittings. These blocks are adjustable for height, which makes them particularly serviceable when the work is to be supported at points having different diameters.

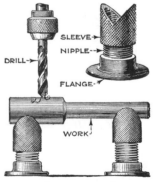

The base of each block is made from a pipe flange, which needs no machining whatever. The standard is a short nipple screwed tightly into the flange. The "V" proper is made from a threaded sleeve or coupling, having a knurled outer surface. The 90° "V" can be cut out with a saw and finished by filing.

Supporting Long Bars in a Speed Lathe

Speed lathes are not, as a rule, equipped with any means for supporting long bars, and, as it is impossible to run these at any

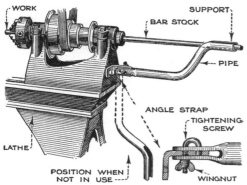

A Support for the Speed Lathe Makes It Possible to Work from the Bar without Cutting the Stock into Short Lengths

speed without support of some kind, the general practice is to cut the long stock into short lengths. In this manner a pile of short ends, which have no more than junk value, soon accumulates. This type of lathe is not always used for bar work, so the support illustrated has the advantage of being readily dropped out of the way, yet remaining a part of the machine.

A piece of iron, bent to form a right-angled bracket, is bolted to the end of the machine, and a piece of pipe is slotted at one end to fit over the bracket. The pipe is then bent at a convenient distance, and the top bend is ground or cut away to allow the bars to pass through. The two parts of the support are connected by a U-bolt, as shown, the long end of which is threaded for a wingnut, so that the device can be swung up into position or released in a few seconds, the only necessary operation being the tightening or releasing of the hook bolt.

Finding Unusual Armature Trouble

The armature of an automobile generator had been rewound, and it tested perfectly until assembled in the frame; then it refused to develop full voltage, and, when run as a motor, it turned with a strong torque even when the field coils were disconnected. Ordinarily this would immediately suggest a wrong brush position, but the brushes on this machine were fixed and nonadjustable. The only remaining possibility was that the armature-coil ends were all brought the wrong

distance around the commutator before being connected. Before this accusation could be brought against the armature winder, who had otherwise done a good job, it was necessary to prove the fact by a test. The test used was simply to touch two brushes to the commutator, the proper angular distance apart, and find with a compass the axis on which the armature iron was magnetized. If the armature had been properly wound, the armature poles should have come out about midway between the field poles; as they came out far from this position, it proved that the leads were all connected to the wrong bars.

Compressor for Cage-Valve Springs

Usually it is a difficult and slow job to compress the springs and remove the keys in the cage-type valves used on a

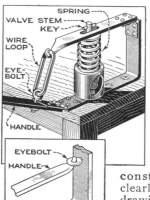

number of automobiles, but the easily made device illustrated makes it possible to do this very quickly. The compressor is made of $\frac{1}{4}$-in. flat-iron stock, and is bolted to the workbench, its construction being clearly shown in the drawing. The valve cages are placed as shown, and the handle pushed downward, the valve stem and key extending through a slot cut in the top member. With this rig, the keys can be removed and replaced almost as fast as the cages can be placed in position.

In the insert a type of construction is shown in which the handle has a hooked end that is placed in eyebolts spaced at intervals along the upright member; this device will take valves of any size. However, a simpler method would be to bore $\frac{3}{8}$-in. holes in the upright through which the hook could be inserted. This construction may also be used in place of the lower hinge, which requires more work in assembling than the eyebolt method, although it possesses the advantage of having all parts connected, so that no individual parts can be lost or mislaid—a decided advantage in most shops.—D. C. Stephenson, Augusta, Kan.

Using Old Blueprint Paper

Having some blueprint paper that had become "stale" in the roll, that is, darkened without having been exposed to the light, and receiving a small order for prints that amounted to less than the cost of a new roll, I decided to make an attempt to use the old paper on hand. The print was exposed in bright sunlight, but, instead of using cold water, the exposed print was washed in hot water, the result being a perfectly legible blueprint. —Edwin J. Bachman, Fullerton, Pa.

Lapping Wristpin Centers

After a large number of air-compressor wristpins had been made up and hardened in the usual way, it was discovered that the steel used was different from that customarily used for this work. The heat-treating process had caused the work to warp so badly that most of the pins would not clean up in the finish-grinding operation, and to save the pieces the centers were lapped with a copper lap which was charged with emery.

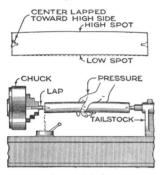

The high spot in the center of the pin was marked with chalk and pressure exerted in an opposite direction when the piece was placed on a speed lathe in the manner illustrated. The lap was first turned up to a 60° angle and then smeared with medium emery and oil. When, after continued lapping, the lap had worn out of shape it was again brought to shape by using a file and center gauge. The amount the centers were lapped depended upon the amount of warp, most of the pins cleaning up with a lapping of .01 in. off center.

Keyseating Fixture for Use on the Shaper Head

Keyseating operations in small shops are usually assigned to the shaper, but to do the work in this manner is objectionable because of the chattering of the gooseneck tool and the breaking away of the front edge of the keyseat. All these and other difficulties can be overcome and heavier cuts taken by the use of the cutter bar shown in the drawing. The bar is fastened to the clapper box in place of the regular toolholder, and a locknut is provided to hold the bar in the proper position. The tool bit is held in the slot

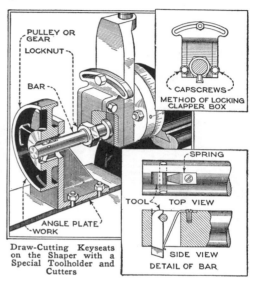

Draw-Cutting Keyseats on the Shaper with a Special Toolholder and Cutters

of the bar by a tool-steel pin. The upper end of the tool bit is ground off to a radius that allows it to swing in an arc and lift on the return stroke. A flat spring, fastened to the top of the bar, holds the tool in the cutting position, but allows it to lift on the noncutting stroke of the ram. Although a single tool of this description will not answer for all sizes of work, it is simple to make, and a variety can be kept on hand, or made up as required.

To use a draw-cut tool bar, the clapper box must be tightly held; so holes are drilled and tapped in the outer flanges of the box, and capscrews and washers are used to clamp it and prevent lifting.

The work is mounted on an angle plate in alinement with a hole of sufficient diameter to permit passage of the bar. Greater accuracy and heavier cuts are possible with the draw-cut method, and all causes of chatter and vibration are overcome. Also, the ability to work to the layout line, which is not broken away, is another advantage of such a tool.

In fitting up the cutter for the draw-cut bar, grind it to make a neat sliding fit in the bar slot, and also grind a notch in the tool bit, to allow it to move in an arc without any lost motion on the pin.

Attachment Makes Drilling Machine from Horizontal Miller

Drilling, reaming, and other operations usually done on a drill press, can be done

Making a Drilling Machine from the Horizontal Miller by the Addition of a Simple Attachment: Power is Provided by a Separate Motor

on a milling machine by the use of an attachment similar to the one illustrated. The attachment is a simple casting with an arm cast at an angle to the perpendicular section, the arm being machined to fit into the overarm of the miller. The vertical part of the device is cast hollow and bored for spindle bushings; to the upper end of the spindle a pulley is attached. The power to drive the drill is provided by a separate motor through a quarter-turn belt.—J. H. Rouse, San Francisco, Calif.

Corrosion of Oil Tanks

Investigations carried out on behalf of insurance associations have shown that steel oil tanks, buried in cinders, show greater corrosion than when buried in other materials, probably because of electrolytic action between the steel and carbon in the cinders.

The best coverings, in the order of merit, are: oily sand, sand, gravel, clay, loam, and cinders. It was also shown that ground or tide water do not stimulate corrosion to any great extent. Steel tanks, buried under favorable conditions, should last more than 30 years. In damp ground this time will be reduced to between 15 and 20 years.

Tanks should be coated with red lead and asphalt and buried 3 ft. or more below the surface; ground and tide water should be avoided as far as possible.

Emergency Repair for Stripped Thread on an Auto Axle

A trouble that is frequently met with in rear-axle shafts of some types of automobiles, is the stripping of the threaded end and consequent failure of the nut, which holds the wheel in place, to grip on the axle. An emergency repair that will hold until a new shaft can be obtained, is effected by drilling a ¼-in. hole about 1 in. deep into the center of the axle, parallel with its axis. A tapered punch is driven into the drilled hole to expand the stripped end. It is only necessary to expand the end of the shaft a small fraction of an inch, after which a new thread can be cut. For the purpose of recutting the thread, in the absence of a regular die, the castellated nut can be run up on the axle in an inverted position. The nut, in most cases, is casehardened, and a serviceable thread will result, especially if portions of the original thread remain as a guide for the improvised threading die.

Locking a Fan-Pulley Pin

An expedient by which the fan pulley of a standard light automobile can be

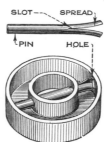

securely locked on the crankshaft, is indicated in the drawing. The pin, as commonly used, frequently works loose and drops out; this is prevented by splitting the outer end of the pin with a hacksaw. The ends are bent apart and the pin is driven into the hole. After the end of the pin has passed the rim of the fan pulley, the ends expand in such a manner that they must be compressed with a pair of pliers before the pin can be removed.

Dressing and Cleaning Leather Belts

In service, a belt gradually loses a portion of its lubricating material, so that, unless this is renewed at suitable intervals, the durability of the belt is impaired. A good grease or dressing gives the belt sufficient flexibility, and at the same time causes it to cling to the pulley, but does not subsequently stiffen or injure it in any way. Among the best belt dressings are mixtures of cod and neat's-foot oils, with tallow, and wool grease free from mineral acid.

Clean the belt well, especially on the pulley side, by washing it with warm water and a good neutral soap, such as castile or white toilet soap, and, if necessary, scrape it on the pulley side to remove any dressing and dirt that may be caked there. Caking of dressings is injurious to the belt and also causes it to run unevenly. Wash rapidly and under no circumstances permit the belt to become wet, as it will then stretch and slip, and cemented joints may become loosened. Apply the dressing, which may be either liquid or solid at ordinary temperature, to the outside of the belt, while it

is at rest, and allow it to soak overnight. It should be applied very evenly and rubbed in with cotton waste, felt, or similar material. If absolutely necessary, a very light dressing may be applied to the pulley side of the belt, using cotton waste or felt lightly coated with the dressing. Even distribution and penetration should be aimed at. Resin, or greases containing it, weaken the belt and shorten its period of service. The use of too much dressing causes undue stretching and loss of grip. Belts should never feel greasy or look greasier than when they were installed. Because a little belt dressing is good for belts, it does not follow that more is better; just as little as possible should be used, but enough to make the belt flexible, and cause it to cling to the pulleys.

How to Make a Motorcycle Trailer

By J. R. KOONTZ

THE painter, carpenter, paperhanger, mason, or other tradesman doing a jobbing business, or the farmer, will find a trailer for a side-car motorcycle a practical addition to his equipment.

The trailer shown in the illustrations is mounted on a pair of wheels taken from an old hay-rake, and runs on a

ladders, lumber, or other long articles. The sideboards are fastened to the bed with bolts, in the same manner as on an ordinary farm wagon. When finished, the box is balanced on the axle so that the weight will be uniformly distributed. The axle may be bolted to the center of the box by drilling holes

An Easily Made Trailer for Attachment to a Motorcycle and Sidecar: The Pictures at the Center and Left Show the Use of Such an Outfit for Hauling Painting Equipment. Right: The Same Equipment Used for Hauling Supplies to the Farm

pipe axle, although one of solid steel could be used. The axle should be long enough so that the wheels will track with a regular wagon, 56 in. center to center, or with the motorcycle and sidecar. The box bed of the trailer is 4½ ft. long by 3 ft. wide, and 8 or 10 in. deep. Make it with loose end gates so that they can be removed in case it is necessary to haul

through the metal and wood, or fastened, as in the drawing, by using brackets or straps, forged from flat iron, and collars to prevent sideplay; all should be provided with setscrews.

The trailer hitch is made either of angle iron or wood; the latter will perhaps be the easier to get, and for this purpose, a piece of 2 by 4-in. hardwood will answer; it must be long enough to reach from the axle and project about 30 in. beyond the front of the box. An iron

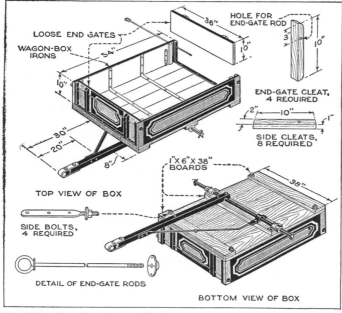

HOLE FOR END-GATE ROD

36"

LOOSE END GATES

WAGON-BOX IRONS

54"

10"

10"

3"

10"

END-GATE CLEAT, 4 REQUIRED

2"

10"

1"

SIDE CLEATS, 8 REQUIRED

30"

20"

8"

1"X 6"X 38" BOARDS

38"

TOP VIEW OF BOX

SIDE BOLTS, 4 REQUIRED

DETAIL OF END-GATE RODS

BOTTOM VIEW OF BOX

Detail Drawings, Showing the Simplicity of Construction of the Motorcycle Trailer: Such a Trailer can be Easily Built in the Farm Shop

brace is also required, and this should be bent so that it will meet the hitch about 20 in. from the end, and extend back at

an angle to the right-hand side of the bed. This arrangement makes the hitch solid, helps to equalize the draft, and distributes the pull without undue strain on the motorcycle or sidecar. The hitch must be placed on the left-hand side of the trailer, so that the latter will track with the motorcycle and sidecar, and should be attached to the sidecar frame as closely as possible to the main frame of the motorcycle, so that the pull will be nearly behind the latter; otherwise too great a strain would be placed on the frame of the sidecar.

If something of neater appearance is desired, two old motorcycle wheels, mounted on suitable axle spindles, can be used instead of the iron wheels; this will reduce the noise and allow the trailer to run much more smoothly.

In the winter months, when the ground is covered with snow or ice, the wheels can be removed from the trailer and a pair of runners substituted.

Making Invisible Molding Joints

Amateur craftsmen who have had occasion to use odd pieces of molding know some of the difficulties of making

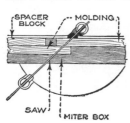

SPACER BLOCK

MOLDING

SAW

MITER BOX

good joints. The method illustrated makes a joint that is practically invisible, and is very easily followed. The pieces to be cut are both placed in the miter box and the ends that are to be fitted together have their angles formed by a single cut of the saw; as both pieces are cut exactly alike, a perfect joint will result. A spacer block, of the same thickness as the molding, is necessary to fill up the space between the side of the miter box and the second piece of molding.—L. H. Georger, Buffalo, N. Y.

Simplifying a Difficult Soldering Job

When soldering the joints on the brine tank of a small refrigerating machine, trouble was experienced in making the solder take hold on the galvanized sheet iron used in the construction. After a number of futile attempts with different fluxes, each resulting in a gaping, leaking seam, the method illustrated was used with success.

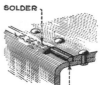

SOLDER

COPPER WIRE

The sheet metal was fairly heavy, so some No. 18 copper wire was skinned of its insulation, brightened with sandpaper, covered with soldering paste, and laid along the edge of the seam. Undiluted muriatic acid was applied to the adjacent galvanized metal, and, with a hot iron, the solder was wiped on smoothly; it flowed easily over both metals, and a perfect joint was made.

Improved Small Generator Brushes

Where carbon brushes are used, the generators on some makes of automobiles often fail to charge the storage battery as they should, on account of poor contact. To overcome this trouble, drill a hole through the brushes from face to top, and insert a bunch of very fine copper wires that will fill the hole as tightly as possible, then trim them off flush with the face of the brush. This will increase the output considerably. The copper cores should be staggered so that they will bear on the commutator in different places.—O. G. Crooks, Newcastle, Pa.

Caliper Attachment for Scale

By attaching a caliper leg to a 12-in. scale a tool is obtained that can be used to test whether or not a long hole has been bored straight. Every mechanic knows that a slight taper in a long hole is easily overlooked when calipers are used to measure the diameter, and also, unless the bore is large enough to admit the hand, it is sometimes impossible to gauge the bottom end of a blind hole at all. A 12-in. power-hacksaw blade, ground to shape, makes an excellent caliper leg,

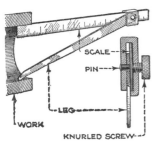

and can be attached to a scale of the same length in the manner illustrated by the drawing.

Bend a piece of 1/8-in. flat steel, and drill one side for a tight-fitting pin, which projects inside and serves as a pivot for the saw-blade leg. A hole is drilled and tapped on the opposite side for a knurled screw with which the attachment is clamped to the scale.

The caliper is set to the proper dimension by means of another scale, and as the leg is opened the holder is pushed forward to keep the caliper point in line with the end of the scale. In use, the tool is pushed into the bore, with the scale held firmly against one side of the hole. Any variation in size can then be felt immediately as the caliper is moved forward. In addition to being handy for long holes of medium diameter, the tool is also useful for larger holes of short length which must be perfectly straight.

Dipping Tank for Brick and Tile

In the laying of face brick and some forms of ornamental tile, it is necessary that the materials be soaked in water or

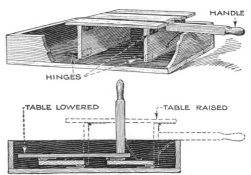

Tile Setters and Bricklayers Who must Soak Certain Kinds of Materials in Water or Other Solutions, will Find the Dipping Vat Illustrated Very Convenient

other fluid so that the cement will adhere to them. In such cases, the dipping tank illustrated is a most convenient accessory. The tile or brick is placed on a horizontal platform, which is hinged to two parallel supports, the latter being fastened to the bottom of the tank with hinges. A handle is attached to one of the endpieces, for raising or lowering the material into the solution. This enables the worker to do the work rapidly without placing his hands in the bath.

Underground Garbage-Can Receiver

A convenient and inexpensive garbage-can container is easily made from a section of glazed sewer tile, as shown in the drawing. This arrangement conceals the garbage receptacle under the surface of the ground. A section of tile, large enough to receive the can, is set into a pit dug in the ground so that the shoulder end is just flush with the surface.

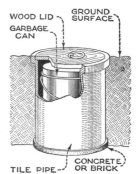

A mixture of sand and cement is poured into the bottom, to a depth of several inches, so that the container can be easily kept clean. A wooden cover, which fits neatly into the shoulder of the tile, is provided to keep flies and animals from the refuse.

A Multiple Fuse Block

A multiple fuse block is a very handy thing to have in the workshop or experimental laboratory, because, when a

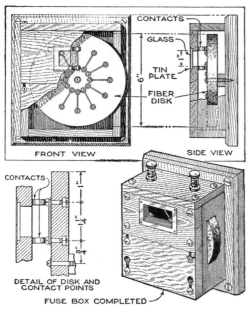

FRONT VIEW   SIDE VIEW

DETAIL OF DISK AND CONTACT POINTS

FUSE BOX COMPLETED

A Fuse Block That Enables a New Fuse to be Put into an Electrical Circuit, to Take the Place of One That has Blown, by the Mere Turn of a Fiber Disk

fuse is blown, a new one can be brought into the circuit by the mere turn of a disk.

Cut out a 6-in. disk from ½-in. fiber and drill 12 equally spaced holes on a circle 2 in. from the center. Then drill 12 more holes, on a 4-in. circle, in such a manner that the holes in the outer circle will be in a radial line with those on the inner one. Obtain 24 small brass machine screws, ⅜ in. long, with brass nuts and washers to fit. Counterbore the holes on one side of the disk to a depth of ¼ in., with a drill slightly smaller in diameter than the width of the nuts across their corners, and drive the nuts into the counterbores with a flat-ended stick. If the nuts do not fit tightly, small wooden plugs should be driven in around them to hold them in place. Place a washer on each machine screw, and screw them into the nuts from the opposite side of the disk.

Build a case, as shown, a slot being cut in one side so that the edge of the disk will protrude, and mount the disk as indicated. The screw used as a bearing should be fairly large, in order to present a large wearing surface; a washer should be placed under the screw head and the screw tightened just enough to make the disk turn stiffly. The cover for the case should be made in two pieces. The upper part is permanently fastened to the case, while the lower section is fastened in such a manner that, by slightly loosening the screws, it can be quickly removed. The object of making half of the cover removable is to make possible reloading of the fuses on the disk. A slot is made in the upper part of the case, and recessed so that the small light of glass used will come flush with the surface; a piece of tin or brass, cut to the shape shown, is fastened over the glass with brads to hold the glass in place. Two brass fingers are cut and shaped as in the drawing; these are mounted on the inside of the upper half of the cover, in such a manner that they will coincide and make contact with the two brass screws of one fuse wire. Wires are led from these fingers to binding posts on the top of the case or any other convenient position.

To load the fuse disk, remove the lower cover, loosen the machine screws, and place lengths of standard fuse wire under the screw heads; then tighten the screws. After loading the disk, the cover is replaced, and the disk is turned by its protruding edge until a fuse wire appears immediately behind the glass window. The fuse that appears through the window is the one in the circuit, and if it blows out, it is a simple matter to turn the disk until another fuse is in place.—I. B. Jackson, Lafayette, Ind.

Bottle Cap Prevents Bolt from Turning

While a man was repairing some of the body irons of a wagon, he found that the

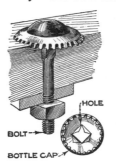

holes had become enlarged so that it was hardly possible to prevent the bolts from turning while tightening the nuts. In order to prevent this, the simple method illustrated was successfully used. Square holes were punched through the centers of crown bottle caps; the bolts were driven through the punched holes and the nuts tightened, drawing the corrugated edges of the caps into the wood, and thus anchoring the heads of the bolts securely.

Mary Alice Cash, LPN works as a surgical scrub nurse in a hospital in New York State. She is married and has one daughter. Mary Alice enjoys reading, knitting, crocheting, quilting, and her "grand puppy" Jake.

Kathy Castille-Aliffi, RN, MSN, FNP-C is currently working in an occupational health setting. She has been a nurse practitioner for several years and has extensive critical care experience, working in a variety of settings from Navy Reserves to primary care in a rural setting. Cathy always finds herself looking for humor in everyday events.

Kelly A. Cavins, RN wanted to be a nurse for as long as she can remember. Perhaps being the oldest of seven children influenced her. In 1983 she earned her Diploma in Nursing from Lutheran Hospital for Nurses. Kelly has enjoyed a wonderful career working in a variety of settings as diverse as neuroscience and high-risk obstetrics. She is currently the Pediatric Epilepsy Nurse Coordinator at the Medical University of South Carolina.

Kim Ceccarelli, RN, BSN, CSN has been a nurse for 24 years and a school nurse for 10 of those years. She lives in Dayton, Ohio with her husband, three children, two dogs and two cats. Kim loves to golf, play tennis, paint, read, and travel. She strives to convince parents, teachers, and others in the community that the well-being of children must come first.

Annmarie Centrone-Cefoli, RN, BSN, COHN-S began her nursing career as a hospital nurse. Once she moved to employee health, she never looked back, enjoying the challenges and the rewards. Annmarie enjoys caring for tropical fish, going to the theater, reading biographies or watching them on television, and listening to oldies music. Annmarie also walks for various charities.

Eva Oi Wah Chan, MSc, BSN, RTN, RMN graduated with her master's degree in health promotion from the London School of Hygiene and Tropical Medicine. Currently she works as a nurse specialist in the field of community psychiatric nursing. Eva serves as a consultant for organizations on psychiatric rehabilitation, youth and community services. Her activities have been repeatedly awarded, including appreciation by the Chief Executive of Hong Kong Special Administrative Region of the People's Republic of China.

Stephanie F. Chomos, RN, MSNc is a native of northeast Ohio. She graduated from Kent State University, Ashtabula Campus, with an Associate Degree in Nursing in 1981. After graduating, she worked the next 9 years in a small community hospital in northwestern Pennsylvania. In 1991 she moved to the 'low country' of South Carolina and began working in a fast-paced ED where she gained a wealth of knowledge and experience. From there she went to the Medical University of South Carolina Level 1 Trauma Center. Currently, she is finishing her RN – MSN degree in Nurse Education at the MUSC College of Nursing. She has two children, Eric and Denise, who are both out in the world as young adults. She lives in a modest little home with her partner, two birds, and a beagle. She is a licensed pilot, rides a "cruiser"-style motorcycle and enjoys kayaking in a lovely little "blow-up" boat.

Arlene M. Clarke-Coughlin, RN, MSN has been in nursing for 30 years. Of her job she says, "I love it just as much now as when I first became a nurse." Arlene has enjoyed teaching for over 20 years, before which she was a critical care nurse. She has been published in the past in various nursing journals. Her long-term goal is to write a book on death and dying.

Marcia Keck Cline, RN, BSN, CCRN is a nurse in the intensive care unit Defiance Regional Medical Center in Defiance, Ohio. She is a member of the American Association of Critical Care Nurses and Sigma Theta Tau (the International Honor Society of Nursing). She loves to teach and mentor other nurses. Marcia's hobbies are playing with her dogs (Yorkshire terriers), working in her flower garden and writing poetry.

Jean Sheerin Coffey, RN, MS, CPNP has worked in pediatric nursing most of her career. She is currently a doctoral candidate at the University of Connecticut with a research concentration in pediatric asthma care. Jean has four children. She resides in Vermont and takes full advantage of great outdoor activities the state offers.

Amy S. Coghill, RN, BSN, OCN graduated from Virginia Commonwealth University/Medical College of Virginia School of Nursing in 1997. After two years in cardiology, she moved to bone marrow transplant. Amy is currently the nurse educator for the bone marrow transplant unit at the University of North Carolina Hospitals in Chapel Hill, NC. She will be moving into the role of nurse educator for oncology services in the future.

Helen June Daniels, RN, MSN has over 30 years experience working as a bedside nurse. She is currently employed as a staff nurse at St. Vincent's Medical Center in Jacksonville, Florida. Helen believes that pet therapy is important to add to the healthcare team because it brightens people's days as pets offer a distraction from worries and illness.

Marie Daniel, RN, CNIII has been a nurse for almost 40 years. She has achieved many rewards from her patients and profession, including the Nursing Excellence Award and advancing to a Clinical Nurse III at the Medical University of South Carolina. As a Certified Parish Nurse, she had the opportunity to use her nursing knowledge in conjunction with her faith. Marie has been married for 37 years and is the grandmother of nine.

Pennie DeBoard, RN, ADN, DNC has been a nurse for over 20 years. She is the daughter of a nurse and hopes her baby granddaughter will carry on the tradition. Her most recent experience is as a part-time American Red Cross Nurse. Additionally, Pennie manages the family business, a trucking company with nine employees. Her hobbies include writing, organic gardening, and riding her Harley motorcycle.

E. Rosellen Dedlow, RN, MSN had her life changed when she cared for her niece Patricia Elaine Flowers, a youngster with special respiratory needs. In 1992 she completed her master's degree with a dual specialization in Child Health and Pediatric Primary Care. Rosellen coordinated programs at the University of Florida Department of Pediatrics. Rosellen plays the mountain dulcimer, collects rocks, gardens, swims, and flies kites, all with greater enthusiasm than skill.

Mary Kate Dilts Skaggs, RN, MSN has over 25 years experience as a nurse. She has spent many years in Renal and Emergency Nursing, doing patient care and managing the area. She lives in Ohio. Mary Kate likes butterflies and believes they are a sign of hope, which she shares with patients and staff. She has spoken nationally on her topics of expertise.

Judith Dorward, RN, BSN, MSN graduated from Pilgrim State Hospital School of Nursing in 1966. She has been a school nurse for over 25 years. She is widely published and wrote a newspaper column, "Your Child's Health" for three years. Judith currently resides on a farmette in central California with her husband, six horses, a dog, various fowl, and five or eight cats. She is contemplating a book, *School Nurse: the Bug Stops Here.*

Deborah J. Downes, RN, BSN, CRRN began her career in nursing after spending some time as a full-time mom. For her, nursing is about nurturing and making someone's quality of life better. Nursing has taught Deborah the value of little things that can make a big difference in a person's life, whether her family, her patients, or her community.

Janet M. Duda, RN, MS, ANP has experience in many areas of nursing, including obstetrics, flight nursing, kidney dialysis, and as a manager. She currently works with a psychiatrist in caring for older adults in long-term care facilities. Janet is married with a daughter and two stepsons. She enjoys hiking, bowling, kayaking, camping, and traveling with her husband. She has a passion for animals of all kinds.

Debbie Dulaney, RN, NHV works for the State of Louisiana in an innovative program called the Nurse-Family Partnership. She makes home visits to first-time mothers, educating them in areas of healthy pregnancy, fetal development, and healthy infancy and toddler stages. Debbie works with the client to achieve the client's life goals. The visits start early in pregnancy and continue until the child's second birthday.

Catherine M. Duren, RN, BSN, CTCRN began her career as a medic in the Army during the Persian Gulf War. While she was born in Florida and spent most of her life there, she is currently a resident of California. Catherine works at the Veterans Administration Hospital of Loma Linda. Here she works with veterans, like herself, from different wars. Although the population is elderly, they always find something in common.

Alice Facente, RN, MSN has been a nurse for 30 years, the last 15 years as a visiting nurse. She is currently beginning a new endeavor, that of nurse educator. Alice does a lot of writing and quilting. She and her husband Brian have two grown children, and they are enjoying the empty nest experience.

Lois Finelli, RN, APRN, BC began her career in medicine and cardiology. Gradually, she transitioned to mental health. Lois lives with her husband, two teenage children, and four guinea pigs in northern Virginia. In her spare time, she enjoys reading, writing, photography, and listening to music, especially folk and bluegrass.

Marilyn Fletcher, RN, CEN is a self-described "dinosaur diploma" nurse, having graduated in 1959 from Milford Hospital School of Nursing. She is still working there per-diem in the emergency department. She has seen nursing grow and change, but caring remains the uniting force. Her husband, children, and grandchildren keep her on her toes.

Karen Fontaine, RN, BSN began her career as a nurse working with cancer patients. Karen has worked in home health and hospice in staff and managerial positions. She currently lives in Reno, Nevada and is a full-time instructor in the nursing program at Truckee Meadows Community College. She loves making life better one person at a time.

Janice Kay Hibler Freeman, RN, BSN, OCN is an oncology emergency room nurse and nurse ombudsperson at the M. D. Anderson Cancer Center in Houston, Texas. She has performed many roles in nursing, including manager. Janice is active with various volunteer programs, including the Anderson Ambassador program at the hospital and with the American Red Cross. She is a member of the Ombudsman Association.

Teresa Lynn Greeson, RN works as a charge nurse in a long term care facility in Florida. She has been a nurse for two years. Teresa loves meeting the day-to-day challenges of nursing her patients and knowing she makes a difference in their lives. A perfect day for her would be spent riding roller coasters with her fiancé or in the kitchen baking and cooking up a storm.

Marla Gundle, RN became intensely curious about the effects of hospitalization on patients and their families. Fueled by this question, she pursued diverse nursing experiences that included working at Headstart and in a county jail. Over time, Marla has come to value to profundity of the ordinary, that a simple word or gesture can be as effective as an astute clinical judgement.

Kathy Hageseth, RN, BSN, CCRN graduated in 1966 and began her lifelong passion for critical care nursing six years later. She has worked in intensive care units of all sizes and the privilege of being allowed into the sacred space of patients and their families is an awesome experience. In her spare time, she enjoys reading, skiing, and being outside. She lives with her husband; they have two grown children.

Kristi B. Haldeman, RN, MSN is an Assistant Professor at the Buntain School of Nursing at Northwest College in Kirkland, Washington. She teaches junior level nursing students in beginning medical-surgical nursing and psychiatric nursing. Kris is also interested in transcultural nursing. She has three adolescent children and competes in sprint distance triathlons in the summer months.

Janelle Harris, RN, MSN, GNP completed her bachelors degree in 1991 and her masters degree in 1996. She works at the San Francisco Veterans Administration Medical Center, currently at a satellite clinic in rural Eureka, California. She has three young children. Janelle is active in her parish where her husband is the pastor.

Patrice E. Harris, RN graduated from a small diploma school in New York. She wanted more excitement in her life and moved to Florida and then traveled around Europe for a while. She settled down in Miami at Mercy Hospital where she worked for 25 years in critical care and other areas. She is currently retired and enjoys being a grandmother.

Amy Zlomek Hedden, RN, MS, NP is a nurse practitioner who teaches and works with new mothers and children at Bakersfield Memorial Hospital. Amy runs an active consulting business. She is married and the mother of two children whose soccer teams she coaches. She also likes to read, swim, play softball, and drive her dirt track race car.

Eileen Hession Laband, RN, BSN, MBA is a nursing project manager at Children's Hospital in Boston. Her responsibilities include analysis and implementation of a wide variety of clinical, operational, and financial projects. At the current time, Eileen is the Magnet Recognition Program project director as the hospital pursues this designation from the American Nurses Credentialing Center.

Violet Horst, RN, CPNP, MSN has been a nurse for 40 years. For 22 of those years, she has been a faculty member at Eastern Mennonite University. She teaches full time and practices nursing part time. Violet is married with two adult daughters.

Pia Labio Inguito, RN, MSN is finishing her doctoral degree at the University of Maryland, Baltimore. The emphasis of her doctoral studies is gerontology. Prior to returning to school, Pia taught, was on active duty with the Army, and worked in orthopedic surgery and trauma caring for older persons. She resides in Delaware with her husband and two children.

Linda Johnson, RN, BSN, CDE is a graduate and employee of the Medical University of South Carolina. She has been employed in intensive care and home health areas. Linda is the recipient of the Medical University's Clinical Services Recognition Award and the Trident Black Nurses association Nurse of the Year Award. Linda lives in Charleston with her daughter and son.

Teresa Julich, RN, BSN is currently a traveling nurse with her husband, a respiratory therapist. They enjoy seeing different parts of the country while doing what they love. Teresa's passion is intensive care nursing where the complexity of patient need and the multi-disciplinary collaboration is at its highest. Future goals include becoming a flight nurse and becoming a collegiate teacher.

Kate Bracy Kalb, RN, MS, ARNP is a nurse practitioner living in Seattle, Washington. Her main job is staff development in the county health department, where Kate observes public health nurses doing magic everyday. She and her partner live on Bainbridge Island where they raised two daughters and currently have custody of a couple of grand pets.

Coleen Kenny, RN, MS, ANP is a nurse practitioner who works with the elderly. She began writing three years ago and has self-published three booklets of poetry, as well as having articles published in *Believe! Magazine* and in *Positive Thinking*. Coleen is currently finishing her first book, *How to Meet Chicks: A Practical Guide for Single Men*, which is dedicated to the men in her church's singles group. She is an avid hiker and the editor of her trail club's newsletter.

Noel A. Kline, RN, BA, ASN began his nursing career after five years in television and radio broadcasting. His focus is end-of-life care and hospice. Noel lives in Waynesboro, Pennsylvania and shares his home with a majestic German Shepherd named Keiser. His hobbies include Civil War history, personal fitness, and photography. He is also an active member of a Masonic Lodge.

Ruth Nelson Knollmueller, RN, PhD has spent her career of over 40 years in Community Health Nursing and Public Health. She has worked as a clinician and educator. Ruth has held numerous elected and appointed offices from the local level to the national level in her specialty. She lives in Connecticut with her husband and two daughters.

Pamela Daley LaFrentz, RN, MA also has an MA in English. She has co-authored academic publications. She has frequently contributed nursing stories to the Sun-Sentinel's Vital Signs Magazine and has been reprinted in the Chicago Tribune. Pamela has published numerous humor articles in regional newspapers in Florida. She has acquired a New York literary agent and has completed her first young adult novel. She lives in Florida with her husband and three cats.

Patricia A. Layton, RN, BSN was born and raised in Indiana. She moved to Texas, married, and had a child. Later she divorced, returned to Indiana where she raised her daughter as a single parent. During this time, Patricia put herself through college pursuing a nursing degree. She is currently working on a degree in the ministry. She has re-married.

Heather Tomlinson Levy, RN, BSN is a 1994 graduate of the Medical University of South Carolina College of Nursing. Heather has worked in inpatient, home and outpatient settings. Currently she is on the staff of the Department of Otolaryngology, Head and Neck Surgery at her alma mater. She is married and the proud mother of twin boys. Heather enjoys yard work and baking, especially wedding cakes.

Ann E. Marsh, RN, BSN, CEN, EMT-p always knew she wanted to be a nurse. As life would have it, she had several arrested attempts at higher education before she was able to settle in one area and concentrate on it. Ann began her nursing career in her late twenties. She worked in intensive care and in long-term care before finding her niche in emergency nursing.

Grayce Massi-Ventura, RN went to Boston to attend nursing school. There she fell in love with the city and her husband. She is a Clinical Nurse Educator in Ambulatory Surgery at the Lahey Clinic in Burlington, Massachusetts. Grace has been associated with perianesthesia nursing for over 25 years. Grace loves rock concerts, the Red Sox, dinners with friends, and every minute she can spend on Martha's Vineyard.

Mary C. McCarthy, RN, BSN is a third-generation nurse. She has spent most of her life and career in Iowa. She received her bachelors of science in nursing from Marycrest College in Davenport, Iowa. Mary currently works at Mercy Hospital in Iowa City.

Janice M. McCoy, RN, MS, CNAA has practiced nursing for almost 40 years and for 25 of those years, she has been a nurse executive. She is currently the Vice President of Patient Care Services at Cape Canaveral Hospital in Cocoa beach, Florida. She is a frequent speaker. She has published several articles and book chapters. Janice serves on professional nursing advisory boards and is an adjunct faculty member for a local nursing program. She enjoys singing in the Chancel Choir and participates in community groups.

Marge McDowell, RN has been a nurse for over 35 years, the last 15 spent in oncology nursing. She is a member of the Long Island Writers Guild. Marge has published articles and poems. Photography is also important to her and the marriage of words and pictures continually fascinates her.

Sandra McLaughlin, RN, MSHSA, MSN works as a cardiovascular nurse practitioner. In addition to her nursing degrees, she has a master's degree in Health Services Administration. She is a certified case manager and certified by the American Academy of Nurse Practitioners. Sandra enjoys spending time with her family and her scrapbook.

Aquilla T. Miller is a 30-year-old African American who was the client in the Nurse-Family Partnership described by Debbie Dulaney. Aquilla is the mother of a three-year-old and is married to her beloved Ernest. She works in a community home.

Carrie A. Moore, RN, BSN currently lives in Greenville, South Carolina where she works in a Mother/Baby unit. She enjoys witnessing the interactions between each parent and their new baby. Carrie is involved in several nursing committees within the hospital. She also enjoys reading and playing the piano.

Donna M. Nickitas, RN, PhD, CNAA, BC is an Associate Professor and Graduate Program Specialty Coordinator, Nursing Administration and Hunter College in New York City. She has held many nursing positions. Donna is a grass-roots community activist and is known for her civic engagement activities. Her yellow Lab, three children and husband keep her celebrating life.

Fran Nielsen, RN loves helping others in a time of great need. Her patients have been her greatest teachers and have taught her about suffering and personal victory. She is a grandparent. Fran is involved in jogging, biking, watercoloring, writing short stories and poetry, and she grows roses.

Irene O'Day, RN is retired from active nursing after practicing for 50 years. Her interest in stress management grew from an internship with Bernie Siegel, MD. She volunteers at a state prison, teaching stress management as part of the Sisters of Mercy chaplaincy program. Irene also likes to travel and read. She is active in nursing organizations dedicated to holistic nursing practices.

Nikki Odango Ongtawco, RN, BSN is currently the office manager in an Obstetric and Gynecology practice in Virginia. She also works in labor and delivery in a local hospital. She has worked in women's health for over 20 years. Nikki was born in the Philippines and pursued her nursing career after moving to the United States.

Bozena M. Padykula, RN, MSN, HNC, is a staff nurse on a medical/psychiatry unit at a hospital in Connecticut. She also does clinical teaching for the University of Connecticut School of Nursing. Bozena is the mother of three children. To maintain balance in her life, she recharges her energy by taking long walks on the beach and long bike rides.

J. M. Pantatello is 80 years young. He has been writing seriously for the last eight years. He claims writing has saved his life and preserved his sanity. He enjoys writing fantasy, mystery, and a bit of romance to please his wife, Caroline, his severest critic. They live in New York and are happily contemplating the arrival of a new puppy.

Michele N. Pedulla, RN, MSN, ARNP, PNP has been a nurse for 19 years. Presently, she works with children of all ages in a school-based health clinic as a pediatric nurse practitioner. Michele has found another passion...teaching. She shares her years of experience with nursing students in a nearby community college. As one of 11 children, family is at the center of her life. She is an accomplished sports mom, theater mom, and chaperone mom.

Mary E. Perrine, RNC, BSN wanted to be a nurse since she was eight years old. After trying a couple of areas of practice, Mary discovered the special care nursery where she worked for 18 years. She was disabled following neck surgery in 2002 but continues to work on special projects for Winchester Hospital. She is very active in her community and church.

Toni L. Phillips, BSN, C has been practicing as a registered nurse for twenty four years. She administered care at Shands Hospital, unit 75, and shared her knowledge within the nursing programs at Santa Fe Community College. Her most recent appointment is at the VA Medical Center in Gainesville where she is practicing as a Nursing Information Coordinator. She is currently enrolled in the masters program at the University of Central Florida.

Caryl A. Pratt, RN, MSN, MSEd is nearing retirement after a fulfilling career in nursing. Much of her career was in the field of Public Health Nursing. Caryl is an avid football fan. Currently she is in Oklahoma where she is an active member of the Oklahoma Parish Nurse Network. She is part of a group who are creating an informational website to support parish/congregational nursing in Oklahoma.

Patrice Rancour, RN, MS, CS has been a mental health nurse for over 30 years as a clinician educator and consultant. Her professional interests include psychoneuroimmunology, integrative healing modalities, and working with folks facing life threatening illnesses. Patrice enjoys reading, art, gardening and travel.

L. M. Rasmussen, RN, MS, CEN currently works in the emergency department at Mad River Community Hospital, as well as at St. Mary's in San Francisco. She takes calls for the Humboldt County Sexual Assault Response Team. She is a volunteer for an advocacy group for abused and neglected children in her community. L. M. is a wife, mother, and yogini. Her family lives with two cats in an old home by the bay.

Elizabeth Samer, RN, BSN, CEN was an emergency room nurse for 20 years. She currently works in an outpatient setting and does freelance writing. Personally, Elizabeth is enjoying the second part of her life with her soul mate, looking forward to what the future will hold. She is the mother of four young adults, the eldest of whom is in the United States Army serving his country in Iraq.

Beka Serdans, RN, BSN has worked for 17 years in critical care areas. In the early 1990s she developed distain, a movement disorder. She has written two books on the topic and founded a non-profit group, Care4Dystonia whose mission is to set the pace in areas of awareness, education, patient care, and collaboration with other movement disorder advocacy and non-profit groups. Her spare time is spent gardening, writing, and traveling.

Tracie Shields, RN, CAPA had several relatives who were nurses who she admired. A deep religious faith and her natural tendency to care for people have motivated her career. She worked in Oncology nursing, then moved to a day surgery unit, where she currently works part time. Tracie enjoys being active with her family and her church and playing the piano.

Lynn Coletta Simko, RN, PhD, CCRN has made a career of working in coronary care and going to school. Once she completed her bachelor's degree in nursing, she achieved two master's degrees, one in Public Health, the other in Nursing. Then Lynn embarked upon doctoral study. Currently, she is an Associate Professor of Nursing at Duquesne University. She has two adult children and two needy cats.

Kendra L. Smith, RN, BSN, IBCLC moved to Ithaca when she was 14 months old and stayed there her whole life. Her children attended the same schools she did. She is an obstetric nurse. Kendra worked the night shift in the local hospital for 16 years. Currently, she teaches childbirth classes and is a Lactation Consultant. She is a grandmother.

Ida A. Souza, LPN, OTTP has been at St. Luke's Hospital in New Bedford, Massachusetts for 37 years. Her current position is on an acute medical/surgical geriatric unit. She is active on hospital committees and councils. Ida and her husband have two children and two grandchildren. They are avid travelers.

Anne St. Germaine, RN, PhD works in the school health program for the Seattle School District. She has made a career of improving the health of children. When Anne isn't involved in helping kids stay well enough to learn, she likes to kayak in some of the quiet inlets around Puget Sound.

Lorraine Steefel, RN, MSN, CTN has occupied various positions from medical/surgical nursing in a hospital to school, camp and clinical research nursing. She also did staff education and served as an adjunct faculty member of a school of nursing. Lorraine has written for several nursing and health-related publications. She is a senior staff writer for *Nursing Spectrum*. She is a certified transcultural nurse.

Barbara A. Stevenson, RN, MS is a retired member of the Army Nurse Corps. She served in Vietnam and as a reservist in the Gulf War. Barbara Ann practiced in emergency and intensive care nursing. Currently she lectures baccalaureate students, is active in the children's Miracle Network, and does AIDS education.

Pamela Sturtevant, RN specializes in cardiac and anticoagulant nursing. She has published in *The American Journal of Nursing* and *On call Magazine*. She lives with one husband, four pets, congregations of wildlife, and enough gardens to make the strongest spine cry. Pamela enjoys writing about perennial miracles that self-sow into our personal landscapes.

Catherine Thompson, RN, BA, BSN worked for several years on a medical service that specialized in HIV and palliative care. Recently, Catherine transferred to a geriatrics unit as she is pursuing her master's degree as a geriatric nurse. She splits her time between New Jersey and the Pocono's. She and her husband are avid travelers and love the countryside.

Ellen R. Thompson, RN has been a nurse for 35 years. She has worked in intensive care units, medical surgery floors, in public health, and home health care. In 1993 she also earned a MSW. Following that she worked as a psychiatric nurse liason and as a patient care coordinator in an Emergency Department. She also has been a discharge planner. Currently she is working part-time as a staff nurse at a city-county hospital in Denver, CO. She is a member of the Colorado Nurses Association and works to raise awareness about the inadequate coverage of health insurance in our country. She has a grown son, a teen-age daughter, and two grandchildren. Her hobbies include gardening, reading, and spending time with friends.

Page M. Vandewater, RN, MS is an accomplished home health nurse. She is currently the Director of Health Care Services, Walnut Street Center, Day Rehabilitation Program in Somerville, Massachusetts. Page is a Specialized Home Care Provider for Mentor, Inc.

Claudia Vepraskas, RN, BSN, NCSN, has been practicing nursing for 30 years in a variety of settings. She has been a school nurse for the past 14 years covering all student levels. She published an article in the journal of *School Nursing* in August 2002 addressing heat and dehydration in marching band students, a topic of great interest to her as a Band Mom. She is married to a university professor. Their two children are currently in college. Claudia sings in her church choir and is becoming reacquainted with activities she enjoyed "BC" (before children), such as needlework and reading.

Debra C. Wadell, RN, BSN, CCS lives in Georgia with her husband, Steve and two children, Rachel and Rebecca. She is a graduate of Georgia Baptist College and Graceland University. She is also a certified coding specialist. Her work experience has been primarily in home health, SNF, and acute care. Debra is considering a career in forensic nursing and is interested in future writing projects.

Lenore B. Weinstein, RN, MA is an Adjunct Associate Professor (Clinical) at Marquette University School of Dentistry. She is a certified interviewer for the Holocaust Documentation and Education Center, Inc. and a Master Interviewer for the Survivors of the Shoah Visual History Foundation. Additionally, Lenore is Book/Media Editor for the journal *Activities, Adaptation & Aging.* She is also a grandmother, her favorite role.

Bonnie Whaite, RN, MSN has been a nurse for 30 years. Her area of expertise is Pediatric Nursing. She has worked in a variety of positions. Bonnie is interested in Florence Nightingale's life and work. For the past seven years, she has been an educator. She is married and has three children.

Hazel Marie Barmore Wiegert, RN, MA is passionate about post-anesthesia care. She has worked in the field since 1976. She is active and national and state Perianesthesia groups, serving as an officer and committee member. Hazel currently works at the Hennepin County Medical Center in Minneapolis, Minnesota. She is becoming certified as a Parish Nurse. She lives with her husband and 10-year-old dog.

Kathy Wilmering, RN, MSW, APRN, BC has had 22 years of notable success helping and healing people in need where other therapies have failed. She has presented workshops on mental health topics to professional and lay groups in the United States and Canada. Kathy is certified in the complementary therapies of Therapeutic Touch, Qigong, and the use of music/sound in therapy. She blends these with psychotherapy.

Laurie L. Wise, RN, BSN, ET, OCN began her career in 1970, specializing in the care of cancer patients. She is currently the Oncology Care Specialist and ET nurse for clients with colorectal and prostate caner. In this role, Laurie educates clients, staff, and the community. She is a member of several cancer-focused organizations. She is married, has a grown daughter, and two grandchildren.